Practical
Encyclopedia of

KEEPING AND BREEDING TORTOISES AND FRESHWATER TURTLES

A. C. Highfield

Line drawings by Andrew Barrowman

Book design by A. C. Highfield

Additional photographs by : R. D. Bartlett, Dr. Indraneil Das, John Dickson, G. & A. Beck, D. Peterson

First Edition, 1996
Second Edition, 2002
Third Edition, 2008

ISBN 1 873943 06 7 (Soft cover)
ISBN 1 873943 11 3 (Cloth cover)

British Library Cataloguing in Publication Data. A catalogue record for this book is available from the British Library.

Published by:
Carapace Press,
c/o The Tortoise Trust,
BM Tortoise,
London,
WC1N 3XX,
England

Printed and bound by Gomer Press, Llandysul, Ceredigion, Wales SA44 4JL

CONTENTS

Acknowledgements

The author would like to thank the following for their assistance during the preparation of this work: Indraneil Das, R.D. Bartlett, Suzanne O'Leary, Bill McCord, Jim Buskirk, Richard Ross, Ken Welch, Ramon Mascort Brugarolas, Ashley Woods, Jaco Bruekers, Tahar Slimani, Jarmo Perala, Paul Eversfield, Elaine Harland, Lance Jepson, John Dickson, Alison Kay, Lin King, Sean McKeown, Richard Inskeep, Esther Wenman, Eric and Kathy Thiss, Jill Martin, the membership of the Tortoise Trust, and my wife, Jane Bayley.

PREFACE

This book was prepared in response to the many requests I have received from enthusiasts and professionals around the world for an accessible, thoroughly practical and comprehensive guide to breeding tortoises and turtles in captivity. It substantially expands upon and updates my earlier work *Keeping and Breeding Tortoises in Captivity* (R&A Publishing Ltd., 1990). Much of the information presented in that early edition remains fresh and relevant today. However, new research has cast more light upon certain areas and, in the veterinary field in particular, several important new drugs and treatments have emerged. These are detailed in Chapters Eight and Nine. I have retained text from the earlier edition that remains relevant but have also included a substantial amount of completely new information, including, for the first time, comprehensive data on the maintenance and breeding of aquatic and semi-aquatic testudines.

By means of this volume I hope to show that the technology of captive breeding can make an invaluable contribution to conservation, not only by encouraging enthusiasts to breed their animals in captivity rather than by sourcing them from the wild, thereby depleting natural populations, but also by enabling critically endangered populations to be replenished by the careful application of the same techniques.

The threats against tortoises and turtles are greater than before; habitats continue to disappear and usage for food and medicines (particularly in Asia) is a serious problem. The good news is that many species which previously had not been captive bred in significant numbers are now regularly reproducing under captive conditions. This is leading to a corresponding reduction in demand for wild-caught specimens. In general, captive bred stocks are healthier and far less stressed than imports and contribute to, rather than detract from, the continued survival of the species. Zoos, private keepers, and institutions all have a role to play in this battle, and I sincerely hope that this new *Encyclopedia* will also make a useful contribution to the preservation of these most remarkable animals.

Andy C. Highfield

Chapter One

THE ROLE OF CAPTIVE BREEDING

The ultimate objective of most serious and conservation-conscious reptile keepers is to achieve consistent and sustainable captive reproduction; only in this way can we really justify the keeping of rare or endangered species in captivity. Breeding threatened species of reptiles in captivity is increasingly becoming the only method by which fellow enthusiasts can obtain specimens; it is no longer acceptable to make extensive collections in the wild in order to supply this need. Furthermore, the technical knowledge gained in captive breeding projects can contribute greatly to the success of other projects based in the natural habitat.

It is important to question the role that we, as individuals, play in this process. If we seek to acquire animals taken from the wild simply in order to say we have bred them in captivity, then our role is not a positive one. We must at all times question our role, and try to ensure that our efforts do actually result in some tangible benefit to the species involved.

As this book was going to press I was called to a major European airport to examine a consignment of some 80 *T. graeca* complex tortoises bound for eventual sale in the United States. The animals were in a very sorry condition indeed, badly packed and extremely mal-

A tortoise emerges from its egg.The importanance of captive breeding as a conservation tool is considerable.

Wild-caught *Testudo kleinmanni* and Libyan *T. graeca* on sale in a Cairo street market. Literally millions of tortoises have been collected from North Africa to supply the demands of the European, and latterly, American, pet trade.

nourished and dehydrated. Many had serious eye infections and others had nasal discharges. A considerable number were very aged tortoises indeed. They had originally been collected in Libya and it was evident from their condition that they had been held in captivity for a considerable period before being loaded aboard their aircraft in Cairo, Egypt. The tortoises were confiscated by officials on the grounds of their packing not meeting IATA regulations (a set of regulations governing the conditions of transport of animals) and they were then given into the care of the Tortoise Trust's veterinary hospital for treatment. Eventually, they would be rehomed with caring enthusiasts. Sadly, this state of affairs is all too typical of the wild-caught trade. One is also moved to wonder what people's reaction would be if a pet store were to offer malnourished, dehydrated geriatric dogs or cats suffering from multiple pathologies for sale? I suspect that they would certainly not find as many gullible customers as this consignment would have attracted. If more purchasers were to insist on captive-bred stock only, this would certainly represent a considerable step in the right direction. Not only is captive-bred stock less damaging ecologically, it is generally far healthier.

The captive breeding of tortoises or turtles is an extremely challenging undertaking, as these are by no means easy animals to induce to breed successfully and consistently; raising the hatchlings to a healthy adulthood and hopefully managing these well enough to produce second and third captive-bred generations is if anything an even bigger challenge. Yet with dedication and good management it can be done.

The conservation role that can be played by captive breeding is nowhere better illustrated than on the Galapagos.

By the late 1960's the future of the handful of surviving Galapagos Hood Island tortoises *Geochelone (Chelonoidis) elephantopus hoodensis,* was looking bleak. Thousands had been slaughtered in the 19th century by visiting whalers (between them, two ship's logs record taking 585 tortoises in 1831 alone), and by 1847 the population was effectively devastated. The number of tortoises was reduced to such an extent that even the whalers considered it no longer worth their while to continue the hunt. Scientific search parties in 1906 man-

A Galapagos giant tortoise at the Charles Darwin Research Station on Santa Cruz Island

aged to locate only three living tortoises. The population faced total extinction. Indeed, some believed that this may already have occurred. Nonetheless, fresh expeditions set out and finally during the 1960's a total of fourteen adults comprising twelve females and two males were located. These were removed to the safety of the Charles Darwin Research Station on Santa Cruz and by 1971 the first eggs were successfully incubated.

The Hood island tortoises, along with other races from different islands are now breeding regularly and successfully at the Darwin Station. Reintroductions into the wild of captive reared juveniles are gradually swelling the populations of the most critically endangered races, and the evidence is that survivorship is good. Young tortoises are susceptible to predation not only by natural enemies such as birds, but also by introduced predators such as rats and feral domestic animals. By head-starting hatchlings past the age of peak predation, the maximum conservation benefit of captive breeding can be attained.

It is not only on the Galapagos where captive breeding is seen as an answer to the tortoises plight. In the South of France, in Spain, and in Italy, *Testudo hermanni hermanni* is being captive bred by similar means for release into their native habitats. Again, the head-start technique is proving highly successful. Other programs around the world are using similar methods to fend off extinction in critically endangered populations. In Mexico the extremely rare endemic Chihuahuan desert tortoise, *Gopherus flavomarginatus*, had been hunted for food to such an extent that total extinction was feared within 20 years. An enlightened educational effort involving local people in conservation activities (one of the area's best known ex-tortoise hunters now works for the program) combined with stiff penalties for illegally taking a tortoise has reversed the trend, but once again captive breeding holds the most promise for eventual repopulation. In Madagascar, similar efforts are being made on behalf of the beautiful radiated tortoises, *Asterochelys (Geochelone) radiata* and *Asterochelys (Geochelone) yniphora*.

In North Africa, the Tortoise Survival Project is for the first time attempting to assess, and ultimately reverse, some of the damage done by 50 years of intensive trade collecting. It has been estimated that over 1 million tortoises were taken from Morocco alone between 1967 and 1981. Collections were indiscriminate and vast numbers perished en-route to the pet shops of Europe. More died during their first hibernation. The Tortoise Survival Project has recently established that genetic diversity in this region is very profound and that almost certainly numerous undescribed species were included, unrecognised, in this vast trade. One species, only found in Algeria, and which was described in the 19th century was *Testudo whitei*. This tortoise was named after Gilbert White's famous "Timothy" tortoise of Selborne, first described in 1836 and thereafter forgotten, synonymised with *Testudo graeca graeca*, about until re-discovered by the Project in 1989 - exactly 200 years after the first publication of White's classic *Natural History*. A urgent effort is now underway to save it, and similar recently discovered rare endemic forms, from eventual extinction. Along with efforts directed towards habitat conservation and the elimination of a grisly tourist souvenir trade using tortoise carapaces, captive breeding will play an important role.

Captive breeding projects involving marine turtles have been established for many years and are well known. It is not so well known that many freshwater turtles are equally (or more) endangered and that breeding projects to help them also exist. As an example, *Pseudemydura umbrina*, the Western swamp turtle, is probably the world's most endangered turtle; fewer than 15 - 25 wild specimens were known to exist in Australia. By 1989 12 eggs had been produced by a small captive group. Of these, 11 hatched and probably represented up to 25% of the world's total population of this species (Kuchling, 1989).

The core of all these programs is essentially the same. A small breeding stock of endangered tortoises or turtles is removed to a safe area where eggs can be laid without risk of the nests being attacked by predators, human or animal. In some programs it is possible to simply protect the nests by means of wire mesh and allow incubation to occur naturally, in the ground. At other times it is preferable to remove the eggs from the nest once the female has finished laying and place them in an artificial incubator whilst development takes place.

In many wild situations, egg predation can affect up to 80% of all nests with wild pigs, foxes, pine martens and even hedge-hogs being particularly effective and systematic predators. Today, introduced predators are also a serious threat in many localities. These attrition rates can be reduced to nil by artificial incubation, thus dramatically boosting the recovery potential of a depressed population.

One particularly crucial problem facing all conservation based captive programs, that may not be immediately obvious, is to ensure that only true and genetically compatible pairs are used for breeding purposes. If random cross-breeding occurs, then an endangered species or subspecies could literally be bred to the point of extinction. This is where the roles of taxonomist, geneticist, ecologist, and zoo keeper can combine to ensure that only the correct species and subspecies are bred and re-introduced into native habitats. No introductions of captive-bred stock should ever be made until the situation has been thoroughly investigated and the impact of such an operation has been very carefully assessed.

This form of genetic management must extend not only to the species and subspecies level, but must also be applied at the level of individual populations. Where eventual release of captive bred stock is intended, therefore, the genetic integrity of the original populations must be carefully maintained.

Genetics and cross-breeding

For obvious reasons it is undesirable to produce hybrid offspring from different species. Fortunately in the case of tortoises and turtles, it is also, usually, extremely difficult. Despite looking for evidence of successful cross-matings between recognised species for several years, I have only ever encountered a few genuine cases at first hand. Most cases of alleged hybridisation reported to us and subsequently investigated were based upon simple misidentification of the parents, others upon pre-fertilisation of the female by a male of identical type subsequently mated by male of a different species which was then assumed to be a parent. The sometimes very extended gestation periods of tortoises between conception and laying frequently leads to this type of mistake. Some hybridisation may indeed occur naturally between some geographically adjacent races, and it may be possible to induce it between normally widely separated races when both are held in captivity. One well documented case involved hybridisation between *G. radiata* and *G. carbonaria* in a captive group on Reunion Island (Gonzalez, 1993). Any such instances must be regarded as unusual and certainly the physical construction of some species, the size of their eggs, and unique biotypic adaptations would suggest that reports must be treated with scepticism until carefully verified.

There are reports in the literature of cross-breeding between *Testudo marginata* and *Testudo ibera* ,both of which occur in Greece, and also of hybridisation between *Testudo hermanni* and *Testudo horsfieldi*. In one case, I observed cross-bred hatchlings from non-sympatric Turkish *T. ibera* and North African *T. graeca*. The most curious feature was that in both of these cases the hatchlings appeared to inherit all their visible (external) characters from the male, and displayed no characters whatsoever typical of the female. They also did not demonstrate any other combination of traits to suggest that cross-breeding had occurred. This is certainly an extremely interesting result and is now undergoing further investigation.

The capacity of turtles for sperm storage for long periods, and even multiple paternity, the occurrence within a single clutch of offspring descended from more than one male (Galbraith, 1993), can further complicate the question of managing captive-breeding colonies. It is also worth noting that whilst cross-matings very rarely produce fertile eggs, almost any mating activity seems able to stimulate females to generate eggs. The following practical guidelines are suggested for routine adoption:

- Do not deliberately induce cross-matings between different species or subspecies. Fertility is likely to be nil or very greatly reduced and the offspring may be infertile. It is also ecologically damaging to produce such hybrids.

- Do not breed from siblings or from closely related pairs. Inbreeding suppression, although not an immediate consequence, may occur in the long term when such practices are sustained.

- Introduce new genetic input into any captive breeding program frequently by means of breeding loans and exchanges etc.

- Never release captive-bred stock into wild habitats. Any such releases should only occur after the most exhaustive scientific studies and preferably even then only after DNA or genetic screening has confirmed that it is safe to do so.

- If at all possible, maintain animals from individual populations separately, and breed only from truly compatible pairs from similar genetic and zoogeographic backgrounds. Keep careful records of all resulting hatchlings.

Finally, do not assume that the taxonomic nomenclature and status of tortoises is fully understood and is fixed. It is not. Taxonomy is a continually developing science. Until only recently, for example, it was thought that only a single species (*Testudo graeca graeca* Linnaeus 1758) occurred throughout North Africa - this has subsequently proven to be far from the case. Similar conditions apply to many species. *Geochelone (Chelonoidis) carbonaria, Geochelone (Chelonoidis) chilensis*, *Kinixys belliana*, *Testudo graeca* and *Testudo hermanni* are all highly complex taxonomic units which are formed of many individual populations, some demonstrating a great deal of individual variety and divergence. It is highly likely that certain of these taxa will, on further investigation, prove to comprise more than one simple species. The same is even more true of numerous aquatic species, the taxonomy and phylogeny of which is often very poorly understood.

Subspecies are always problematic and the criteria used to define them are very variable. What one researcher proposes as a subspecies another may consider a full species. There is in fact a good argument for dispensing with subspecies altogether. If a geographical population has diverged sufficiently to be *a)* recognisably different and *b)* considered worthy of separate nomenclatural status, it can be argued that it is in actuality a biological species. Where one draws the line on these matters is open to a great deal of personal interpretation and is always the cause of much heated debate among taxonomists.

The message for those intending to captive breed tortoises is therefore very clear. Treat all taxa and nomenclature with caution, and, if possible, base captive breeding colonies not simply upon currently accepted taxonomic divisions (which may change) but on geographic populations. Not only is this approach consistently the most successful, but it also avoids any possibility of inadvertently causing genetic pollution.

Albino and leucistic animals

Many commercially oriented snake breeders invest a great deal of effort in the production of unusual colour phase animals. Recently, some attention has also been given to the production of albino and leucistic tortoises and turtles. There is no doubt that rare examples of such do occur naturally. On a visit to the impressive Aquarium of the Americas in New Orleans for example, I was struck by the ghostly appearance of two leucistic Atlantic Ridley turtles (*Lepidochelys kempii*) gliding through the water in the company of several large sharks in their dramatically presented giant aquarium. I have also encountered a curious albino North African *T. graeca graeca* (see plates) and a leucistic Common Snapping turtle (*Chelydra serpentina*). Occasional reports surface of breeders offering albino and leucistic animals for sale at very high prices. Unfortunately, the temptation is obviously there for the deliberate breeding of such specimens. This is regrettable and it is not a practice which should be encouraged. One would not wish to see a situation where artificial blood-lines are deliberately being created; this would only serve to remove and separate captive-bred stocks from those that occur naturally. As one of the prime objectives of captive breeding is the propagation and conservation of naturally occurring species the creation of artificial animals is counter-productive to that cause.

It should also be pointed out that albino tortoises and turtles often demonstrate serious feeding difficulties and some exhibit obvious discomfort under bright lighting conditions. It is evident, on observing such specimens, that their vision is often impaired. The mortality rate among albino hatchlings also tends to be far greater than among normal specimens.

Sexual maturity and age of breeding stock

Careful observations on a wide range of species indicate that primarily physical size rather than age is the indicator and initiator of sexual maturity in tortoises. Size is of course related to age but as captive-bred specimens often grow much faster than equivalent wild specimens, due to the normally better availability of food, these often mature sexually and attain breeding capability much earlier than their wild counterparts. For example, in the wild *T. graeca* and *G. pardalis* usually mature at approximately 12 to 15 years of age. Captive-bred examples can easily mature at less than half this time, in 5 to 7 years. In one instance, we know of the successful mating of an adult female *G. pardalis* by a 4-year-old captive-reared male.

At the other end of the scale, extreme caution should be exercised in attempting to use elderly females for captive breeding purposes. When eggs have not been produced for many years severe obstetric difficulties can ensue (see chapter nine for more details of female reproductive problems and suggested treatments). In our own captive breeding programs all elderly females are automatically excluded and are maintained separately from the males to avoid undue stress or the danger of egg retention.

Above: Male *Testudo hermanni*. In many species, adult males are distinguished by a tail which is longer than that of females, and which is carried sideways when walking. This characteristic is a fairly reliable indicator of gender.

Above: Female *Testudo hermanni*. Note much shorter tail.

Overall body shape is often a very useful indicator of sex. Compare the female *Geochelone carbonaria* (left) with the male (right). In many species, females are broader at the 'waist' than males.

The plastra of male tortoises is often depressed, or indented. In some species, such as *G. carbonaria* (above) this feature is very evident. In other species, however, the degree of depression may be only slight.

Sexual dimorphism in tortoises and turtles

In most species of tortoises and turtles it is comparatively easy to determine the sex of specimens by using the following primary sexual characteristics:

- *Tail length*
  In mature males the tail is almost always longer that of females. In juveniles there may be little or no observable difference, however.
- *Plastron*
  In many species the plastron of males is deeply curved or indented. The anal plates of the plastron also differ in size and shape between male and female specimens in many species.
- *Size*
  In most species, adult males are considerably smaller than adult females. In the case of aquatic turtles, the length of the male's front claws may also be a useful indicator.
- *Carapace shape*
  There are often significant differences between males and females. In many species females are broader at the waist than males. The rear marginal scutes of male specimens may be more serrated or flared than that of females and the supracaudal scutes of males are, in some species, extended and introflexed whereas those of females are shorter and straight.

There are, in addition to these primary characters, a large number of secondary characters which are often unique to individual species. These include sexual dichromatism, or colour differences between males and females. Head stripes and markings may also differ, especially in freshwater turtles. Often these characters are difficult to evaluate until considerable experience has been gained. Even the above primary characters are not universally applicable. For example, the plastrons of male *Geochelone pardalis* (the Leopard tortoise) are sometimes as flat as those of females, and there is very little difference in tail length between male and female *Geochelone (Chelonoidis) chilensis* (the Chaco tortoise) also, male *Geochelone (Chelonoidis) elephantopus* (Galapagos tortoises) and Leopard tortoises are usually considerably larger than females. However, the above guidelines do hold true for the majority of species likely to be encountered.

Major dimorphic characters within individual species are discussed in part two which deals with identification and breeding notes.

Sexual behaviour, vocalisation and aggression

Details of courtship behaviour varies considerably between different species. *Geochelone carbonaria* (the Red-foot tortoise), for example, engages in a strange pre-nuptial head nodding ritual where the male extends his neck and rapidly shakes his head up and down whilst making a unique "clucking" noise; something similar (but without the accompanying noise) is seen in *Testudo horsfieldi*. North African *Testudo graeca* and trans-Caucasian *Testudo ibera* ram and butt the females prior to mating (although the North African *graeca's* performance is notably less violent than that of *ibera*); in *Testudo hermanni* ramming behaviour is rarely seen, but head and leg biting is commonplace. Mating males frequently emit species-characteristic sounds. These sounds are so unique to each species that it is possible for experienced observers to identify them merely by listening to a tape

A pair of mating Pancake tortoises, *Malacochersus tornieri*. During copulation, the male engages in a series of rapid head movements and distinctive vocalisations.

recording of the various vocalisations. One of the most curious examples is the sound made by *Testudo kleinmanni*, the Egyptian tortoise. These tiny animals are capable of making a remarkably loud noise during courtship which sounds very much like a dove calling. No other tortoise makes a similar sound.

During times of breeding activity, it is also important to monitor the animals for signs of excessive aggression; quite severe injuries can be sustained if this gets out of control. In some species males not only engage in ramming behaviour but also inflict potentially serious bites. These are most often situated on the female's limbs or face. The potential for secondary infection is obvious. The carapace condition in particular should be monitored for signs of excessive bruising which can lead to necrotic dermatitis (shell rot or SCUD - the acronym for Septicaemic Cutaneous Ulcerative Disease). Inter-male combat can prove equally dangerous. In all cases it is vital that all animals within the collection are checked regularly for early signs of injury and that troublesome animals are, if necessary, removed temporarily. The precise mix of the breeding group can have a major effect upon the behaviour of animals within the group. An excess of males can be especially problematic. Typically, a 3:1 ratio of females to males is the most satisfactory arrangement.

With aquatic or semiaquatic turtles the potential for injury in the breeding phase is even more acute. These animals tend to be not only highly aggressive but are also equipped with highly effective jaws designed for tearing flesh. With many such species, introduction of males to females is an operation fraught with difficulty and danger. Some species require the male to be introduced to the female's tank or territory; with others the opposite may be true. Unfortunately, even within species, aggressive behaviour often varies greatly from one individual to another. Only careful observation and monitoring on the part of the keeper can prevent disaster in such circumstances.

Some species, such as *Carretochelys insculpta*, present special difficulties in terms of their aggressive behaviour. In other species, aggression and competition between males may actually be a prerequisite to achieving interest in mating. Similarly, a violent advance towards females may, in some species, play a role in stimulating egg production or receptivity.

For obvious physical reasons the mating postures adopted by the various species of land tortoises are all very similar. The male assumes a mounted position, the tail probes for and locates the females cloacal opening. The male's engorged penis is then inserted into the cloaca of the female. The majority of aquatic species also adopt a similar mating posture, with the male typically grasping the female's carapace with his front claws and, frequently, also grasping her neck in his jaws. In most aquatic species, mating takes place underwater rather than on land or on the surface.

Size of females and sexual attractiveness

It has been frequently observed that if a male is exposed to two or more females, a definite preference is exhibited by many males for the largest. This effect can be observed in many terrestrial species including *G. pardalis* and *T. graeca* where it is very marked, but it may also play a role with many aquatic species. This can have negative consequences when a small male persistently attempts to mate the largest female present but is physically unable to perform the act properly. At the same time, available females of more suitable dimensions may be entirely ignored. The solution in such circumstances is to match pairs taking size into account and to remove large, tempting, but non-viable females from the breeding compound.

Temporary separation and introductions

Many long-established potential breeding groups may persistently refuse to engage in sexual behaviour. In many cases, interest can be stimulated by temporarily separating males and females for a few days to several weeks, then reintroducing them. This technique has proved highly effective with the majority of terrestrial and aquatic species. Another method is to obtain additional stock and introduce this, on a one-to-one basis, to selected members of the existing group. Sometimes separating males together will result in aggression and competitive behaviour; this may be a precursor to re-establishing reproductive activity.

Artificial insemination

The techniques of AI have infrequently been applied to tortoises or turtles. These techniques tend to be prohibitively expensive, have a low overall success rate, and are rarely justifiable in the case of testudines. A rare exception is where genuinely seriously endangered species are involved, as with *Asterochelys (Geochelone) yniphora*, the Madagascan Ploughshare tortoise at Honolulu Zoo. The attempt produced inconclusive results (Juvick, Meier and McKeown 1990), but is clearly worth considering in special cases when working with critically endangered, and uncooperative, tortoises and turtles.

Pre-nesting behaviour

Careful observation of a breeding group of tortoises will soon reveal clear indications that a particular female is carrying eggs and is getting ready to lay. These indicators are somewhat dependent upon the species involved, but can be summarised as a reduction in food intake; territorial type behaviour, i.e., attacking or mounting other females in sex-reversal type activity, climbing, or perimeter walking. The competent keeper will quickly learn to recognise these signs. The diagnosis can be confirmed, if necessary, by manually probing the female, by regular monitoring of weight (most females peak in weight around laying time) or by X-ray examination if a problem is suspected. Ultrasound scanning has also been used in tortoises and turtles, but the very nature of a turtle's shell presents unique difficulties for the method. Nonetheless, despite these difficulties, the technique holds much promise. In particular, ultrasound scanning can detect ovarian follicles and oviductal eggs (Kuchling, 1989). With this knowledge, it is possible to improve management of captive breeding groups. At present, the technique is infrequently available, expensive, and requires interpretation by skilled opera-

Average clutch density and sex determination methods of selected species

Species	Average density	Sex determination
Asterochelys (G.) radiata	9	Probable ESD
Chelodina longicollis	7-12	Genetic
Chersina angulata	1	Probable ESD
Chinemys reevesi	4-7	Unknown
Clemmys guttata	2-4	ESD
Clemmys insculpta	4-7	Genetic
Clemmys muhlenbergii	2-4	ESD
Cuora amboinensis	2-4	Unknown
Cyclemys dentata	2-4	Unknown
Furculacheys whitei	12-18	Probable ESD
Geochelone carbonaria	7-12	Probable ESD
Geochelone chilensis	2-4	Probable ESD
Geochelone elegans	2-4	Probable ESD
Geochelone pardalis	15-20	Probable ESD
Gopherus agassizii	4-7	Probable ESD
Homopus areolatus	2-4	Unknown
Kinosternon bauri	2-4	ESD
Malacochersus tornieri	1	Probable ESD
Manouria emys phayrei	40	Unknown
Manouria impressa	20	Unknown
Pelomedusa subrufa	12-15	Unknown
Pelusios castanoides	20	ESD
Pelusios subniger	5-9	Probable ESD
Platemys platycephala	4-7	Unknown
Rhinoclemmys funerea	2-4	Probable ESD
Rhinoclemmys punctularia	2-4	Probable ESD
Testudo graeca graeca	4-7	ESD
Testudo horsfieldi	4-7	Probable ESD

ESD, or TSD, occures in various pattern types in turtles. In one pattern there is a single transition zone below which incubation results in 100% male offspring and above which incubation results in 100% female offspring. In a second pattern, males predominate at intermediate temperatures and females result at either extreme. Some species may utilise a combination of ESD and genetic methods; it is suspected that *Emys orbicularis*, the European pond turtle, may be one such case.

Average egg dimensions of selected species

Species	Length	Width
Aldabrachelys (G.) gigantea	55.00 mm	50.00 mm
Asterochelys (G.) radiata	38.00 mm	38.00 mm
Chelodina longicollis	30.00 mm	20.00 mm
Chelodina oblonga	34.00 mm	20.00 mm
Chelus fimbriatus	36.00 mm	35.00 mm
Clemmys guttata	29.00 mm	16.00 mm
Cuora amboinensis	52.00 mm	30.00 mm
Emydura subglobosa	40.00 mm	20.00 mm
G. (X.) agassizii	44.00 mm	39.00 mm
G. *berlandieri*	48.00 mm	35.00 mm
G. p. babcocki	43.00 mm	43.00 mm
Geochelone chilensis	45.00 mm	33.00 mm
Geochelone sulcata	41.00 mm	41.00 mm
K. b. belliana	48.00 mm	38.00 mm
Kinosternon minor	27.00 mm	15.00 mm
M. e. phayrei	54.00 mm	54.00 mm
M. tornieri	47.00 mm	31.00 mm
Pelomedusa subrufa	32.00 mm	22.00 mm
Rhinoclemmys pulcherrima	51.00 mm	30.00 mm
T. c. carolina	32.00 mm	20.00 mm
T. g. graeca	30.00 mm	27.50 mm
T. h. boettgeri	40.00 mm	29.25 mm
T. h. hermanni	29.75 mm	24.00 mm
T. horsfieldi	47.00 mm	34.00 mm
T. ibera	36.00 mm	30.00 mm
T. kleinmanni	32.50 mm	23.50 mm
T. marginata	30.50 mm	28.00 mm

Egg dimensions are, in many species, highly variable. In other species they are remarkably consistent. Marked differences may occur between geographic subspecies, as is illustrated in the case of *Testudo hermanni*. In some species the size of the laying female exerts a direct influence upon egg dimensions. Young females also frequently produce abnormally sized eggs.

tors. It is therefore of principal interest in the management of critically endangered turtles. Ultrasound has also been employed with great success with other gravid reptiles, especially in the case of large snakes and iguanas.

Clutch size and egg dimensions

Land tortoises are by no means as prolific in egg production as most aquatic turtles - although some, i.e. *Manouria emys*, come close. The number of eggs laid in a clutch also varies considerably between species - from 1 single egg in the case of *Malacochersus tornieri* (the Pancake tortoise) to 20 or more eggs per clutch in *Geochelone pardalis* (table 1) and over 50 eggs per clutch in *M. emys phayrei*. Egg size also differs among species (and often subspecies) as table 2 shows. Fertility within clutches is usually high, at about 80% on average in most species. In the wild between 50% and 90% of hatchlings fail to reach adult breeding age due to predation and other causes. In captivity, with careful management, juvenile mortality can be reduced to practically nil. Many species also have more than one clutch of eggs per year. The reproductive potential of a small, but well managed, captive colony can therefore be quite high. With aquatic turtles even high rates of success can often be achieved due to the higher clutch density often produced (table 1). It should be noted that clutch density and egg size may be affected by the size and age of the producing female. Young females, early in their reproductive life, often lay unusually small eggs. Larger females often lay more and larger eggs than smaller specimens of the same species reflecting parallel increases in the dimensions of the pelvic opening (Congdon and Gibbons, 1987). It also appears that, in some species, egg dimensions may vary seasonally in a regular pattern. This has been observed in *Cuora amboinensis* (Inskeep, pers. comm.)

Above: Mating Red-foot tortoises, *Geochelone (Chelonoidis) carbonaria*

Chapter Two

EGGS AND INCUBATION

Most tortoise and turtle eggs have a very similar structure although the shape and size may vary considerably from species to species (table 2). They are formed from calcium carbonate in the form of aragonite rather than from calcite as found in bird eggs. The ratio of shell to yolk and albumen is also much higher than that found in birds, typically 16% in tortoises as opposed to a typical figure of 12% for most birds. The eggs of *Testudo graeca* for example consist on average of 44% albumen, 40% yolk, and 16% shell. There is a thick fibrous membrane between the inner surface of the shell and albumen. Shortly after laying contraction of the yolk and other contents causes an air cell to appear, usually at one end. This effect can be seen quite clearly if the egg is examined against a bright light source.

Eggs are usually round although some species produce elongate forms. In general large species tend to produce spherical eggs and small species to produce more elongate eggs. In general, rainforest and tropical tortoises and turtles also produce larger eggs than those from temperate habitats. The thickness and resilience of the shell wall also varies between species from the parchment-like thin and soft shell of *Terrapene carolina* (and many aquatic turtles) to the very hard and resilient eggs of *Testudo graeca*. If hard-shelled eggs are examined under the microscope, it will be seen that the surface comprises a series of radiating crystals of a spherical shape called sphaerulites; in some species pores occur at interstices between crystals. These pores are found in *G. elegans* but not in *T. graeca*, although externally, to the naked eye, their surfaces appear very similar.

Even the hardest of tortoise egg shells are permeable to a certain degree. Measurements of *Testudo graeca* eggs incubated at 30°C in a dry environment revealed weight losses of between 10% - 50% as a result of evaporation over a 12 week incubation period. This weight loss is interesting in that it contrasts directly with the situation pertaining to many other species of reptile some of which actually increase in weight over their incubation period by as much as 70% (i.e. cobra eggs increase not only in weight but also in size). Among the turtles, an increase in size during incubation is often noted in species which lay soft-shelled eggs, *Terrapene carolina,* for example.

Incubation humidity

In a series of tests I conducted some years ago it was observed that fertile eggs dehydrated the least whilst infertile eggs dehydrated the most. After 8 weeks at 30°C in a very dry incubation environment it became relatively easy to detect which eggs were fertile and which were infertile by weighing them on a set of sensitive electronic digital scales. For example, one batch of 7 eggs produced 4 fertile eggs which after 8 weeks all weighed between 11.25 grams and 13.00 grams and 3 infertile eggs which weighed between 6.00 grams and 8.5 grams. Comparative studies produced the further result that at least in the case of *Testudo graeca* no difference in hatching rates were noted irrespective of whether the incubation humidity was low (30%), moderate (50 - 60%) or high (90%+). However, infertile eggs dehydrated much more rapidly when the ambient humidity was very low.

It is probable that the formation of the various membranes and other tissue within fertile eggs serves to conserve internal fluids, and that the reason infertile eggs dehydrate so acutely is that lacking such membranes there is less of a barrier to the migration of fluids. It would seem that fertile hard-shelled eggs are relatively immune to variations in incubation humidity, at least within the limits tested. Nonetheless, it is probably sensible not to incubate at either extreme of humidity, just in case. Our experiments all took place within an incubator which had very little airflow over the eggs. We have since received reports that attempts at incubating *T. graeca* eggs in incubators intended for bird eggs have failed due to embryonic dehydration. The airflow in such incubators is much higher than that of our own static-air tortoise egg incubators and we felt that this factor was probably responsible for the failures. Sustaining a high incubation humidity is much more critical when soft-shelled turtle eggs are to be incubated. There is a temptation in such instances to reduce airflow as this makes it much easier to maintain high humidity but this could prove to be a costly mistake. Certainly, sealing eggs within plastic bags will keep them damp, but it will also cause anoxia. It is far better to use a properly designed incubator with a suitable substrate maintained at an appropriate level of humidity, for example vermiculite hydrated with water. Incubation substrates for soft-shelled eggs play an especially critical role. A mixture of sand, vermiculite, and sphagnum moss has proved consistently successful for this type of egg. In general, soft-shelled turtle eggs should be incubated at close to 100% relative humidity. For most other eggs, an incubation humidity of approximately 70% is suggested.

Oxygen and the developing embryo

The eggshell is not only permeable to water but also to respiratory and other gasses and this performs important metabolic functions during embryonic development. When this requirement is ignored in artificial incubation, deaths from anoxia must be considered a distinct possibility. The practice of incubating eggs in totally airtight containers is therefore to be strongly discouraged.

Whilst it is easier to maintain high levels of humidity in a sealed environment, tests have shown that carbon dioxide (CO_2) levels can accumulate rapidly in such situations. Embryonic anoxia is quite possibly the hidden factor responsible for many dead-in-shell and premature hatchlings encountered by captive breeders where other explanations such as incubator failure or genetic incompatibility can be discounted.

Where a sealed incubation environment has been used and high levels of mortality encountered, a change to a more natural and aerated incubation method will often produce an immediate and dramatic improvement in survivorship. It is a myth that because eggs are buried underground they require no oxygen or do not need to ventilate waste gasses. In fact, soil oxygen levels of most nesting sites are usually good and permeability comparatively high. Some turtle nests, excavated in damp sand, may be an exception to this general rule, however.

Developing tortoise and turtle eggs possess a functional internal lung in the form of the chorio-allantoic membrane. This allows gaseous exchange to occur through the eggshell. CO_2 is produced which must be expirated and fresh oxygen must be obtained from the outside world. In a sealed incubation environment CO_2 builds up and the oxygen supply eventually becomes depleted. A very high mortality is noted, particularly of full-term hatchlings. Survivors may be weak and in some cases display evidence of brain damage.

Other signs that embryonic anoxia may have occurred include a very high post-hatching mortality and hatchlings leaving the egg carrying excessively large egg-sacs, e.g. too early.

Certainly if full-term embryos are developing but suffering pre-hatching mortality the incubation technique is the most likely causal factor. Other possibilities include genetic defects and trace element (micro-nutritional) deficiencies. If the problem is occurring with several different species or sets of parents within the same program then the genetic factor is ruled out leaving only incubation technique or trace element deficiencies.

Finally, prospective turtle and tortoise breeders are advised to avoid living at high altitudes as this can profoundly affect the oxygen metabolism of eggs. Studies with birds have shown that at 3,800 meters only 16% of fertile eggs hatched compared to 90% at sea level.

The internal metabolism of the egg

The yolk of testudine eggs performs the same function as that of bird eggs providing lipoproteins (combined fats and proteins) originally manufactured in the liver of the female and transported via the blood-stream to the oviducts where it is formed into the yolk. In addition to fat and protein the yolk also contains other trace elements and vitamins including calcium, phosphorus and vitamin E. However, direct measurements of the calcium content of egg-yolks indicates that these contain insufficient calcium to supply the very heavy calcium demand of an embryonic developing tortoise. In the case of sea-turtles (the testudine species most intensively studied thus far) the disparity between yolk-calcium and the calcium content of a hatchling is approximately 400%. The excess requirement is met by the osteo-genesis of the calcium tied up in the shell. It is therefore also highly probable that mineral and other nutritional deficiencies in the adult female can seriously impair breeding viability and this will be discussed in some detail in chapter seven.

After the egg has been fertilised the embryo begins at once to draw upon the yolk for its sustenance. The exact site of fertilisation is unclear but is probably in the ifundibular area. The egg then rapidly moves along the albumen secreting magnum where it is propelled by muscular activity and pulsating hair-like cilia. The function of the albumen is again similar to that of the albumen of birds' eggs, providing fluid support and a small additional reserve of food. Most freshly laid tortoise eggs contain albumen which is gelatinous in parts and extremely fluid in others. Chalazae, the twisted fibrous spirals found in birds' eggs, are absent in tortoise eggs as they are in all reptilian eggs. Reptiles, unlike birds, do not turn their eggs during incubation and certainly, the lack of chalazae does tend to make the embryo more susceptible to disturbance.

In addition to the main yolk-sac three other important membranes occur within the testudine egg: the chorion, the amnion, and the allantois. The chorion, which is formed of ectoderm and mesoderm, occurs just beneath the inside surface of the eggshell. The amnion is similarly formed of ectoderm coated with mesoderm and develops into a fluid-filled sac which envelopes the growing embryo. The third membrane, the allantois, forms a receptacle for some of the nitrogenous waste of the embryo including precipitated uric acid and at the point of fusion with the allantois (chorio-allantois) performs the vital function of allowing oxygen and carbon dioxide exchange to take place through the walls of the egg.

It has been pointed out (Needham, 1931), that the difference between vertebrates which form urea (mammals and amphibians), and those that form uric acid (reptiles and birds), is closely connected with their mode of reproduction. The amphibian egg develops in water and the mammal embryo in the uterus where waste products are carried away by the blood of the mother. The embryonic development of birds and reptiles, however, takes place is a closed egg where only gasses are exchanged with the outside world. Waste products must remain within the shell. If urea were to be produced it would accumulate in solution. Uric acid, however, can be precipitated and therefore effectively eliminated.

Natural incubation and nest-site selection

Incubation in the wild consists of the female selecting a suitable nest site, then digging a suitable hole and depositing the eggs, leaving nature to do the rest. Although on the surface this may appear perfectly straightforward, in reality, her task is a complex one.

The selected area must comprise earth of the correct texture and humidity. If it is too loose or too stony emerging hatchlings may be trapped and suffocated. If it is too damp the eggs may rot and develop fungal growths. If too dry they may desiccate. Sites which are subject to flash flooding are also unsuitable. Anyone who has observed female tortoises or turtles in search of nest sites will readily attest to the tremendous care taken over the operation. Several test nests are often laboriously excavated then rejected for various reasons. This care is repeated in captivity.

The temperature of the nesting site is perhaps the most critical of all as successful incubation can only occur within a relatively narrow temperature band. The precise mechanisms by which female tortoises select nesting sites remain unclear but this is certainly an area worthy of detailed study.

Temperature measurements taken by the author at nest sites revealed that for *T. graeca* a ground surface temperature between 38°C and 42°C is often preferred. At approximately 75 mm below the surface, temperatures of between 27 °C and 31 °C were recorded at the same sites. In captivity provision of a suitable nest site is extremely important. Failure to provide an egg-bearing female with acceptable facilities frequently results in egg retention and consequent obstetric difficulties. Nesting can take some considerable time. Between 1 and 3 hours is average for most species although some take much longer. During this period the female carefully excavates a bell-shaped pit with her back legs before laying the eggs which comprise the clutch in rapid succession. The nest is then filled in, again

The nest is carefully excavated in a selected position using the hind legs. The nest may take several hours to prepare to the female's satisfaction.

using the back legs alone. Once deposited, the eggs should be removed as soon as possible for artificial incubation.

As stated above, in the wild nest site selection is obviously very critical and in captivity females usually take equal care. This can present problems, as it is not always easy to provide a suitable site which will satisfy her natural instincts.

Design of breeding accommodation

The provision of satisfactory breeding and nesting areas is critical to the success of any captive breeding project. Very often, however, this aspect is overlooked. If properly implemented a good breeding pen and nesting site will have a dramatic impact upon the number of eggs and hatchlings produced, and an equally dramatic reduction in stress caused to the animals and consequential disease problems.

Some useful guidelines for the design of breeding accommodation are as follows:

- Flat, featureless hard floor surfaces in breeding areas are associated with high rates of failure to obtain effective fertilisation. In the wild mating takes place on slopes, or on a natural earth surfaces which allow the female to raise her rear plastron sufficiently for the male to gain access. On a naturally undulating surface this is facilitated: on a flat concrete or grass floor, as seen in many collections, it is seriously inhibited. The larger the animals involved, the more important this appears to be. With Leopard, African Spurred, Galapagos and Seychelles tortoises it is vital that the mating area surface is adequately sculptured.

- Breeding areas require adequate cover for animals to retreat, and careful attention must be paid to stress and aggression levels. Females which are stressed may experience laying problems later. Provide plenty of space, and above all provide a few plants and hilly areas for animals to hide themselves. Exterior enclosure walls should be opaque; if they are transparent many animals will spend much of their time trying to climb either over or through them.

- Nesting areas should be raised, and preferably gently sloped. South-facing slopes and terraces are ideal. Flat and featureless nesting areas are associated with a high rate of egg retention problems. Nesting boxes should have an adequate substrate depth. For large tortoises a considerable depth of laying site substrate is essential. For *Geochelone carbonaria*, *G. sulcata* or *G. pardalis* at least 50 cm is required. More for very large specimens. Smaller species will often accept a substrate depth approximately equal to their own carapace length. If an adequate depth not is provided, this can easily result in aborted laying attempts and secondary complications. After many trials, we have found that providing each penned area with two separate nesting mounds is much preferred by the tortoises. Ours are made from a mixture of clay-type earth and sand, retained in position on three sides by surrounding timber logs. One side, gently sloped, is left open for easy access. A selection of plants is grown on the nesting mound, and the fine root structure of these greatly facilitates excavation of the nest chamber. In the wild, most nest sites adjoin similar root-infiltrated slopes. The extra element of choice allowed by providing more than one laying site in captivity definitely appears to reduce stress and facilitates problem-free nesting.

One special technique has proved useful with several species, terrestrial as well as aquatic, where the female seems to be experiencing problems in locating a suitable laying site. In this situation it is worth removing her to a separate area with a good depth of substrate of the appropriate type and with a 100 watt reflector lamp suspended about 50 cm above ground level. The female should be disturbed as little as possible. After a day or two in this environment, many otherwise reluctant females will lay without further difficulty. We have observed that some tortoises and turtles will lay in the early evening if maintained under a basking lamp, so when working with a problematic female, it may prove worthwhile persevering beyond normal activity times.

Oviposition and aquatic turtles

The problems associated with providing satisfactory laying sites for aquatic turtles are legion. There are several possible solutions but which is the most appropriate in the prevailing circumstances will depend upon the species concerned and space available. If an adequate laying area is not provided, females will usually lay their eggs in the water. This can lead to saturation of the eggs and consequent non-viability, or to the eggs being viewed as an interesting new food. For this reason it is important to make provision for safe laying and egg recovery. These various approaches can be summarised as follows:

Provision of a land area within turtle aquariums

A raised land area positioned under a basking lamp, provided it has sufficient depth, may be accepted as a laying site. A few plants located on the land area may assist acceptance. For pond-based installations, provision of a suitable bank or laying area is usually straightforward. Although flat laying areas are easier to provide, female turtles seem to greatly prefer sloped banks. These are well worth the extra effort involved in their construction as they substantially reduce egg-retention problems. Moistened peat, moss, and sandy soil are usually favoured substrate materials. In tank-based systems, however, the situation is more complex. Care must be taken to avoid the area becoming water-logged. To avoid water-logging I have often used deep plastic bowls or buckets heavily weighted with rock. The laying substrate is placed on top of this base material. Turtles can also be rather destructive animals, so expect to

A clutch of turtle eggs deposited in a natural nest of moist earth. For artificial incubation, they should be carefully removed and transported to the incubator as quickly as possible.

see large quantities of substrate deposited in the water. This can rapidly clog filters. A larger than normal tank will also be required if vital water area is not to be reduced. A new tank design which includes excellent laying facilities for aquatic specimens is described in chapter six.

Temporary removal to laying site

The success of this technique depends upon good observation of the breeding stock. When the female turtle reduces her food intake and behavioural changes indicate laying is imminent she should be removed to a separate laying tank. Thereafter she should be monitored constantly. In most cases, females which are ready to lay will do so within 2 - 3 days of relocation. Unfortunately, the upheaval of removal to a strange new environment may itself result in complications and refusal to lay. Some turtles accept this without evident stress; others are obviously distressed and may not accept the laying area on offer. Only time and experience with the particular specimens in question will determine the effectiveness of this method in a specific situation.

Artificial induction

This technique is also reliant upon early recognition of imminent oviposition. An experienced keeper will usually recognise when a female is about to lay and will confirm this diagnosis by manually palpating the female to establish the presence of eggs. These are usually best felt by probing gently in the region of the body cavity above the hind legs. X-rays can also be used to confirm the presence, number, and density of eggs. It should be noted that an experienced interpretation of X-ray results is important. If it is determined that the female is ready to lay, an injection of calcium followed by the hormone oxytocin should be given. In most cases the eggs will be deposited within 1-4 hours. This may take a little longer in some instances. For the psychological well-being of the female I feel that it is important that she is placed in an environment that has a suitable laying site during oxytocin induction. The results of this technique are very fast and one of the most successful turtle breeders I know uses this method almost exclusively. Neither females nor offspring demonstrate any long-term adverse effects. For suggested dosing schedules of calcium and oxytocin see under the heading of *Egg retention and dystocia* in Chapter 9.

Chapter Three

DESIGNING AND CONSTRUCTING AN INCUBATOR FOR TORTOISE OR TURTLE EGGS

Various suggestions for testudine egg incubators have been published. Some are excellent and well suited to the purpose, others leave much to be desired. The author is strongly opposed to any incubator which is dependent upon light bulbs for a heat source as these are simply not reliable enough for the purpose and the constant on-off cycle demanded by incubator use is almost guaranteed to induce filament failure sooner or later. This may well occur during the most critical phase of incubation and can result in the total loss of every egg within the unit. Fortunately, various low cost reliable and safe heaters of suitable design are fairly readily available from electrical and animal hobbyist sources. These can usefully be classified as follows:

Heating pads

These are widely available from exotic animal and aquarium suppliers in a range of sizes and wattage ratings. For use in a well-insulated incubator a small 35 - 50 W unit is generally more than adequate. The better quality brands are extremely reliable but some cheaper brands are liable to failure so should be avoided.

Miniature industrial heating elements and compact thermo-tubes

These are generally only available through industrial electronics suppliers and are intended for use in process control, drying cabinets and commercial installations. They may not be easily obtainable through ordinary retail channels although electronic hobbyist suppliers can sometimes help. Most consist of a low wattage (typically 60 - 100 W) ceramic element contained within a metal shielding. The thermo-tube variety are often sold as window demisters and as greenhouse heaters. This type of heater is typically sold by length rather than by wattage. For incubator use a 300 to 400 mm model is generally adequate.

The advantage of such units is their low cost and extremely high reliability. I have had one installed in an incubator of my own for over 10 years which has seen almost constant service and which looks like carrying on for at least as long again. For moderate humidity static air incubator use they are difficult to better and are definitely my own preference.

Submersible aquarium heaters

This sort of heater can be useful where it is necessary to maintain very high humidity levels. The heater (typically not more than 60 - 100 watts rating) is submerged in a water tray located in the base of the incubator cabinet or instead heats a water jacket surrounding the incubation media . This type of heating may be useful for incubating very soft eggs such as those produced by box turtles or aquatic turtles where humidity is especially critical. However, it has its dangers. The first and most important point is that should the water tray dry out, overheating of the element will occur very rapidly. At best the element will simply fail. At worst a fire could result. Although some breeders use this type of heater with entirely satisfactory results, my own view is that the dangers far outweigh the benefits and I do not recommend it.

Incubators for tortoise and turtle eggs, and reptile eggs generally, fall into two main groups, "dry" incubators and "wet" incubators:

Type I "dry" static air incubator design

A highly effective incubator which was designed by the author especially for incubating tortoise eggs which do not require a high incubation humidity is shown below. Although simple to construct, this incubator offers very precise temperature regulation and an easy inspection facility. The incubator is constructed from 15 mm chipboard, a material with excellent insulating properties. A transparent secondary lid is fitted to allow examination without heat loss; for this, Perspex® or polycarbonate sheet rather than glass is suggested. In the author's own incubators a 60 watt industrial heating element is fixed to the base but a heating pad would be equally suitable. The eggs are placed in plastic ice-cream or margarine cartons within the incubator and rest on a lattice-work of wooden bars suspended above the heater. A water tray and sponge provides a degree of ambient humidity, and the vermiculite substrate is also lightly dampened. The overall humidity is adjusted to around 70%.

Temperature control presents more of a problem. Two main types of temperature switch or thermostat are generally available. The first type relies upon a bi-metalic strip and electro-mechanical action. This sort is widely available in the form of both aquarium thermostats or central heating air-temperature thermostats. Provided one is selected which encompasses the temperature range required these may be perfectly satisfactory for general

A still-air tortoise egg incubator with electronic temperature control and a built-in digital thermometer. The heat source is a 60 watt element in the base. Eggs rest in plastic ice-cream tubs on a vermiculite or other suitable substrate.

For reliable temperature measurement, the remote probe from an electronic thermometer may be positioned in close proximity to the eggs.

use. They do however have their disadvantages. The first is that they are rarely very accurate and temperature swings or deviations of several degrees are quite possible. The other disadvantage is that should they ever fail they can jam either fully open or closed thereby causing a catastrophe.

The author now prefers entirely electronic non-mechanical thermostats. These are widely available at reasonable cost and offer much increased precision and reliability over mechanical types. Such devices should be available from specialist aquatic and exotic animal suppliers or alternatively from electronic component sources. This type of temperature controller is becoming increasingly popular with tropical fish hobbyists so locating a suitable unit should not be too difficult.

Using an advanced proportional electronic thermostat, a temperature tolerance of +/-0.25°C (measured directly at the egg container) was maintained over a 3 month period using the incubator illustrated. Whilst this sort of precision will not be required for general purpose incubation, where experiments into embryonic development or environmental sex determination (ESD) are concerned, extreme accuracy will be vital.

As a method of accurate temperature control the proportional method has few equals. Unlike on-off controllers (whether mechanical or electronic) there is no time-lag whilst heating elements warm up from cold and consequently much less chance of thermal overshoot. A time period, generally 10 seconds or so, is defined during which power is applied

A complete kit of parts for constructing an incubator, consisting of: a 40 watt heating pad, a small digital thermometer with remote probe, an electronic thermostat and a suitable enclosure made out of coated chipboard and glass.

For the high-humidity incubation of turtle eggs, a standard 'dry' tortoise egg incubator can quickly be adapted to provide a high humidity environment by means of a seed-tray propagator which includes a damp vermiculite substrate. The propagator is placed within the main incubator with its own plastic lid in place. This type of adaption is much safer and more effective than incubators which rely upon submersible aquarium heaters and a water bath.

to the heating load for a variable percentage of the proportional band. This percentage is determined by reference to an integrated circuit which measures deviation from the set point and either increases or decreases the percentage of power on time accordingly. The heating element itself remains warm, varying in temperature according to the percentage of time power is applied throughout the proportional band. There is no sudden surge of heat which has the additional benefit of reducing the likelihood of thermal shock damage to the element - a primary cause of failure in on-off type systems.

Type II high humidity incubator

Where a high humidity level is required throughout incubation the incubator shown above is recommended. Because of the humidity levels attained internally this unit must be constructed from moisture resistant materials; plastic, glass and marine grade plywood are all suitable. If plywood is used, be sure to seal with a thick coat of varnish - but ensure that this is thoroughly dry and well aired before use to allow potentially toxic fumes to dissipate. I would recommend leaving the unit for at least 8 weeks before use.

A 60 watt heat-pad rests beneath plastic plant propagators containing a vermiculite and sphagnum moss substrate which is hydrated 1:1 with water. To sustain local humidity, the plastic lids these units are normally supplied with are also utilised. Temperature control is provided by means of a proportional-type controller and is monitored by means of an electronic digital thermometer fitted with a remote sensing probe. Incubation humidity in this type of incubator can easily be maintained in excess of 90%. The use of an electronic relative humidity meter is also highly recommended in conjunction with the incubator.

This type of incubator has proved highly successful with a wide range of aquatic and semiaquatic species which produce soft-shelled eggs and is used routinely for such at the Tortoise Trust. It is much safer in use and more reliable than the "wet" type incubators used previously which relied upon a submerged aquarium heater.

Emergency or field research incubators

On many occasions I have adapted the Styrofoam® or polystyrene cartons which tropical fish are sometimes packed in to form very functional and low-cost incubators. Where only a very few eggs are to be incubated these can make an ideal base for conversion. The inside can be lined with plywood sheeting, and a heat pad can provide the heat source. It may sometimes be necessary to use an incubator in a region where high-technology components are simply not available, or even where a reliable power source is unavailable. The key to success in these circumstances is to minimise heat loss via good insulation and, by that route, reduce the amount of input power required by the system. The better the insulation the more practical the incubator becomes. Low voltage heaters can often be obtained from automobile sources. Even car headlamp bulbs can be pressed into use - two of these wired in series and run on reduced voltage will produce considerable heat and minimal light. Aquarium heaters (provided low voltage models can be found) are also ideal. For power, solar cells combined with an automobile battery offers great potential. In most tropical research situations, this power source is probably by far the best option. Even in the total absence of electrical power it is possible to make a functional incubator. Black coloured water storage drums placed in the sun will accumulate a great deal of heat which can be used to provide overnight warmth for incubating eggs. The greater the mass of the heat accumulator, the more stable the improvised incubator will be.

Warm room or ambient incubation

In large-scale installations, it is not uncommon to find a particular room which is maintained at a more or less constant temperature. A tropical room in a snake house is a good example. Provided temperatures within the room are relatively stable, and within normal incubation parameters it may be possible to use a convenient shelf within the room for egg incubation. Checks can be made for suitability using the digital thermometers described below. One of the most successful turtle breeders I know uses his basement for egg incubation; no additional local heating of the eggs is required. The basement is heated to approximately 29°C and the humidity is high due to the large number of turtle aquaria it contains. Both turtle and tortoise eggs are contained within plastic trays, lightly covered with a lid, and placed on a shoulder-high shelf in a draught-free location. There is some slight fall in temperature overnight, but generally temperature management in this installation is excellent. If such a facility is available, it is certainly worth investigating its incubation potential.

Stabilising the incubator

Most incubators will require 24 hours or so to stabilise, so it is worth ensuring that an incubator is running satisfactorily well before it is actually required. Temperature adjustments take time to make and do not register instantly. One important point to note is that the thermal mass present within the incubator plays a critical role in temperature stabilisation. The greater the mass present the more stable the incubator will tend to become. In practical terms, a fully loaded incubator will, therefore, tend to behave with greater thermal stability than an almost empty one.

Even if only a single clutch of eggs is to be incubated, it is well worth placing substrate in the unused egg trays as this will impart a greater thermal mass and consequently better overall stability. Similarly, if you wish to measure the actual or true temperature of the incubating eggs, this is best achieved by placing the thermometer probe right next to the eggs, and in contact with the substrate. The air temperature inside the incubator will fluctuate much more rapidly and may give a misleading impression, so do not rely upon internal air temperature readings. It is also important to be aware of the fact that the upper reaches of the incubator

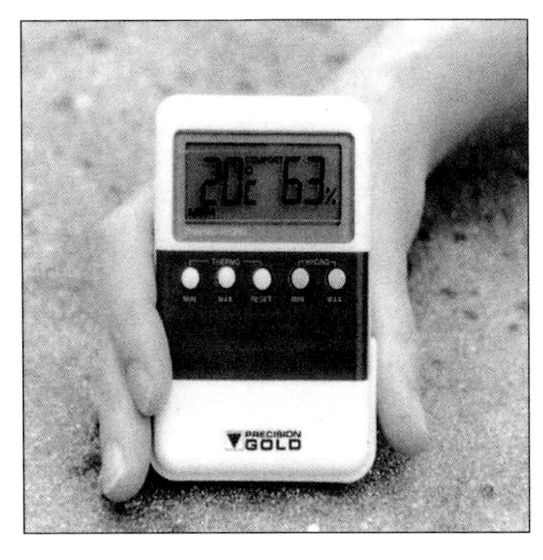

A combined digital thermometer and relative humidity meter. Such devices are ideal for environmental monitoring in incubators and for many other herpetological applications.

will be warmer than the bottom. To incubate a large number of eggs at the same temperature an incubator with a large internal horizontal surface area will be required. Stacking egg trays can certainly work, but they will not all be at the same temperature (this can prove useful, however, when seeking to influence sex by temperature and only one incubator is available). A few minutes experimentation with a fast reacting digital thermometer will prove both instructive and fruitful.

Dual temperature range incubation

It is a relatively simple matter to construct an incubator which will provide a cyclic incubation temperature. This may be required for experimental purposes, or to replicate a natural diurnal temperature pattern. The easiest way of achieving this is to use two (or more) pre-set electronic thermostats operated by a time switch. At a pre-determined time the active thermostat is changed over. In this way, an overnight temperature drop or mid-day peak can easily be achieved.

Temperature measurement

Although equally as important as temperature control, temperature measurement is often overlooked. There is little point in adjusting highly accurate thermostats on the basis of incorrect readings from unreliable thermometers. Experiments with alcohol and mercury thermometers revealed that low-cost types were almost invariably inaccurate. If such thermometers are to be employed, then those supplied for use in photographic processing are often the most satisfactory.

Modern electronics provides another option in the form of low cost and very satisfactory self-contained Liquid Crystal Digital (LCD) temperature modules which operate from 1.5 volt miniature batteries. Such units are now available at relatively low cost compared to a few years ago when they were exclusively in the domain of the laboratory and industrial user . The modules regularly used by the author provide a LCD display calibrated either in °C or in °F and are accurate to 0.1 °C in most cases. In addition, some models can be set to sound an audible alarm at certain temperatures, a very useful facility indeed where heater or thermostat failure can have such catastrophic consequences.

It can sometimes be useful to know the degree of variation both above and below the target temperature set during any given period; for example if a batch of eggs are incubated at 31.5 °C it would be very advantageous to know if overnight this temperature was actually maintained or if it suffered a fall. Such a measurement can be taken with a maximum-minimum recording thermometer and both mercury/alcohol and electronic versions are available. I much prefer electronic maximum - minimum types as these do not require physical removal to re-set (most mercury types have to be vigorously shaken down or a button pressed after each reading has been taken). With electronic models everything can be carried out remotely by means of a switch conveniently positioned outside the incubator thereby avoiding the need to disturb the unit unnecessarily.

Humidity control and measurement

The easiest way to control incident humidity within the incubator is to position a tray of water in the base and to remember to re-fill it from time to time. Very accurate laboratory quality electronic relative humidity meters and controllers are available but are at present comparatively expensive. Whilst this may be justified in the case of research activities for day-to-day incubation purposes they are hardly essential. New, low cost designs which are almost (but not quite) as accurate have now appeared on the market. These operate in much the same way as the digital thermometers mentioned earlier; indeed, some models combine the functions of a humidity meter and thermometer. These are ideal for zoological use and in tests conducted by the author have proved more than accurate enough for incubation monitoring purposes.

Incubation substrates

It is recommended that the eggs be placed in an open-topped plastic lunch box type container within the incubator and that vermiculite or a similar insulating particle medium should be used instead of sand. Other suitable alternatives include polystyrene packaging material or agricultural potting medium combined with vermiculite - the latter is especially suitable where high humidity levels are required. Sand, which is perhaps the most obvious choice, should definitely be avoided as it can set very hard indeed during the prolonged incubation period and can entomb emerging hatchlings. It is also extremely dangerous if ingested and its well known abrasive qualities can all too easily cause serious damage to delicate eyes or mouths. For high humidity incubation of turtle eggs, both damp vermiculite and a mixture of peat, moss and sand have proved consistently successful.

Bio-erosion of turtle eggshells

There are some indications that in the case of certain aquatic testudines the pH of the incubation media may affect viability. Unfortunately, specific data on this topic is not readily available and it is evident that further research is called for. The eggs of certain alligators have, however, been investigated in this respect (Ferguson, 1981). The problem appears to affect South American chelid turtles to a greater extent than other species. *Chelus fimbriatus*, *Phrynops* and *Platemys* species in particular appeared sensitive to pH in incubation (Lehmann, 1987). In these species it was found that eggs incubated in a sterile media experienced mortality at a late stage in development whilst those incubated in an acidic media hatched normally. It is evident that the micro climate surrounding a naturally incubating egg has a far higher level of biological (and chemical) activity than is normal in most artificial incubation situations. The mechanism appears to involve carbonic acid from decaying vegetation producing a slightly acidic region (pH 6) around the eggshell. Calcium degradation in turn will affect oxygen permeability and structural integrity. Soil bacterial activity may also play a role. It is also likely that these factors affect different species in different ways. The practical techniques described here are based upon practical experience and reports from numerous breeders around the world. In the vast majority of cases they will suffice without modification. If problems are experienced, especially with rare or little studied species, then experiments with different incubation media are probably justified. A useful acidic incubation medium is peaty soil. This holds moisture well and tends to be biologically active. It can easily be combined with vermiculite.

Egg positioning

It is not generally advisable to completely bury the eggs. In a stable incubator half-burying or even resting them on the surface should be perfectly adequate. With soft-shelled eggs I generally half-bury them; with hard-shelled eggs I find surface incubation consistently satisfactory. However, if it is suspected that soil pH may be a factor then the eggs should be covered to allow all-round contact with the incubation medium.

As the time for hatching approaches, the open top of the incubating box can be carefully covered with coarse linen gauze or netting. Otherwise unexpected hatchlings might escape within the incubator and injure themselves.

Incubation period, temperature and sex determination

Incubation time is typically determined not only by species but also by temperature. The higher the temperature the faster development tends to occur. This is not an absolute rule and some clutches seem to defy the general trend. Very high temperatures however can lead to deformity and death so it is vital to establish acceptable ranges for each species of egg it that is intended to incubate. Typical symptoms of excessive incubation temperature include hatchlings with distorted or deformed scutes, or eye, mouth and limb deformities.

As a guide, the normal parameters for the eggs of *T. hermanni* are as follows:

<26 °C = Incubation normally ineffective.

26 °C - 29.5 °C = All male offspring within 75-140 days.

30 °C - 32 °C = Typically mixed brood within 65-80 days (but see comments below).

32.5 °C - 33 °C = All female offspring within 60-75 days.

>34 °C = Deformed or dead-in-shell hatchlings likely.

For *Geochelone carbonaria*, the Red-foot tortoise, incubation at 32°C will produce predominantly female hatchlings whilst 27.5°C and below will result in mainly males.

Note that this also introduces the effects of ESD, or Environmental Sex Determination, sometimes also called Temperature dependant Sex Determination, or TSD. Whilst ESD parameters have now been established for some common species, at the time of writing many species have not been investigated at all in this respect. Much field and laboratory work is crying out to be done in this fascinating and potentially highly rewarding area which has very profound implications for the conservation of endangered species of reptiles world-wide. It is not yet clear, for example, if localised populations of the same species have differing ESD points within a wider geographical range. There is some suggestion that they might. Only further experimentation with examples from precisely known localities will tell.

In the case of tortoises, terrapins, and turtles low temperatures typically produce male offspring, whilst higher temperatures usually produce females. This is in marked contrast to certain other reptiles where sex is determined by temperature, particularly alligators and some lizards where the reverse is true. It also appears that some species possess multiple ESD threshold points, for example, see *Chelydra serpentina* in the species profile section in part two of this volume. The situation is further complicated by the fact that it appears that soft-shell turtles (genus *Apalone/Trionyx*) and members of the genus *Clemmys* possess sex chromosomes and hence do not employ ESD. In the case of most terrestrial testudines, the practical relevance of all this is that even when dealing with a species where precise details of critical ESD points (or threshold temperatures) are unknown, the best general advice that can be offered is to incubate at 30°C. In many cases this will result in a mixed-sex brood. However, there is some evidence that incubating at constant temperatures in the threshold region may contribute toward the production of intersexed specimens (these are also known to occur naturally), i.e. hermaphrodite turtles (Pieau, 1975). Also, it is often more desirable from the reproductive potential aspect to produce more females than males. Few natural populations contain a 1:1 male-female ratio, and in practice, from the reproductive potential aspect a female to male ratio of at least 3:1 is likely to prove most beneficial.

Most incubators are set to provide a constant temperature throughout the entire incubation period. In fact, for ESD, although an accurate incubator is required it is not necessarily the case that a constant temperature is required throughout the entire incubation process. In most species so far studied, a critical factor is the time in the embryonic development process at which different temperatures are experienced. In some species this sex determination window may be very narrow or precise; in others more latitude may exist. Unfortunately, a great deal is still unknown, and very few species have yet been studied in adequate detail. In those species which have been studied in detail (mainly North American aquatic species; virtually nothing is known about the majority of tropical species), environmental temperatures during the middle third of the incubation period appear to be most critical in determining sex. In some species, it also appears that a daily exposure to a certain temperature can influence sex; *Chelydra serpentina* eggs exposed to 30°C for 4 hours or more a day result in all-female neonates (Wilhoft, 1983).

These points need to be considered when planning ESD based incubation projects. The published literature on ESD is not (yet) a sufficiently reliable guide upon which to base large or important incubation projects. There are too many variables and too few certainties. The wisest course of action is undoubtedly to conduct experiments in determining what ESD thresholds (if any) apply for the specific reproductive group involved. This will obviously take time (it can prove difficult to sex turtles reliably until they have attained a certain size) but is ultimately the only reliable method of managing gender in captive-bred turtles. If there is not sufficient time to conduct such experiments, then the next best option is probably to run at least two separate incubators - one set at the estimated "female" end of the temperature spectrum, the other at the estimated "male" end. This will at least reduce the chances of large numbers of an unwanted sex being produced in isolation. Unfortunately, many books and articles available to the would-be captive breeder suggest incubation temperatures which are far too low, often in the 22 - 27°C range. At these temperatures, in the majority of species,

Transilluminating eggs can provide a useful guide to viability. In viable eggs, the formation of blood vessels may be seen. In non-viable eggs (as shown) the yolk may precipitate and dehydrate. Viable eggs will gradually become opaque as the embryo develops. A small air-space may, however, remain visible.

either all male neonates would result or incubation would fail altogether.

Handling tortoise and turtle eggs

The effects of handling upon reptile eggs is also an area where all is by no means clear. The indications are that gentle handling following laying should not have any deleterious effect but that rough handling should definitely be avoided after embryonic development is advanced to a point where any physical trauma could damage delicate blood vessels. Fragile soft-shelled eggs are clearly in greater danger from rough handling than hard-shelled varieties. I have conducted a series experiments, using several species, where eggs have been gently inverted at mid-point in the incubation cycle. This did not appear to affect overall viability, although several hatchlings emerged upside down. Other researchers have carried out similar experiments with very much the same result. One possible exception, however, is *Chelydra serpentina* where rotated eggs do appear to have a lower hatch rate. Feldman (1983) noted a 50% mortality following rotation.

It is actually nothing more than a myth that eggs must be transported to the incubator the same way up as they were deposited in the nest. At this stage the egg contains no more than a few active cells and these are in no way affected by orientation. Later, after an embryo has formed, orientation becomes increasingly important, so after the first few days, eggs should not be inverted or otherwise handled unnecessarily.

Examination of eggs during incubation

It is often possible to determine whether or not incubating eggs are fertile by carefully examining them against a strong light source. A small box, containing a 15 watt bulb with a hole cut in the top to hold the egg, is ideal for this purpose. Miniature pocket torches are also a useful tool for this purpose. When subject to transillumination in this way, an egg can be examined at various stages of its development.

Such examination can usually reveal entirely infertile eggs quite easily, and those containing large embryos are also quite easy to detect; however, it is not always possible to be 100% certain in borderline cases. I would certainly be very reluctant to discard any egg merely on the basis of a visual examination unless the evidence was absolutely conclusive. Another considerably more advanced technique which has been employed with success to determine egg tortoise and turtle egg viability is that employing Doppler ultrasound examination. This can actually reveal embryonic heart-beat and blood flow within the egg.

One very useful visual check which can be carried out without physically disturbing the eggs is to note any colour change. Fertile eggs usually darken and gradually lose the pinkish hue of fresh laid examples. This change is actually caused by expansion of the vitelline sac and the way in which it occurs varies between species. In North American mud turtles, for example, a white band appears around the mid-line of the egg. In other species, a white spot may form; in yet other species, the whitening is more general. Their surface texture also becomes less reflective and somewhat less smooth to the touch - this is due to elements such as calcium being gradually lost from the shell as embryonic development continues. In the case of infertile eggs, the composition of the eggshell remains unchanged.

It is worth noting some particular problems which may come to light during routine examination:

Fungal infections of eggs

This condition is usually associated with high humidity incubation of turtle or terrapin eggs. The presence of fungus does not necessarily indicate that the affected egg is infertile. Affected eggs are, however, best removed to a separate container to avoid the possibility cross-infection. Biochemical analysis of turtle and tortoise eggs has shown that healthy eggs may possess inherent antibiotic and antimycotic properties. *Aspergilus* and *Penicillium* fungus spores were killed by albumen from *Testudo horsfieldi* eggs, for example (Movchan, 1964 and 1966). Some bacterium were similarly affected, but other notorious pathogens including *Pseudomonas* species were unaffected - emphasising the overall need to avoid cross contamination from possible carrier adults or infected incubation media.

Collapsed and dented eggs

This is most frequently encountered with soft-shelled eggs. It usually indicates infertility or inadequate incubation humidity. However, some hard-shelled eggs may be subject to distortion before laying and subsequently manifest with this condition. By no means are all such eggs non-viable, and it is certainly worth incubating them.

Cracked eggs

This usually indicates that the egg is infertile, especially if accompanied by foul smelling discharge. Eggs in this condition should normally be discarded. Some eggs crack without any evident discharge. These may remain viable and should not be discarded. An emergency repair can sometimes be achieved using a thin smear of silicone aquarium sealer; this technique has worked with the eggs of both aquatic and terrestrial species. Cracking may also be caused by out-of-range temperature or humidity.

Colour changes

Colour changes are not necessarily diagnostic of failure. Eggs may darken considerably and still remain viable. Some eggs, mainly soft-shelled varieties, have been observed to take on a wide range of strange hues; blue, yellow and green - despite this, some have remained viable. Some degree of darkening, the loss of an initial pink hue and gradual dulling of the egg surface is perfectly normal and is associated with expansion of the vitaline sac and absorption by the embryo of calcium from the surrounding shell as discussed previously.

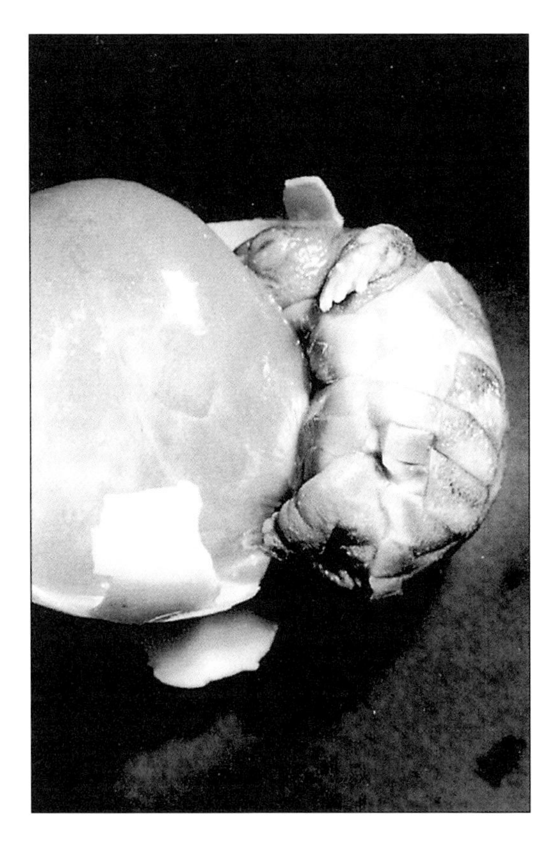

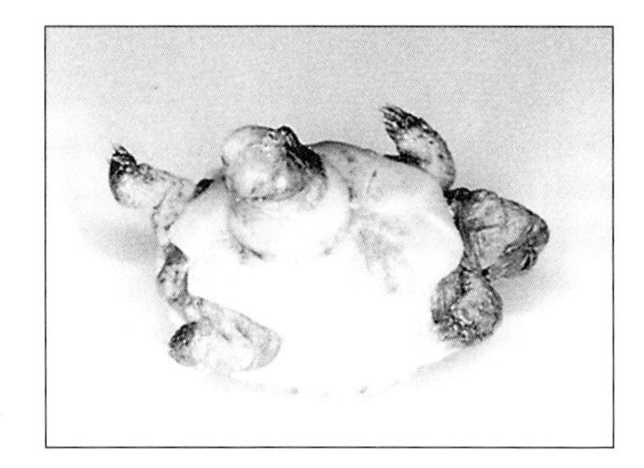

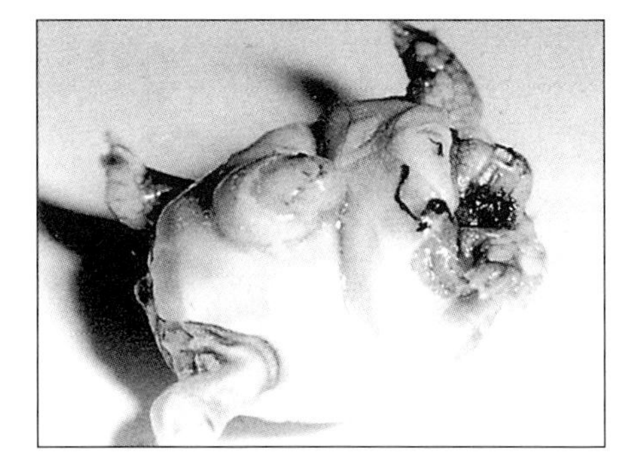

Above left: An abnormally large egg-sac is present on this very premature hatchling. It has no chance of survival. *Top right:* This hatchling has a fairly large egg-sac and is slightly premature. Normally, it would have remained within the egg until it had been fully absorbed. *Bottom right*: An average sized egg-sac on a normal hatchling.

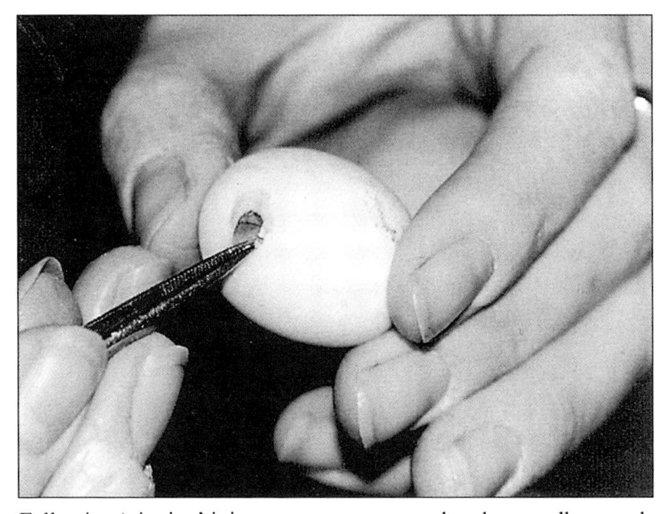

Above: Following 'pipping' it is necessary to ensure that the egg albumen does not dry out and form a 'glue' which can obstruct the neonate's airway. This is not a common problem, but nonetheless can lead to mortalities.

Above: Immediately after hatching, the neonate is rounded in appearance. The body shape will develop normally after a few days. Note the vertebral scute deformities present in this otherwise perfectly healthy hatchling *T. graeca*

Above: The plastron is also folded immediately following hatching. It straightens out over a period of 24 to 48 hours.

Fly larvae and turtle eggs

Fly larvae have been reported to infect turtle eggs, but are generally only encountered in natural nests. Acuna-Mesen and Hanson (1990), however, describe a case of *Rhinoclemmys pulcherrima* eggs becoming infected by *Phorid* fly larvae within an artificial incubator. Obviously, where this is a possibility extra hygiene precautions should be adopted. The presence of small dust mites within the incubator, however, should not give rise to concern. These are entirely harmless and will affect neither the egg nor hatching neonates.

Finally, it is worth remembering to guard against power failures when incubating eggs. Some power services, especially in rural areas, can be unreliable. A short failure, except in winter, is unlikely to prove disastrous, but long cuts in supply can wipe out months of effort at a stroke. For really important projects, or for the naturally cautious, a small standby generator may be considered a worthwhile investment. Alternatively, consider including a secondary low voltage heating element which will automatically cut in should a mains failure occur. In a dire emergency, the small chemically-based hand warmers sold by outdoor suppliers can supply several hours of useful heat. These can also be used should it ever be necessary to re-locate incubating eggs. I have transported eggs in a Styrofoam® container this way several times with no apparent ill effects.

Diagnosis of incubation failures and neonate mortality

If hatching rates are consistently below 70% this indicates that in all probability there is a defect either in incubation technique (see above) or in the overall viability of the eggs themselves. A large number of dead-in-shell or hatchlings which emerge in a weakened condition is a positive indicator that a serious problem exists.

Excluding incubation failures which are discussed above, such as embryonic anoxia, special substrate pH requirements or temperature drift outside safe parameters, some common causes of embryonic or neonate mortality are:

- Genetic defects inherited from one or both parents. In such cases, a high percentage of surviving offspring may exhibit developmental defects and deformities. This is usually relatively straightforward to diagnose as only eggs from a specific parentage will be affected. Changing the combination of parents or excluding a suspected carrier of genetic defects from the breeding program will produce a complete solution to the problem.

- Trace element deficiencies. These are extremely difficult to diagnose accurately and often the only method is to proceed on an empirical basis, testing the addition of appropriate supplements to the diet of breeding stock and monitoring results. Little specific research has been carried out in this field with reptiles, but dramatic results have been reported in the case of avian egg incubation. For example, hatch rates of commercially bred poultry increased from 50% to 80% following supplementation with a range of mineral trace elements. Selenium, zinc, copper, and manganese appear to be particularly important in this respect. A selenium deficiency has been indicated as a cause of thickened amniotic membranes, for example. It also seems probable that vitamin A, E, C and D deficiencies in adult breeding stock may have a profound effect upon egg viability. It would seem prudent, therefore, to ensure that adult breeding stock is always provided with an adequate intake of essential trace elements and that other aspects of their diet are also carefully regulated.

- Breeding exhaustion. An unfortunately rather vague term which describes a syndrome whereby previously highly productive reproductive pairs generate offspring which are increasingly weak and prone to ever increasing rates of mortality. The precise cause is difficult to identify and it is probable that many factors are involved. Genetic weaknesses, egg and sperm counts and micro-nutritional (trace element) deficiencies probably number among these. The best corrective treatment is prevention. Subjecting animals to a continual breeding cycle is not recommended. A season's rest occasionally can improve long-term breeding condition and viability.

Other possible, but much less common, causes of embryonic or neonatal mortality include toxicity from materials used in incubator construction (new chipboard has a high formaldehyde content), paint fumes, or organophosphorous poisoning either from fly killers or airborne over-spray from pesticide application. Caution should be exercised with all these products in the vicinity of incubating eggs and juveniles.

Above: Additional, missing, or asymmetrical scutes are a minor, but common deformity. Most are caused as a result of genetic factors. Adult wild tortoises and turtles with such deformities are often encountered. There is evidence that similar deformities can be caused in some turtles by incubation at excessively high temperatures or at an incorrect level of humidity.

Chapter Four

HATCHING AND JUVENILE CARE

As a developing embryo within the egg increases in size its metabolism produces an increasing quantity of carbon dioxide. Eventually, this rises to a level in excess of that which can be diffused via the allantois and the pores in the eggshell (the gradual utilisation of calcium from the eggshell actually increases this porosity and gradually weakens the shell as development continues). Eventually the embryo's blood and tissue CO_2 levels rise to such an extent that the embryo begins to convulse in an effort to breath normally. The head moves into the airspace within the egg created by evaporation, and lung breathing begins. This airspace rapidly becomes foul, however, and even stronger contractions and convulsions commence. The shape of an egg dictates that it resists compression but has little tensile strength. Only slight pressure from within is sufficient to fracture it.

In many cases, hatching in the wild coincides with the first rainfall following the hot summer incubation period. As the ground becomes saturated by water, its permeability to oxygen is drastically reduced. This causes a corresponding rise in CO_2 levels within the buried eggs which in turn triggers emergence.

Some years ago the author conducted a few experiments involving different levels of incubation humidity and the effect upon hatching. I observed that if, towards the expected hatching time, the air humidity level in the incubator was raised sharply this would tend to result in a much greater proportion of eggs hatching simultaneously than if the air humidity was not raised.

The phenomenon of bimodality in tortoise and turtle hatching times has been noted but is not by any means well understood. Bimodality in the context of hatching is defined as eggs from the same clutch, incubated under identical conditions, but which actually hatch at different times. It is well known that marine turtle eggs typically hatch over a very short period and that the young tend to leave the nest together. However, in tortoise eggs, it has been noted that often the time between the first hatching and the last within a clutch can be very extended. Examples include *Asterochelys (Geochelone) radiata* where one egg hatched after 121 days but another from the same clutch took 211 days to emerge, and *Geochelone pardalis* where quite frequently in can take 3 - 4 weeks for a clutch to complete hatching. In both *Testudo ibera* and *T. hermanni* a delay between the first and last emergence from a clutch of between 7 - 12 days is not at all uncommon. Even longer delays are not unheard of.

It is normal for neonates to remain within the egg for many hours, or even days, once 'pipping' has occurred. During this time, any remaining egg-sac is gradually absorbed.

The biological reasons for this effect remain unclear. However, in one experiment I carefully monitored the incubation temperature differential between several eggs all from the same clutch which I incubated artificially using a precision incubator. At no time did the eggs differ in temperature from one another by more than 0.3°C throughout the entire incubation process. However, periodic examination of the eggs by transillumination revealed startling differences in the rate of embryonic development, the most extreme example being that of one egg which attained hatching proportions whilst its nearest neighbour remained less than half its size. For some reason or another it appears that on occasions embryonic development is temporarily arrested in individual eggs within a clutch.

There is clearly a biochemical mechanism at work here, sometimes known as diapause, which requires further investigation. So far, research has confirmed that the process occurs regularly in the North American Chicken turtle (*Deirochelys reticulata*) and revealed that the trigger for resumed development is a drop in incubation temperature at a critical time. Unfortunately, we do not, at present, know how common the same phenomenon is among other testudines.

The crucial lesson for captive breeders is not to expect all eggs to hatch "on time" and under no circumstances to make the (usually fatal) mistake of artificially cracking open what are assumed to be late eggs. That said, in the case of certain aquatic testudines truly synchronous hatching is commonplace. Clearly, the first hatchlings initiate a 'message' to their siblings that it is time to emerge. If this first hatchling is premature, then a serious situation ensues. Unfortunately, there is not much which can be done about this other than to remove the premature hatching initiator as quickly as possible - hopefully before a full scale hatch is triggered.

As the hatching process begins, hatchlings first abrade and then pierce the eggshell using an egg-tooth like appendage, actually an egg caruncle, gradually enlarging this opening by biting small pieces from the eggshell and pushing with the front legs. As soon as hatching begins the eggs should be kept under continuous observation. Hatching can take some time; between 2-5 hours is average for *T. graeca* and *T. hermanni*. Once access to air has been gained, the young tortoise will often stay in the egg for a day or more gradually gaining in strength and allowing time for the egg-sac to be properly absorbed. If a hatchling is in obvious trouble and is clearly weakening then careful assistance can be given. Provided that hatching is in full progress, giving such aid will not do any harm. One particular problem, frequently observed, involves the neonate becoming glued to the eggshell by highly adhesive albumen or gelatinous membrane residues. The eyes, nares and mouth in particular are often involved. Should this occur, gentle wiping with sterile water on a cotton tipped probe will usually assist removal of the offending substance. If the eggshell appears to be unusually thick and is causing real problems then assistance is recommended. This can occur if the eggs have been retained in the female for a longer-than-usual period. Indeed, on occasions, twin-walled eggs are found. Such eggs are extremely hard and very likely to cause an emerging hatchling serious trouble. Usually however the walls in such cases are so thick that mortality from anoxia would have occurred long before full development has been attained.

Unless hatching has commenced naturally and it is quite clear that the time for emergence is at hand the eggs should not be otherwise disturbed. Under no circumstances should eggs be artificially cracked open on the supposition that they are 'late' and hence must be in difficulty. This type of action, which is often initiated by inexpert and impatient keepers can only result in tragedy with half formed and doomed hatchlings being suddenly being torn from their eggs.

Immediately hatching is complete, each young tortoise as it emerges should be removed from the incubator into a previously prepared hatching vivarium or nursery unit. The now-vacant eggshells should also be removed to the hatchling unit as these provide an excellent source of calcium in the critical early days. Many hatchlings will avidly gnaw at them - failure to provide access to the eggshells, often discarded as of no value by many keepers, can result in early-stage calcium deficiencies. Recently, during field-work in Morocco, I examined a number of wild *T. graeca graeca* faeces samples under the microscope. Both tortoise egg and snail shell fragments were evident, demonstrating that these valuable sources of calcium are utilised where possible. As will be seen from the table below, in the first month the percentage growth and weight gain of hatchlings is very considerable.

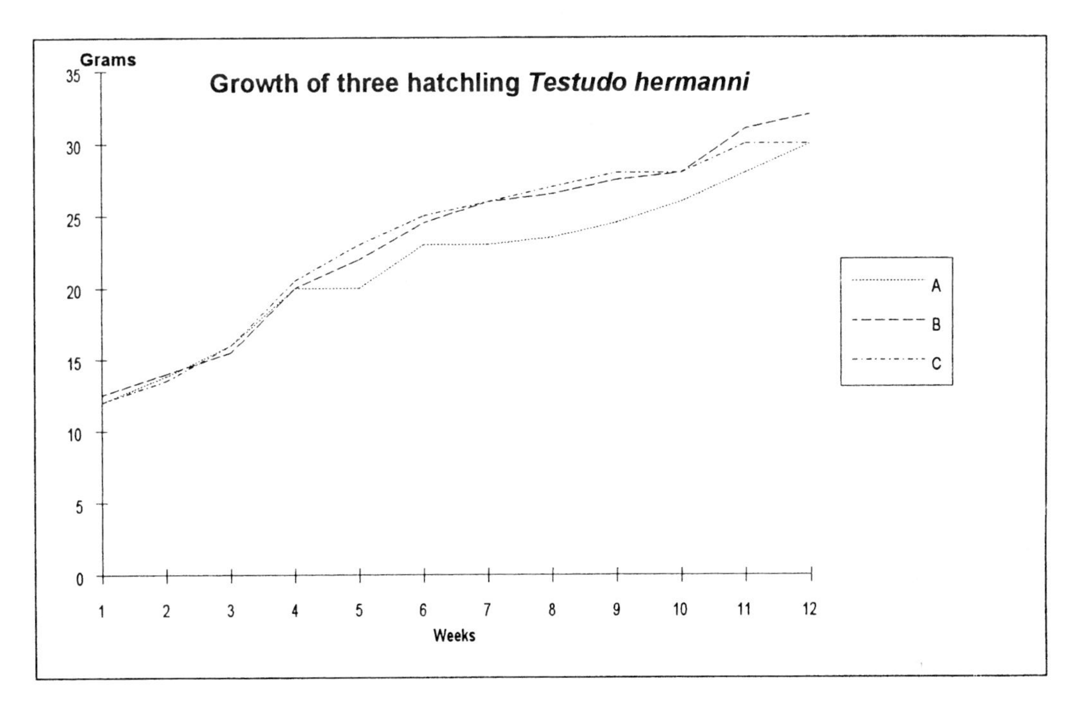

Their calcium demand during this time is also considerable and deficiencies can easily occur. At this point in the hatchling's life the balance between the calcium-mineral metabolism and protein metabolism is extremely fragile. Inadequate levels of dietary minerals or excessive quantities of dietary protein will very rapidly result in the initiation of early stage osteodystrophy leading to the later manifestation of 'soft-shell syndrome' and the carapace deformities so often observed in captive bred testudines.

Initially the hatchling unit should be maintained at approximately the same temperature as the incubator. Within a few hours the environment should be adjusted to that which is normal for adults of the species.

The newly emerged tortoises may still have the yolk-sac attached to their plastrons. Under no circumstances should this be interfered with or any attempt made to remove it. The yolk-sac will be gradually re-absorbed over the next few days. Whilst it is present it represents a risk of infection so any hatchlings displaying a residual yolk-sac must be kept under the most rigorous conditions of hygiene. Sometimes yolk-sacs can adhere to the floor of the vivarium. This can be quite dangerous and steps should be taken to prevent it. One effective method is to line the hatchling's vivarium floor with polythene sheeting. A thin smear of KY® non-toxic jelly on the yolk-sac and on the floor can also help.

Some hatchlings may begin to drink, or feed, almost immediately; others, particularly those with yolk-sacs attached may take longer. We generally find that most hatchlings are eating well within 36 - 72 hours, but some can take a week or more.

Occasionally deformed hatchlings or even twins may emerge from the egg. Siamese twins have also been recorded. There is little to be gained from attempting to maintain grossly deformed hatchlings and should these occur it is better that they are painlessly destroyed as soon as possible. Hatchlings lacking lower jaws or eyes have been encountered on a number of occasions. Minor shell deformities are more common and are usually non-critical. Siamese twins can sometimes be separated and the author has encountered one instance of a small parasitic embryo which was attached to a fully developed twin with which it was sharing the same egg. This was carefully separated and whilst the under-developed parasitic twin died within a few minutes its sibling survived apparently none the worse for the experience. It should be noted that excessively high incubation temperatures, trace-element deficiencies and, in the case of aquatic turtles especially, inadequate incubation humidity have a proven association with developmental abnormalities.

Immediate post-hatching care

In captivity as in the wild, this is the time when young tortoises are at their most vulnerable. In the wild, predation is the major cause of mortality. In captivity, poor dietary management,

A post-hatching unit for neonates constructed from a standard plastic-covered seed propagator. The humidity can easily be adjusted by selecting an appropriate substrate and by removing or replacing the plastic lid. Paper kitchen towels are good for most terrestrial species, whist many semi-terrestrial species react well with damp moss and peat. A combination of base heating, using a heat pad, and an overhead Chromalux® basking lamp provides an ideal environment for tortoises and semi-terrestrial turtles in their first days and weeks of life.

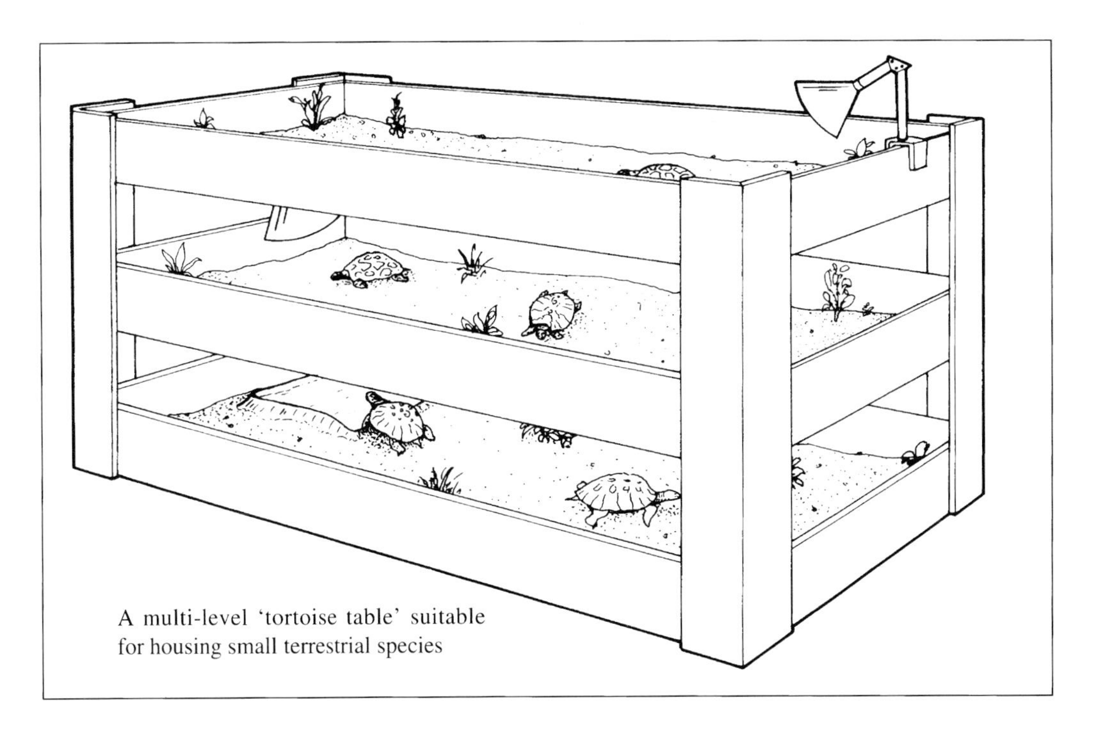
A multi-level 'tortoise table' suitable for housing small terrestrial species

inadequate housing and lack of attention to disease control are among the most common reasons for losses. Our own favourite immediate post-hatching accommodation comprises large plastic seed propagators. These can be used with the transparent lid in place to retain humidity, or with the lid removed to increase ventilation. They can even be used for aquatic species provided models with non-perforated bases are purchased. A combination of gentle base heating via a low wattage heat pad, and radiant heat from a 40 watt reflector lamp situated above the lid seems to suit almost all species. Certainly, we have found that these units produce excellent results with *T. graeca*, *T. kleinmanni*, *K. homeana*, *K. belliana*, *T. marginata*, *G. pardalis*, *Rhinoclemmys* and *Terrapene* among both terrestrial and semi-terrestrial tortoises and turtles. We have also found they ideally suit a wide variety of aquatic species that require shallow water in the post-hatching phase.

Our own juvenile accommodation for terrestrial species, in the months following hatching, consists of wooden outdoor pens covered by welded wire mesh on frames and indoor 'mini-pens' or 'tortoise tables' according to the individual requirements of the species. If weather permits, our terrestrial hatchlings live outdoors on a terraced south-facing slope. Each enclosure is securely protected to prevent predation by foxes, weasels, rats or hedgehogs. The walls of the enclosures are of thick wood or concrete blocks for the same reason. With aquatic and carnivorous turtles beware that adults may view juveniles as a tasty morsel. Juveniles should therefore always be maintained in separate, secure accommodation.

Indoor mini-pens or tortoise tables

This type of housing is extremely versatile and is attractive enough to use in many domestic situations. We have found the design very well suited to small and delicate terrestrial species such as adult *Testudo kleinmanni*, *Psammobates* and *Homopus* as well as the juveniles of many other species. A multi-storey version of this design can accommodate several different species in the same floor area. Basking lights are provided by means of clip-on reflector fittings and full spectrum fluorescent tubes are also provided. Different substrates can be provided as required (see below) and plants can be installed for decoration and to provide cover.

Whether indoor or outdoor, the habitat should be as interesting as possible. Provide an open area for basking, a heavily overgrown area for retreat, and a variety of rocks and native plants for cover, decoration and possibly even for grazing. Juveniles do not have any different temperature, light and humidity requirements from adults. They do, after all, hatch into the same environment as adults in the wild. Provided they are protected from predators and accidental injury they should, therefore, be treated the same.

Substrates for terrestrial species

Provided egg-sacs have been absorbed, newspaper or paper towels make good substrates for the first few days of life. They should be changed regularly. Sand should be avoided for the reasons stated previously.

Another good substrate suitable for use with hatchling tortoises can be made from alfalfa or grass pellets of the sort frequently sold for rabbit food. This provides a firm footing, is very absorbent and is non-problematic if ingested. Avoid medicated varieties. Recently, Astroturf or artificial grass has been used by many breeders. You may care to experiment with this, but beware of the possibility of ingestion. This material may also inhibit natural burrowing, and hence, affect thermoregulatory behaviour. We have recently found that providing juveniles with a natural substrate into which they can burrow at will is highly successful. This encourages normal behaviour patterns, and, due to the amount of time spent in hiding, also reduces excessive feeding and hence artificially accelerated growth. We feel sure that in many cases juveniles feed out of sheer boredom; by providing an interesting environment this behaviour is much reduced.

Artificial lighting

Various types and combinations of lighting units can be employed, but the most consistently successful arrangement with tortoises and turtles is True-lite®, Vitalite® or a similar full-spectrum fluorescent tube combined with a tungsten supplementary lamp to encourage basking. The author finds 40 watt mini-spotlights ideal for this purpose, particularly those available in clamp fixing mobile holders. Species from high altitude or savannah habitats usually demand much higher intensity illumination than those which occupy jungle or forest habitats. Several True-lite® or Vita-lite® type fixtures may be used together to provide higher intensities where indicated.

Very high intensity ultra-violet lighting, as advocated in some reptile husbandry books should generally be avoided. A new type of lighting called Chromalux® has recently become popular; this combines a daylight frequency output with infra-red emission. These would appear to be ideally suited to both tortoises and turtles, and keepers using them report good performance. Their UV-B output is very low, however, and, if this is considered important, then Vita-lite® or a separate UV-B emitter should be employed alongside them. It is worth noting that all ultra-violet and full spectrum lights should be replaced at the manufacturer's recommended intervals as ultra-violet output falls off steeply with age of the lamp. If their UV-B content is being relied upon for vitamin D3 production, the consequences can be catastrophic. In the absence of a specific manufacturer's recommendation, replace tubes every 12 months.

Heating for tortoise and turtle enclosures

A wide variety of heat sources are available from specialist tropical fish accessory and vivarium suppliers as well as from electronics and industrial manufacturers. Certain types commend themselves immediately, however, as particularly well suited to tortoise and turtle housing applications. These include infra-red dull emitters, combined light-heat lamps, thermo-tubes and heat pads:

Infra-red dull emitters

These are a useful heat source for large reptile terraria. They are available in a wide range of powers from 60 watts to 250 watts and are easy to install. Most are shaped rather like spot lamps but instead of being constructed from glass are made from an opaque ceramic material. They get extremely hot in operation so must be installed and positioned with great care using the special heat-proof holders provided. Cables too must be of the heat resisting variety. They are an excellent source of basking heat for tortoises and are much appreciated by all vivarium inhabitants. A note of caution should, however, be sounded. Due to their intensity, these heaters are not safe for juveniles, or indeed for any animal, if it falls on its back directly under the emitter. Death from overheating is a real possibility and can occur surprisingly quickly. The author is aware of young tortoises dying within a few minutes of inversion under a ceramic heater. They must also be positioned well out-of-reach of the animals as severe burns are caused almost instantly on contact. I have found some species, particularly box turtles and some Asiatic semi-terrestrial turtles, to respond badly to high intensity dull emitters. These seem to prefer a gentler, lower-intensity heat source.

Combined light and heat sources

We have found Chromalux® and similar basking lamps to provide a very satisfactory source of both heat and light for juvenile tortoises and aquatic turtles. Note that basking lamps should not be relied upon as adequate sources of UV-B for vitamin D synthesis. In some recent experiments conducted by the author, it was interesting to note that, when given a choice of basking under a dull emitter or a combined light-heat source, the majority of tortoises and turtles preferred the combined source.

Thermo-tubes

These are cylindrical heaters usually rated at 60 watts per 300 mm and are available in many different lengths from 300 mm to 2 m (approximately 1ft to 6ft). They are usually sold for cupboard heating, window demisting or for industrial drying applications. For small vivaria the 600 mm and 900 mm versions are best, larger units will require the 1.5 m or 2 m versions which are rated at 300 W and 360 W respectively. Thermo-tubes are extremely versatile and highly reliable. They may be used individually or in multiples for heating large reptile enclosures. Additional basking heat sources should be provided for most species, however. Combined light-heat lamps as described above are an excellent choice.

Heat pads

Heat-pads are sometimes recommended as a universal solution to the problems of heating reptile cages. This view is not shared by the author who has encountered many behavioural problems linked to their use with tortoises. Heat pads provide very little direct radiant heat and can also seriously impair thermoregulatory behaviour in many species. They should not be relied upon as the sole heat source as they do not encourage natural basking. Some species are also prone to overheating if heat-pads are used. Heat pads can be used effectively in incubators, however, and waterproof types are also very useful for the base heating of aquatic turtle aquariums. Their other uses are somewhat limited with most tortoise species and they are definitely not recommended as the principal daytime source of heating for hatchlings. Heat pads are also well suited to base-heating box turtles and other semiaquatic species, particularly those requiring a high humidity environment and minimal temperature fluctuations, i.e. many equatorial species. We have also found heat pads to be very useful for heating sick tortoises overnight, especially those with respiratory diseases or those on antibiotic therapy where body temperature needs to be maintained within close tolerances in order for drugs to attain maximum effectiveness.

Heating for large installations

Individual vivarium accommodation is the preferred method for small collections, but where many animals are to be accommodated it is both costly and inefficient. The Tortoise Trust's own collection, for example, relied for many years upon individual electrical vivarium heaters: the energy usage (and wastage) proved to be very considerable. A move to new premises presented the opportunity to design everything from the ground up, with energy conservation and efficiency high on the agenda.

The solution ultimately arrived at involved highly insulated main buildings, with polycarbonate twin-wall roofing for maximum natural light transmission and minimum heat-loss. A first building comprising 90 sq. m. (800 sq. ft) included both a humid tropical zone (for Red-foot, Hinge-back and similar tortoises) and an arid semi-desert zone (intended primarily for *G. sulcata*, *G. pardalis* and *G. elegans*). A second building with 70 sq. m. (625 sq. ft). floor area was then designed to provide additional accommodation for tropical semiaquatic turtles such as *Geoemyda*, *Rhinoclemmys*, *Cyclemys* and *Heosemys* species. Roofs were angled at 50 to allow for maximum solar gain (at our latitude of 52°N, the optimum angle will vary according to location) and black plastic water containers were placed against a rear wall to provide a heat store. Additional thermal mass was provided by constructing the internal tortoise enclosures from concrete blocks. These were painted dark brown to increase solar heat absorption during the day - at night they act as an impromptu storage radiator, drastically reducing overnight heating costs. For further design hints on such buildings, organic gardening and permaculture manuals are a good source of advice.

An underfloor hot water heating system comprising:
1) Insulation board
2) Hot water pipes
3) Cement floor
This system has proved very useful with large species such as *Geochelone carbonaria* and *G. sulcata*, etc.

The main heating for our buildings is provided by a combination of under floor hot-water piping and a number of central heating radiators. These are both efficient and economical. The main boiler is oil-fired. This system has proved extremely cost-effective to install, and the running costs are less than 25% of those incurred with our previous electric heating system.

The under floor heating 'pads' were constructed by excavating a 20 cm deep pit and filling this firstly with 15-cm-thick insulation material and then overlaying this with cement containing embedded plastic hot-water heating pipes. This method has proved extremely effective and is greatly appreciated by all tortoises. Some pens were also equipped with wall-mounted central heating radiators. To improve basking possibilities, these were fitted at just above floor-level and a mound of earth positioned just in front of each radiator. The slope facing the radiator is self-selected by tortoises wishing to take advantage of the heat for basking.

The role that insulation can play in reducing heating costs and improving thermal stability should not be underestimated. Our own tropical house was lined with 40 mm thick aluminium foil-lined insulation sheets on all external walls and ceilings. This alone reduced heat losses by 40%. The floors of the tortoise sleeping quarters were also insulated from ground losses by 80 mm thick insulation sheets which reduced overnight heat pad losses to almost zero. Insulation sheet is a very useful material, easy to install, and in conjunction with polycarbonate twin-wall it offers many design possibilities for energy efficient reptile maintenance. With ingenuity, these materials can be employed in most vivarium and terrarium installations to great effect.

Thermostats

It should be noted that the comments made earlier in respect of incubator thermostats and temperature controllers apply equally in regard to heating. Obviously this application is by no means as critical but some reliable method of controlling temperatures is certainly required. In practice, ordinary on-off air temperature thermostats of the central heating type will be found more than adequate for controlling thermo-tubes and similar background sources whilst the precision and security of electronic controllers will be found of enormous benefit where infra-red dull emitters are to be employed.

Accommodation requirements of juvenile aquatic turtles

Most juvenile aquatic turtles are relatively easy to accommodate. A small glass aquarium set to the same temperature range as required for adults of the species will suffice. As an alternative, plastic storage bins may be considered. For filtration, I usually find a small internal canister or hang-on type filter more than adequate, especially if combined with under gravel biological filtration. These are easy to clean and prevent any possibility of cross-contamination from other tanks. Under-gravel filtration alone may be suitable in many cases especially if driven by a powerhead instead of an air-lift. Lighting requirements are very similar to those required for terrestrial tortoises. To avoid the possibility of burns from submersible heaters, base heating using a heat pad is a very safe option. If using a submersible aquarium heater, unbreakable models are best and extra caution needs to be exercised if this type of heater is to be used in shallow water. Many are suitable only for use in deep water. Many small turtles will attempt to rest on the heater itself unless access is restricted. This can result in severe burns. Most species will benefit from provision of a Chromalux® or similar daylight frequency basking lamp. An additional source of UV-B may also be required. Temperate species may be housed outside, at least in fine weather, in an adaptation of our design for terrestrial species, comprising a small pond with surrounding natural habitat and anti-predator guards.

Water depth for neonate and juvenile aquatic turtles

An important point to consider when accommodating neonate and juvenile aquatics is water depth; there is a natural tendency on the part of over-protective keepers to provide water which is far too shallow. In fact, such water can be dangerous as juveniles may flip over onto their backs and be unable to right themselves with the result that they drown. As a general guideline, for most species, the safest water depth is about equal to one and one half to twice their carapace length. At this depth, should a neonate become inverted, it will easily right itself. A gentle slope leading to the basking position or land area should always be provided. With small specimens this depth of water precludes the use of most filters. although under gravel filtration driven by a small powerhead may remain possible. I find that cutting the air-lift tube provided to about 25 mm in length and attaching a small Aquaclear® powerhead just above the water-line works very well. If no filter is present, change the water completely every few days. Shallow-water neonate enclosures should be designed with a built-in drain valve. Water changes and cleaning are then quick and easy. Waste can easily be flushed down the drain using a flexible hose. Change-water should always be pre-heated before use.

Basking and juvenile aquatic turtles

Many juvenile turtles rarely leave the water entirely. For these, small floating platforms of cork or partly submerged bogwood will provide invaluable basking platforms. Another alternative is to free float plastic decorative aquarium plants. These provide adequate support for small turtles to climb on, are easy to clean and visually greatly enhance thc habitat.

A well-filtered aquarium designed for neonate aquatic turtles. The unit shown incorporates both an undergravel filter driven by a powerhead (with venturi) and an Aquaclear® side-mounted filter containing activated carbon which is changed regularly. This combination of biological and chemical filters provides excellent water quality which is ideally suited to the maintenance of delicate species. Adequate basking facilities are also provided.

Humidity and juvenile aquatic turtles

Many aquatic and semiaquatic turtles require high levels of humidity as neonates. Failure to provide sufficient ambient humidity can lead to skin and shell infections, swollen eyes, respiratory symptoms, refusal to feed, and growth deficiencies. In general, terrariums accommodating neonates should be at least half covered to retain relative humidity at approximately 80%. Some species may require even higher levels, for example, species which in the wild inhabit bogs and marshes such as *Clemmys muhlenbergi*, the North American Bog turtle. Neonates of this species normally respond best if ambient humidity is maintained above 90%. The use of seed-tray propagators, complete with the transparent lid in place, as mentioned previously, is one appropriate option.

Above: A large seed-tray propagator with plastic lid in position to create a high humidity environment ideal for many neonate semi-terrestrial species. A heat pad provides gentle base heating to an appropriate temperature. The substrate includes moss, peat and fallen leaves. Approximately 50% of the unit is devoted to an aquatic area, the rest to a terrestrial section. The water is changed daily and is placed within an easy-to-remove inner tray. This type of unit has proved highly successful with numerous species, and especially with South American and Asiatic box turtles such as *Rhinoclemmys* and *Cuora*.

Three-toed American box turtle (*Terrapene carolina triunguis*)

Chapter Five

ENVIRONMENTAL MAINTENANCE

It is extremely important when designing or installing any vivarium lighting or heating system to understand the biological implications for the animals concerned. Tortoises and turtles are reptiles and, as poikilotherms or exotherms, they are largely dependent upon their environment for adjustment and maintenance of body temperature. They have only a very limited ability to compensate for environmental temperatures either above or below their preferred optimum (P.O) level. Outside the P.O temperature, normal metabolic activity will be impaired and at excessively low or high temperatures death will occur. Unfortunately these figures are not known in detail for every species of reptile but almost all reptiles have a P.O temperature range between 20 - 35 °C, and with terrestrial testudines the range is usually between 22 - 30 °C. This is certainly a good starting range when dealing with a species with unknown preferences. Mesic species almost always have a somewhat higher P.O temperature than those species which dwell in lush jungle or undergrowth. The latter are also inclined to display poor thermoregulatory abilities. It is extremely important to note that the critical thermal maxima of many terrestrial species is in the range 34 to 36°C. If maintained at these temperatures without the possibility of escape, death can occur very rapidly. Many accidental deaths in collections occur when tortoises become inverted beneath a heat lamp, for example. It is also important to recognise that as temperatures rise beyond about 28°C many species will show disinterest in feeding and will prepare to enter a state of aestivation.

The term 'preferred optimum' is in itself somewhat misleading and there are some indications that just because a particular temperature range may be favoured by self-selection this is not necessarily the temperature which is most conducive to long-term health or survival. For example, many tortoises will, if allowed to, bask under a heater all day. This can have quite serious metabolic side effects. So, although the 'preferred optimum' temperature should be taken as a general guide, it should not necessarily be available at all times. Temperatures in the wild are cyclic, peaking at about mid-day and falling off towards evening. By far the best guide to ideal captive maintenance conditions will be gained from a careful study of the species' natural habitat and prevailing climate. Ordinary tourist guide-books dealing with the region inhabited by the species are often a very useful source of climatic, seasonal and habitat data. The many technical publications available from geographic and meteorological authorities are also a source of valuable captive maintenance information.

Diurnal cycles and health in captivity

For the vast majority of species, both terrestrial and aquatic, 14 hours of daylight (natural or artificial) will prove entirely satisfactory. Diurnal temperature adjustments may also be required, especially for non-equatorial species, as outlined above. Many species also require an overnight temperature drop; failure to provide this may result in health problems. Failure to provide appropriate light and heat cycling may also have profound effects upon the reproductive process. We have noted an increase in diarrhoea and digestive tract upsets in tortoises which are maintained at unnaturally high overnight temperatures. Stearns (1989) suggests that failure to provide an overnight temperature drop for *G. sulcata* predisposes it to respiratory symptoms. Overnight temperature reductions are not normally appropriate for aquatic species, however.

Humidity control for terrestrial species

The second main factor in the success or failure of the captive environment after temperature is humidity. The importance of this should never be underestimated. Poor humidity control quite probably kills more captive tortoises than any other single environmental influence with the exception of temperature.

Humidity control can, however, present a real problem and unfortunately it is not possible to suggest any universal answer. In large installations de-humidifiers can help for arid habitats and mist sprayers can be very effective in keeping things moist. Smaller installations are more difficult due to cost limitations. We have experimented for some years and so far we have found that substrates are the easiest and cheapest way to provide a fair degree of control.

For arid habitat species a combination of sand, light soil, pebbles, and rocks are suggested, and for rain forest species a combination of pine-bark mulch, peat, and moss appears to work best. This latter will need changing regularly, but stones and rocks can be washed and re-used. Soaking in dilute povidone-iodine solution for 12 hours will provide adequate protection in most cases. It should be noted that some animals will attempt to eat small stones and that this can lead to serious gut impactions. For this reason only pebbles too large to be easily consumed should be employed. The behaviour often ceases if a safe alternative, such as cuttlefish bone, is made available.

The three main habitat types may be summarised as follows:

Mesic and arid habitats

These habitats are characterised by rocky or sandy substrates and low humidity. Good air circulation is essential, as all mesic species are prone to respiratory problems if humidity is excessive or when static air conditions prevail. Direct radiant heat is also essential, with a good gradient, usually at least 10ºC differential between the hottest and coolest part of the habitat. Typically a 32ºC maximum directly under a spot basking source and 20°C daytime in cool areas is appropriate. Overnight, a temperature of 12 to 15ºC is typical. For heat in captivity, a combination of tubular heaters or hot water radiators for background and overnight heating, plus long-wave infra-red (i.e., from dull-emitter ceramic elements) is difficult to better. This arrangement provides excellent thermoregulatory facilities (which are essential for all mesic species) and will prevent immune system depression and consequent disease problems. The lighting is also important. For the best possible environment, Vitalite® or similar full spectrum tubes are highly recommended. Both photo-period (daylength) and intensity of luminescence are obviously also important, but naturally vary according to the species being maintained.

Time switches can certainly prove useful in setting photo-periods based upon geographical data. Where tungsten lighting is used dimmer switches can also give a useful degree of control and enable artificial sunsets or dawn-dusk situations to be replicated.

In large vivaria or indoor habitat areas, several Vitalite® and Chromalux® lamps may be necessary. Certainly for some species very high light intensities are essential. I would suggest a minimum of four or five 40W tubes per vivarium, or even consider using metal halide lighting systems, despite the cost. As indicated previously, good ventilation is essential, but avoid cold draughts. Small 120 mm ex-computer cooling fans can be readily adapted to this application.

Many species may require burrows for retreat and in some cases these must be at specific temperatures or humidity levels if problems are to be avoided.

Medium humidity temperate habitats

This category includes all North African tortoises and most Mediterranean species. The basic requirement is for lush undergrowth, good thermoregulatory facilities, a moderate-to-high level of ambient humidity and good ventilation. Lighting levels should be high, with Vita-lite® or similar highly recommended for indoor installations. For Mediterranean species several fittings may be necessary to produce the required level of illumination.

Outdoor accommodation for these species is preferable to indoor vivarium systems. *Testudo graeca*, *T. ibera*, *F. whitei*, *T. marginata* and *T. hermanni* all have similar requirements although *T. hermanni* and *T. ibera* can tolerate low humidity to a much greater extent than can the North African species (the relative humidity of the environment was measured in the field, in Morocco; most active *T. g. graeca* were found in localities where the relative humidity in their immediate microclimate was 60% or more). In very hot dry weather these species may require spraying regularly with water from a sprinkler system or garden hose to maintain activity. In their wild state, these North African species escape intolerable heat and drought by aestivating underground for several months at a time. The substrate conditions

An outdoor area suited to temperate terrestrial species. A secure perimeter and adequate supply of 'natural' graze are essential. Overnight accommodation is provided by means of wooden huts or artificially excavated dry 'caves'.

required for this can be difficult to replicate in captivity. In addition it should be noted that these same animals will often remain active and feeding in the wild over winter (which is very mild and highly suited to tortoise activity). Again, this is not something it is easy to provide outside their natural bioclimatic range and for this reason our experience suggests that aestivation is best avoided in captivity.

A secure, well-protected garden area is ideal and this should include an open area for basking, an area of shrubs and bushes to provide shade, a raised rocky area for climbing, and a thickly planted weeded area for browsing and retreat. Overnight accommodation can consist of plywood huts or houses.

Keeping tortoises out of doors without artificial support has, to a certain extent, gained a poor reputation as this is usually done badly, by unskilled keepers in unsuitable areas. In fact, if planned and put into practice carefully it offers enormous advantages over indoor accommodation; obviously, it is only possible with temperate species and only in areas which approximate the natural bioclimatic range of the species concerned. Fortunately, most of Europe and the United States is within the safe range for the species mentioned above.

Certainly wherever possible I prefer to see temperate species of tortoise maintained out-of-doors in spacious, well -planted enclosures with plenty of natural cover and graze. This method of captive maintenance is vastly superior to any indoor habitat, no matter how carefully designed. For non-temperate species, however, there is often no alternative to a largely indoor environment and these present special difficulties.

Rain forest and jungle habitats

Rain forest inhabitants require very different facilities and conditions than temperate species. High light intensities are rarely appreciated and can lead to severe stress. Basking heat sources are similarly not favoured. Humidity should be moderately high to very high depending upon the species. It is possible to construct simple automatic misters by utilising automotive windscreen washer pumps linked to a time switch and transformer; alternatively, commercial versions can be purchased from horticultural merchants. Water must be constantly available not only for drinking, but also because many of these species require a bathing pool in which they can semi-immerse themselves for hours on end and which seems to be necessary to defecation. The absence of a bathing pool will lead to serious eye inflammation, respiratory problems and dehydration. Heating is best provided by means of thermostat controlled tubular heaters of sufficient power to heat the entire vivarium to a more or less constant 26 °C - 28 °C (the precise setting will depend upon the species) or an all-round under-floor central heating system in large terrariums.

Infra-red basking heaters are not normally required, although some specimens may take occasional advantage if one is present (i.e. *Kinixys belliana* and *Geochelone (Chelonoidis) carbonaria*). In any case, a low power version is adequate (60 to 100 watts). The temperature gradient should be slight, and not more than +/- 3 C in most cases. Excessive overnight temperature variations should not occur. Lighting should not be excessively bright, and a lower power Vitalite® fitting is usually adequate (i.e. 40 watts). Plenty of cover should be provided as most rain-forest-type tortoises like to be damp, warm and well hidden.

Terrarium construction for terrestrial species

The construction of terrariums suitable for terrestrial tortoises presents considerably more difficulty than is encountered when designing similar units for smaller animals such as lizards or snakes or indeed for most semiaquatic turtles. Without exception, land tortoises require a considerable amount of space for exercise and this can obviously be a difficult criteria to meet in many indoor situations.

Rather than fishtank-type vivaria, which are almost never satisfactory, save for very small specimens, the only viable options for tortoises are likely to consist of converted garages, spare rooms or, best of all, converted greenhouses. Fortunately, in many countries, the maintenance of temperate species may not require much in the way of indoor accommodation at all. If tropical species are to be maintained, then an agricultural merchant's building catalogue is probably a good place to seek out suitable raw materials which, with ingenuity and effort, can be often converted into first-rate terrariums. We have had great success using polycarbonate twinwall material. This has good light transmission properties, possesses an extremely high insulation factor, is virtually unbreakable and can easily be cut with an ordinary saw. For even higher thermal insulation, triple-wall can be used. It is very easy to either improve an existing greenhouse design using bolt-on frames of this material, or to design and build a completely new accommodation unit based upon its unique properties. If doing so, it is worth-while researching energy usage in the proposed unit and integrating as many energy saving features as possible into the design. Energy bills for tropical reptile heating in temperate climates can prove extremely costly. Protect not only the environment but also your finances by building solar heating and energy-conservation features into vivarium systems. The savings can be dramatic.

Terraria for high-humidity environments

Where accommodation for smaller species is required, particularly those requiring high levels of humidity, avoid the use of chipboard-type materials; most of these will deteriorate rapidly in the presence of moisture. Although initially expensive, marine plywood is a good long-term investment as it will last almost indefinitely. Glass vivarium windows lose a considerable amount of heat and consequently result in serious condensation; polycarbonate twin-wall material as discussed above, mounted on a wooden frame for ease of fixing, can also be used to great effect on interior units. I recently constructed a terrarium for the attractive South American wood turtle *Rhinoclemmys pulcherrima* which measured 4 m x 700 mm x 1 m using 9 mm thick marine plywood sealed with polyurethane varnish on a wooden framework. The base was isolated from the ground with 80 mm foam insulation board. The top, sides and ends were covered with 40 mm foil-covered insulation board and the front window made from 16 mm polycarbonate twinwall. The substrate was damp leaf mulch, pine bark and sphagnum. Heating was provided by one thermostatically controlled (750 mm long) hot water radiator mounted on the back wall, but electric thermo-tubes or heat pads would also be suitable. This unit maintains a temperature of 26°C and a humidity in excess of 85% on a minimal energy input. Lighting is by means of two Vita-lite® tubes. An automatic greenhouse-type misting unit has been installed and a number of plants are also included to enhance the environment and to help maintain humidity.

Hibernation of temperate species

Hibernation is a complex biological process and there are many differences between the way in which mammals and reptiles hibernate. In fact, reptile hibernation is often referred to as brumation to reflect these biological differences. It is also not as easy as it may be thought to generalise about which species can and cannot hibernate. Certainly in the wild, some species hibernate in parts of their range and remain active throughout the winter in others. Of such species, it can best be said that they have the biological capacity to hibernate rather than to insist that they always do hibernate. Most, but not all, tortoises from North Africa fall into this category. In the case of *T. graeca graeca* within Morocco for example, animals in the north of the country and those living at high altitudes hibernate whilst those in the south or on the warmer coast remain active. It is interesting to note that within the '*T. graeca*' complex of North Africa certain populations are not biologically suited to hibernation and should not be subjected to it in captivity. Into this category falls the miniature race which inhabits the coast of Tunisia (proposed as *Furculachelys nabeulensis*) and certain populations from Libya.

The essential conditions required for a safe hibernation may be summarised as follows:

- The temperature should remain above 2°C and below 10°C throughout the hibernation period. 5.0°C is an ideal target temperature.

- Animals should not be hibernated whilst the stomach contains undigested food. A fasting period of several weeks beforehand is therefore essential. The precise fasting period will vary according to two factors: the size of the animal and its metabolic rate (which in turn is determined by ambient temperature). Small animals kept at just below normal maintenance temperatures may require a fasting period of no more than 14 days. In the case of larger animals 3 weeks or so may be more appropriate. Failure to ensure an adequate fast can lead to serious digestive tract problems resulting from the decay of semi-digested food in the stomach.

- No animal which is sick or underweight should ever be hibernated.

- Animals should be checked frequently during hibernation. This will not harm them and it is no more than a myth that disturbing a hibernating tortoise is dangerous.

- Small specimens should receive only a short hibernation; 8 to 10 weeks is usually within safe tolerances. Even large specimens should not be subject to excessively long hibernation periods; 12 - 14 weeks is a typical safe maximum.

- In regions where temperature control within safe limits is problematic, hibernating within an artificially refrigerated cool room should be considered. Large domestic refrigerators (not freezers) can also be converted to this task. Excellent temperature stability can be attained, but you may need to replace the existing thermostat with a more sensitive or reliable one. Regular ventilation is also essential to avoid a build-up of carbon dioxide.

- In some areas, it may be possible to arrange a natural hibernaculum. A 1 m deep pit about 75 cm x 75 cm should be excavated, lined with insulation board and rot-proof plywood, then filled with a mixture of light earth, tree bark mulch and sand. For box turtles, the mixture should include a high percentage of leaf litter and moss. A well-insulated tortoise house can be positioned above this and the animals allowed free access as hibernation time approaches. This method offers very good frost protection but has the slight disadvantage that regular inspection of the tortoise is impossible. Nonetheless, the system has a good overall safety record and is used regularly by many successful keepers.

- Many temperate aquatic species appear to require a winter hibernation or dormancy period if they are to remain in peak reproductive condition. Specimens which are maintained in outdoor ponds may hibernate perfectly naturally. It is important, however, that the pond is of sufficient depth to prevent complete freezing and that a layer of organic matter is present on the bottom into which the turtle can burrow. Most aquatic turtles usually hibernate quite safely beneath quite thick ice. Filters and other circulation systems, such as waterfalls and fountains, must be turned off as excessive water movement will serve to prevent the formation of protective thermal layers. Some species leave the water to hibernate in holes or buried under leaf litter. For these species, provision of a natural-type hibernaculum as outlined above is suggested.

If it should become necessary to over winter a normally hibernating temperate species, an indoor vivarium or penned area provided with heat and light as described previously will suffice for terrestrial species whilst aquatic species are easily overwintered in a heated tank.

Finally, although it is sometimes claimed that persistent non-hibernating of captive species which would naturally hibernate in the wild causes no health problems, this is not an opinion we share. We have noted an increased incidence of liver disease in long-term over wintered specimens and a definite decline in fertility. We prefer to see healthy specimens hibernated and only sick or underweight specimens over wintered.

Hibernation of juveniles

Whether or not to hibernate juveniles in their first year is a matter of some contention, with some insisting that species which hibernate should always be hibernated, no matter how young, and others insisting that tortoises and turtles less than 3 or 4 years of age should never be hibernated. The author takes the view that neither dogmatic approach is justified. With very young animals, much depends upon the confidence and ability of the individual keeper and upon the facilities available. Due to their reduced body mass compared to adults, the core temperature of juveniles is obviously more easily influenced by external factors. Therefore, temperature stability during hibernation is especially important. A useful technique is to allow terrestrial juveniles to bury themselves completely in a surrounding mass of substrate, such as earth contained within a deep tray. The additional mass will serve to protect against sudden temperature fluctuations. It may also help to avoid problems due to dehydration during hibernation. This can certainly be a problem if very small animals are hibernated in traditional boxes. On the other hand, if the keeper lacks confidence and a genuinely suitable hibernation area is not available, it is undoubtedly safer to overwinter until the juveniles are somewhat larger. Very much the same comments apply to the hibernation of aquatic juveniles. In this case, however, species which hibernate under water are, to some degree, less likely to be subjected to sudden temperature fluctuations than species which hibernate above ground. Overall, it must be noted that the growth of hibernated juveniles is usually smoother and tends to be closer to natural rates than that recorded for specimens which have been overwintered.

Natural biotypes of aquatic species

Freshwater turtles inhabit a very wide variety of habitats. The situation is complicated by the fact that many species occur in more than one habitat type, and also by the fact that habitats themselves are subject to seasonal fluctuations. Thus, the temperature, flow rate, salinity, pH, and organic content of a habitat may well undergo quite acute changes over a period of months.

Even so, it is possible to arrive at some useful habitat generalisations. These should form the basis of further experimentation and are no more than a starting point when evolving captive-maintenance strategies.

Temperate river habitats

These habitats are typically characterised by acute seasonal changes in temperature, and by varying flow rates and substrate types along the course of the river from source to middle reaches to lowland outflow. At source, typically on a mountain or hillside, the flow is turbulent and the substrate rocky. The water is clear and cold, generally below 10°C even in summer. The pH depends upon local geology. By the middle reaches, turbulence has decreased and the substrate becomes more variable; backwaters featuring sandy substrates are common. The temperature of the water is slightly warmer, typically 15°C. Rocky side pools may provide a good habitat for many temperate turtles; I have found several large colonies of *Mauremys caspica* and *leprosa* living in this type of habitat in Turkey and Spain. Opportunities for basking are generally good. As the river leaves the hills, water temperatures increase further, especially in summer. Break-up of sediment tends to result in finer grained substrates and a consequent increase in rooted aquatic plants. These conditions also encourage a proliferation of sediment-dwelling invertebrates. Along the final section, the river flows slowly over a muddy substrate rich in organic debris. After rain, the water usually carries a heavy load of silt and is of murky appearance. Water temperatures in summer may exceed 20°C. The substrate is very rich in invertebrate life.

Temperate swamps, bogs and marshes

Temperatures in these popular turtle habitats vary according to season and location, but a common factor is the presence of a soft, peat and sphagnum substrate and plentiful aquatic vegetation. Mosses and peripheral plants including sedges, rushes, creeping jenny, and marsh marigolds are also common. The water flow is gentle and very pure. Turtles from these habitats usually exhibit a requirement for very high incubation and neonate humidity.

Tropical hill streams

In Asia, South America, and Equatorial Africa numerous hill streams run through dense forest and their fast rise and fall reflects the sudden and often abundant rainfall typical of these regions. The temperature of these habitats is generally fairly constant and ranges from 24 - 28°C. The main stream may be fast flowing, especially at higher altitudes following rain, but at lower altitudes the current is less and numerous side pools and backwaters exist which offer a variety of habitats well suited to turtles: pH will vary, but is typically between 6 and 7. Air temperatures are usually 5 - 7°C above the temperature of the water.

Equatorial rainforest habitats

The equatorial regions are subject to rainy seasons, and in the Amazon basin over 300 cm of rain falls annually. The wettest periods are between May and July north of the equator and

November and January to the south. The South American Amazon and African Zaire rivers, which span the equator, are therefore subject to two peaks of flooding and in the case of the Amazon its level at such times can rise by as much as 15 m, overflowing into the surrounding forest and creating many temporary marshes. Water temperatures in the main Amazon River itself are typically 28 - 30°C and this remains fairly constant throughout the year. The water is thickly laden with suspended sediments and carries masses of floating vegetation, washed downriver by the current. The substrate is also very muddy. The margins and tributaries of the river offer a much more attractive habitat to turtles, however, and include numerous creeks, oxbows, pools, and sandy banks. The water in these situations is typically much clearer than in the main river, and invertebrate life is much in evidence. Water depth is usually limited to a few metres and the temperature ranges from 25 - 35°C. Although the precise chemistry varies from location to location, many such habitats possess water rich in decaying organic matter which is soft and slightly acidic (typical pH range 6 - 6.5). The substrate of such habitats is varied, but is usually well suited to supporting a good population of aquatic plants, especially water lettuce, giant water lilies, mud plantains, sword plants, and numerous other species which provide both shelter and food for a wide range of fish, turtles and amphibians.

Rain forest pools

Rain forest pools are characterised by waters typically not more than a few metres in depth and heavily laden with decomposing plant debris. The water is stained brown from organic acids released by the decaying material, and the pH is typically between 4 and 5. The oxygen content is very low and the water temperature may exceed 30°C. Seasonal variations occur principally through periodic flooding. The substrate is comprised of black anoxic mud and decaying leaf litter. There is little living plant matter, and in many cases invertebrate life is also at a low level. The entire habitat is heavily shaded by the forest canopy, and is therefore unsuited to basking species.

Tropical swamps

These habitats are characterised by expanses of still water which support a high density of aquatic vegetation. The oxygen content of most tropical swamp waters is low, and the soft bottom is overlaid by decaying vegetation. The pH is typically 6.0 to 6.5, but may be as high as 8.5 in some locations. The water temperature is usually a fairly constant 26°C.

Seasonal rivers

These habitats offer very similar conditions to tropical swamps and are formed by rivers, swollen by rain, flooding large areas of land. These annual floods serve to connect many hitherto isolated pools and ponds and therefore allow many aquatic species to move from one locality to another. Some species are highly active during these flood periods, but resort to aestivation under the dried mud when the floods recede and temperatures rise. Seasonal rivers of this type are common in both Africa and South America.

Tidal estuaries

Tidal estuaries are characterised by frequent influxes of sea water. The conditions in tidal estuaries vary over a period of only a few hours from freshwater to extremely brackish. Salinity typically varies from 1 to 35 parts per 1000 but is uneven due to the effects of river flow rates and retention by pools and sediments. Surrounding plants are saline-tolerant and frequently consist of reed beds. Some 'freshwater' turtles such as *Malaclemys terrapin* (the

Diamondback terrapin) have adopted special strategies to cope with these conditions, including drinking from the thin film of fresh water deposited on top of the brackish water during periods of rain (Davenport and Macedo, 1990).

Tropical lakes

Tropical lakes offer a variety of habitats and may undergo varied seasonal cycles, from periodic flooding to completely drying up. The size of the lake plays a critical role in determining the seasonal changes in water depth, temperature and chemistry experienced. Due to evaporation the salinity may be quite high, and in large lakes, at depth, the water is charged with hydrogen sulphide and contains such low levels of oxygen that few creatures can survive in it. The bulk of life in such lakes is concentrated in the littoral zones. The water temperature at depth is typically a constant 23°C, but in shallower regions is much higher. Turtles are frequently found in these warm littoral zones where an abundance of food is available. There are also good basking sites on reed beds, muddy slopes and semi-submerged vegetation. Turtles living in lakes which dry up in summer may migrate across land to nearby larger lakes, or may aestivate under the mud.

Today, with the effects of agricultural intensification many of these habitats, both aquatic and terrestrial, are seriously threatened. If we wish to secure a future for turtles, preservation of these critical habitats is of the utmost importance. For those responsible for captive tortoises and turtles, careful study of natural habitats can reveal much of value. Stress and disease incidence can be substantially reduced, and reproductive performance increased when environments are modified to take more account of factors critical to the natural behaviour of the species.

Rhinoclemmys funerea, a large semi-terrestrial turtle from tropical central America.

Chapter Six

CAPTIVE MAINTENANCE OF AQUATIC AND SEMI-AQUATIC SPECIES

The most important point to dispose of in connection with keeping turtles is that they are neither smelly nor do they require vast amounts of effort to maintain. I stress this at the very outset simply because there is so much misunderstanding on this topic. In a correctly designed system turtles do not smell at all and require only minimal human intervention. The operative term here is correctly designed. In poorly designed tanks, with no or inadequate filtration and poor dietary management turtles can indeed prove most objectionable. This is hardly their fault. It is the responsibility of their keepers to provide adequate standards of maintenance. This is clearly in the interests of both parties.

The precise accommodation requirements of aquatic species are, of course, very variable and will require special consideration bearing in mind the particular habits of the species in question. Some keepers go to great lengths to provide as near natural habitats as possible using elaborate terrariums; others take quite the opposite approach and accommodate their animals in virtually bare tanks. Both approaches are capable of good results if managed carefully. Most keepers will, however, adopt a middle-of-the road approach and will seek a compromise between visual appeal and ease of maintenance.

Whilst keepers of tropical fish can obtain the majority of their hardware requirements ready-made from specialist supplies, the turtle keeper has non-standard requirements and if good quality accommodation is to be provided must resort to a greater degree of improvisation.

Glass aquarium tanks and construction methods

Standard aquaria intended for tropical fish use are often employed for terrapins and turtles. For small specimens, they are often entirely adequate. For larger animals they are far from ideal. The width to length ratio of tropical fish tanks is typically 1 (W):3 (L) or similar. For turtles, a ratio of 2 (W):3 (L) is preferable. Fish tanks also tend to be excessively deep for turtle use. Most tropical fish hobby stores offer a tank custom-building service and are usually able to construct a tank ideal for turtles at reasonable cost. The tanks I have found to be most satisfactory for medium sized specimens measure 600 mm x 900 mm x 400 mm.

Traditional metal-framed tanks are heavy and exhibit a tendency to leak if moved, or simply deteriorate as a result of ageing. Modern tanks are usually constructed of glass alone fixed with silicone adhesive. Provided the surfaces of the glass are clean and free of grease this type of joint has proved both strong and highly durable.

It is not particularly difficult for a reasonably capable amateur to construct an all glass tank, but it is usually advisable to have the heavy and expensive glass actually cut to size by an expert professional. Working with large sheets of glass is potentially dangerous, so take all precautions necessary and if in any doubt at all seek expert assistance. For a tank of similar dimensions to that mentioned above, 8 mm glass is recommended. Thinner grades of glass should be avoided as they present a serious safety hazard. Larger tanks will require 10 mm or even 12 mm glass and additional reinforcements.

The constructional procedure is as follows:

- Determine the sizes of bottom, sides and reinforcement strips. Obtain pre-cut pieces to these dimensions from a glass merchant. All sharp edges should be abraded smooth and safe to handle with carbide or similar paper. For the base, wire-reinforced glass is often preferred. This does not actually strengthen the glass to any significant degree, but does help to prevent catastrophic break-up in the event of failure.

- Handle all pieces with extreme care throughout the assembly process.

- Carefully clean all surfaces which are to be joined with an alcohol degreasing agent. This is very important, as any trace of grease will render a joint useless.

- Working on a flat, smooth surface, coat one edge of the base with silicone adhesive. Press the back plate into position and secure with masking tape and wooden props if necessary. Work quickly as this type of adhesive has a limited viscosity and its surface hardens rapidly.

- Similarly fix both ends with adhesive, again making sure all seams are well coated with silicone and remain free of grease. Assembly becomes progressively easier as more panes are added. Corners can be held firmly in position using strong masking tape.

- Fix the front pane into position, allow to stand for 24 to 36 hours.

- Finally glue the two top reinforcement strips into place. The tank is now finished. Allow at least another 24 hours for the adhesive to fully set before moving. Excess dried adhesive can be removed with a sharp knife.

- Perform a final check for any remaining sharp edges, paying special attention to corners. Smooth with abrasive paper if necessary.

Before use, rinse the tank out at least three times with fresh water. Using the above methods it is possible to construct tanks of up to 500 litres capacity. It is important to realise that every litre of water weighs approximately 1 kg (2.2 lbs). A 500 litre tank will therefore weigh 500 kg plus the not inconsiderable weight of the thick glass used in its construction, plus the weight of any sand or gravel substrate. From this it is evident that extremely substantial

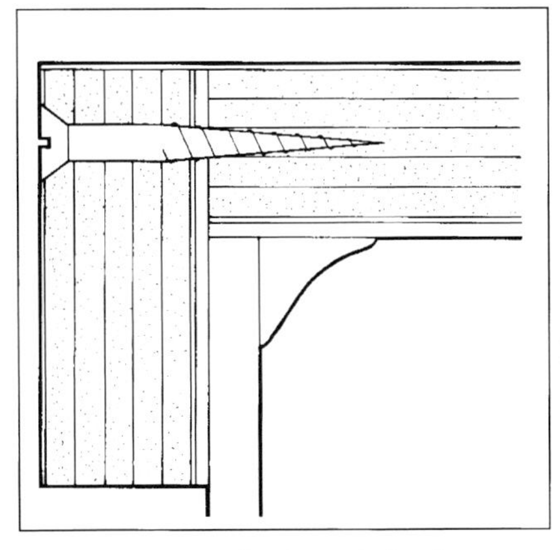

Method of joining hybrid glass-plywood tank seams. Brass screws and high strength silicone sealants are recommended.

stands are required, and for large tanks brick or stone stands are preferred. The base plate should always be carefully positioned on a polystyrene, foam or carpet cushion; one raised screw or nail-head can instantly fracture even 12 mm thick glass under this kind of pressure. Finally, always ensure that floors are safe to bear the weight of tanks to be positioned on them; there are reliable accounts of structural damage occurring in the homes of over-enthusiastic turtle collectors!

Wooden aquarium tanks and construction methods

Wood may at first seem a strange material from which to construct water-retaining tanks, but it fact it is eminently suitable, highly versatile and very durable. It is possible to construct very large and unusually dimensioned tanks using marine plywood and this material can also be used in conjunction with glass very easily. For most tanks, 15 to 20 mm marine-grade ply will be required, and all assembly should be undertaken with waterproof glue and rustproof brass screws. Very large tanks will require external reinforcing braces.

The secret of success in this type of construction is in the water-proofing that follows initial construction. Today some extremely durable epoxy resin coating agents are available which will completely seal the timber against water, permanently. These are sometimes known as two-pack or catalyst lacquers. Moisture-cured polyurethane resins are also available that are equally suitable. Those of a nervous disposition may prefer to coat the inside of the tank with shredded fibreglass and resin, but this is a messy and unpleasant procedure and not really necessary. Provided that good quality marine ply has been used throughout, and the structure is sufficiently rigid, tanks constructed using this method will last as long as any glass model but are much less liable to accidental damage. They also have much better heat retaining properties and can be constructed using simple hand tools.

It is a simple matter to use glass in place of wood for any chosen side in a hybrid tank by routing a channel of the same thickness of the glass and applying silicone sealant when fixing.Alternatively, use the method illustrated above. In practice, for most turtle tanks this will rarely be required. Viewing will mostly occur from above.

I was once asked to design a number of tanks to accommodate small to medium-sized turtles for use in off-exhibit areas. These were mostly intended to house Asiatic and south American turtles which required a well filtered water section combined with a land area with adequate provision for basking and egg laying. The design illustrated on page 62 was eventually adopted. This includes under gravel filtration plus a space for an external canister filter or for an Aquaclear® 600 side-fitting filter. These latter filters are very effective and work well in

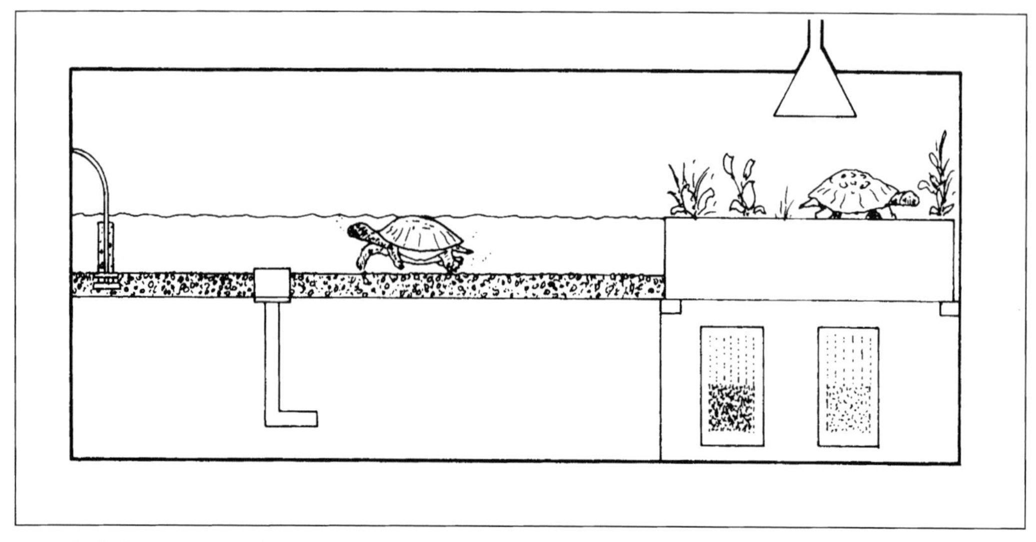

A shallow water surface mounted tank suitable for aquatic species. A pair of canister filters are located beneath the removable land section. A drain valve permits easy water changing and an undergravel system assists with biological filtration.

turtle installations. Their one drawback is that they cannot normally be used in shallow water tanks as used for turtles without a specially adapted tank wall. This is not easy to achieve with a glass walled tank unless built-in at the design stage. The new tank design also includes standard 1 fi" pipe outlets to allow for easy water changes and cleaning. It also provides a more than adequate depth of substrate in the land section. This is fully protected from water saturation and can, if desired, be warmed separately by means of a heat pad. In fact, eggs would probably incubate naturally in this area, but to date I have not actually attempted this.

The versatility of this tank design for turtles is, in my experience, unparalleled; with adaptations, extra land areas or filter arrangements are easily accomplished. As an example of what can be achieved, using this construction system it is perfectly possible to build an artificial river system with banks and flowing water. In its basic form however, the tank is warm, energy efficient, practically indestructible and easily constructed. It is also very inexpensive compared to a glass tank of equivalent dimensions.

The materials required are as follows:

- marine-grade plywood (15 or 20 mm) cut to size for base, sides, top braces and ends
- waterproof woodworking adhesive
- brass screws
- aquarium grade silicone sealant for all joints
- epoxy resin surface sealant (lacquer)

If a glass side wall is required, 6 mm or 8 mm float glass is recommended for small or medium sized units. Fix as shown on page 61. Plywood tanks can also be imaginatively constructed in room alcoves or fitted into other non-standard positions. With care, very attractive and functional turtle habitats can be created using these methods.

Plastic storage bins can provide a quick and effective method of housing small turtles. Here, a central heating radiator provides background heat (but a heat pad could also be used) and clip-on spotlamps provide radiant heat for basking. Filtration can comprise airlift operated undergravel systems or small internal canister filters.

Cascaded tanks

Both wooden and glass aquaria can be cascaded thereby allowing use of a single filter system to service all tanks in the chain. Physically, this arrangement is easily accomplished by positioning the tanks one beneath the other (a fall of 50 mm in water level per stage is recommended) and inter-connecting by means of an overhanging lip or pipe. A very substantial external filter is required if water quality is to be maintained. Because of the potential for cross-infection or contagion an ultra-violet steriliser is also essential. It is not recommended that sensitive species should be accommodated in cascaded tanks.

Plastic storage bins

These stackable containers are sold in hardware and kitchen stores as multipurpose containers and are available in a wide range of sizes. The medium and large sizes (up to 500 mm x 300 mm) make ideal accommodation for small turtles and juveniles. Many breeders use them extensively and report excellent results. Models with flat bases are eminently suitable for base heating via a heat pad. I have also used these containers for turtle housing with great success, especially when a small under gravel filter and powerhead is installed.

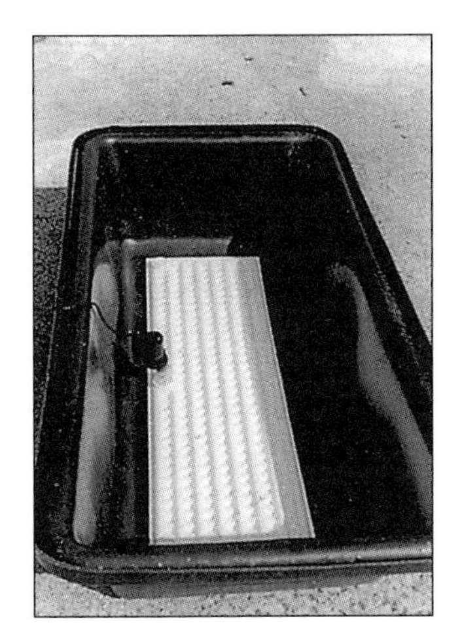

Plastic cement-mixing tubs can easily be converted into turtle accommodation. *Left:* An undergravel filter plate and powerhead is installed. *Below:* A 50 mm deep layer of gravel is added.The result is a tough, reliable and effective habitat for small to medium sized aquatic turtles.

Plastic or fibreglass cement mixing bins

These are often available at farmers' or builders' merchants and can provide a relatively cheap and at the same time high quality turtle habitat. Most measure approximately 600 mm x 900 mm (2 ft x 3 ft) and are both light and unbreakable. They are certainly ideal for emergency or temporary use and we have maintained some smaller turtles in them with excellent results for several years. Again, they work splendidly in conjunction with an under gravel filter and powerhead.

Steel tanks

Steel tanks have regularly been used as turtle housing, but they have a number of serious disadvantages. They have poor insulation properties and are prone to rusting. They are particularly unsuited to housing brackish water species. Other materials are preferable.

Surface mounted ponds

For larger animals a solid fibreglass pond may be more suitable. These can often be purchased read-made from water garden supplies. The addition of a simple wooden framework will permit most designs to be surface mounted. Alternatively, a plywood framework, with suitable reinforcements, can be made and then lined with a standard butyl pond liner.

Another fast and effective method of constructing shallow (up to 200 mm deep) surface mounted ponds, either indoors or outdoors, is to employ standard medium-density concrete blocks as used in buildings to provide the perimeter framework and to overlay this with a good quality flexible PVC or butyl pond-liner. The pond can be finished by overlaying natural-effect capping stones around the edges to hold the liner in place. Fitted with a central basking platform and undergravel filtration, such ponds can be highly effective and are well-suited to many species of turtle.

If using ponds like these in winter out-of-doors, it is important that insulation is applied around the walls and base to prevent the water freezing solid. Such ponds are obviously only suited to tropical species if adequately heated and located in a warm indoor environment.

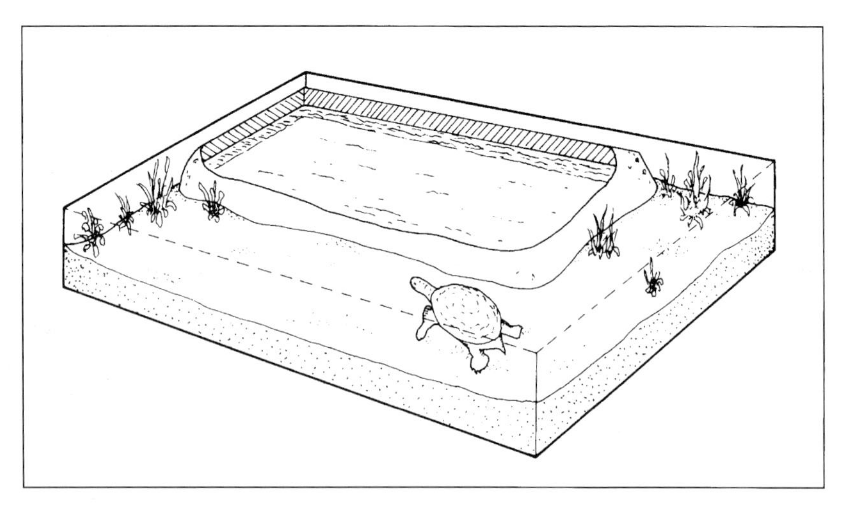

A shallow pond for semi-terrestrial turtles manufactured from resin coated plywood and equipped with a powerhead-operated undergravel filter.

Outdoor and indoor ponds

These range from small ponds suitable for a single turtle to lakes. The size will depend entirely upon available space, the number and size of the proposed inhabitants and inevitable financial constraints. Most will require excavating by mechanical digger. Linings in large sizes tend to be expensive. Depending upon local soil conditions, some ponds may not require lining at all (for this, clay soil is necessary). Most sites will, however, require lining. Butyl tends to be the best material (and the most expensive), followed by heavy duty PVC. Some brands of butyl carry a 20 year guarantee, whilst some cheaper PVC liners have a life expectancy of only 3 years. A good aquatic supplier should be able to explain the good and bad points of the various competing products on the market. Black polythene, as used for lining reservoirs, may be appropriate in very large ponds: note, however, that this is very fragile compared to PVC and butyl and, unless it is completely covered by at least 30 cm of substrate, has a limited life. A good compromise material is heavy duty PVC that has been made especially for pond lining: this has reasonably good abrasion resistance properties and if installed carefully will last for many years. Care should, however, be taken to protect all liners from the turtle's extremely sharp claws. Most damage occurs near the edges, and especially at favourite entry and exit points. Cement-lined ponds are, of course, excellent from the longevity point of view but unfortunately they are extremely costly to build and are in any case not ideal for turtles which tend to suffer abrasions very easily. These abrasions can easily develop into chronic shell rot. For this reason, cement ponds are not generally to be recommended for turtles.

For permanent outdoor use it is important to allow sufficient depth to prevent freezing during winter. The precise depth required will vary according to locality. Again, a local aquatic supplier should be able to advise further. On average, in most temperate locations, a depth of at least 500 mm will be required.

Shallow ponds for semi-aquatic turtles

Shallow ponds for semi-aquatic species are often far more difficult to design than ponds that are designed for entirely aquatic species. The main problem is that of water depth; these ponds are usually required to provide only a shallow depth, typically 75 to 150 mm. This severely limits the choice of filter system, many of which will not work at all unless there is a greater head of pressure. Efficient filtration is especially important in shallow water pools as there is less water volume than in larger tanks and biotoxin levels rapidly attain high concentrations. Because high light levels are also experienced right down to the substrate, proliferation of algae and overgrowth of blanketweed is also a frequent problem.

At the Tortoise Trust, we experimented first with shallow sunken pools lined with butyl pond liner for our tropical and temperate box turtles. For a variety of reasons, these were not very successful. Firstly, they were a chore to clean out (drain holes being almost impossible to install), and we experienced serious problems in achieving adequate filtration of the small volumes of water involved. They were rapidly abandoned.

We finally arrived at the design illustrated on page 64. This is constructed from marine grade plywood and is double coated with brush-on resin to completely seal it against any water penetration. It can be partially set into the ground but is equally satisfactory surface mounted. For filtration an under-gravel system driven by a submersible pump of the aquarium powerhead type is used in combination with an Aquaclear® hang-on-side unit. The under gravel component provides high quality biological filtration, whilst the Aquaclear® filter is loaded with activated charcoal to assist chemical quality. Because parasite levels, especially flagellate organisms, in this type of pool can present a real danger, we also circulate the water through a small ultra-violet steriliser before returning it to the pond. To achieve this a second submersible pump is required. To further enhance the water quality and overall habitat, some aquatic plants are also included.

This design is highly effective, attractive and very versatile in the sense that ponds of unusual dimensions can be readily constructed. To prevent too much terrestrial substrate such as leaf litter and bark mulch from entering the water, the slope leading to the lip of the pond is made from a 20 cm wide bed of medium-sized pea gravel.

The use of logs and timber in pond decoration

Logs can serve a useful purpose in pond construction, most notably to prevent soil erosion into the water. They are also highly decorative and allow the rapid construction of terraces, waterfalls and raised sections. However, extreme care must be taken to avoid the use of logs which have been subjected to toxic chemical preservatives. Tar-based chemicals are particularly toxic to reptiles, fish and amphibians. Modern water-based preservatives are safe, but will take months of curing before they can be submerged. The best option is to coat all timber in contact with the water with pond-quality fibre-glass resin. The protection is excellent, and up to 20 years of service can be expected.

Plants in the aquatic environment

The topic of plants in aquariums is a vast one, and is rightly a specialist subject in itself. Textbooks on tropical fish aquaculture will provide much information on the species available, planting and propagation techniques. However, turtles are much more destructive than tropical fish, and most turtle keepers have found only a relatively restricted range of plants are suitable in practice. Whilst more exotic species can be utilised if desired, the following varieties have proved consistently successful for use in aquaria containing turtles. Such plants not only serve a decorative purpose, but they also provide cover, in some cases food and contribute to overall water quality by utilising nitrates and improving oxygenation.

Java Fern (*Microsorium pteropus*): An extremely vigorous and easy to root plant which thrives at water temperatures from 20-26°C and prefers slightly acidic conditions (pH 6.5 -6.8). Widespread in India and throughout Asia. The leaves and roots are very strong and are not easily destroyed by turtles. It will root easily in a sandy substrate. This plant also enjoys ammonia rich environments, a common state in turtle tanks.

Water Hyacinth (*Eichornia crassipes*, *E. azurea* etc.): Water hyacinths are found in many tropical turtle habitats. The former species, *E. crassipes*, is very vigorous and through introductions has developed into a notorious weed in many areas. However, it is very buoyant and its large floating leaves are favoured by many small turtles for basking purposes. *E. azurea* is a much more delicate plant, suited only to large tanks and low density stocking. The leaves of the water hyacinth are a staple dietary component of several S. American turtles, including *Podocnemis* species. It will thrive in water temperatures from 18 to 27°C and is reasonably tolerant of pH variations.

Water Lettuce (*Pistia stratiotes*): This is very vigorous plant of attractive appearance. Found in many tropical and sub-tropical zones. It does best in water temperatures above 22°C and requires high light levels. This plant is often eaten by turtles.

Java Moss (*Vesicularia dubyana*): This plant is highly tolerant of brackish conditions and is vigorous in growth. It is efficient at utilising nitrates and hence improves water quality. In water it floats, though it also grows up tree trunks, on rocks and river banks out of water. It makes an excellent plant to grow over bogwood and is tough enough to withstand the attention of turtles. It will grow well in a wide range of temperatures.

Common Eel Grass (*Vallisneria spiralis*): Common in clear, fresh waters throughout the world. It propagates easily and is very tolerant. It requires a great deal of light and is best suited to shallow aquariums.

Canadian Pondweed (*Elodea canadensis*): Another highly vigorous and tough plant which is extremely tolerant of water conditions and is able to survive low temperatures. It is an excellent water purifier, a good oxygenator, and will grow either rooted or free-floating.

Crystalwort (*Riccia fluitans*): A useful cover provider for small turtles. Will grow rapidly and improves water quality. Predominantly a still-water and marsh inhabitant, found world-wide.

Arrowhead (*Sagittaria sublata*): Common in the shallow parts of ponds, lakes and rivers in the United States. This is ideal in larger tanks and ponds. It is easy to cultivate and tolerant of a wide range of water conditions.

Hair Grass (*Eleocharis acicularis*): A very hardy plant with extremely fine foliage well suited to cold water ponds and tanks. This is a particularly good underwater oxygenator.

Quillwort (*Isoetes lacustris*): Best suited to acidic conditions. A good oxygenating plant and relatively hardy.

Water Trumpet (*Cryptocoryne cordata*): A semi-hardy member of the widespread genus *Cryptocoryne*, most of which require tropical conditions. It is slow growing and prefers gravel beds and slow moving water. Another versatile member of the genus is *C. ciliata* from India and New Guinea. This latter is tolerant of brackish conditions but also grows well in freshwater. It is also suitable as a tropical terrarium plant out of water, as is *C. nevillii* from Sri Lanka.

In an ideal situation, plants would be selected to match the geographical origin and specific habitat niches of the turtles to be accommodated. This is not always possible, however and the above plants have proved very useful with a wide range of species. With very destructive turtles, and where decorative function is important, plants can be protected by submerging an internal glass or transparent plastic wall within the aquarium tank. If plastic is used a series of small holes can be drilled to permit water flow between the sections; if glass is used, a narrow open slot at the base of the tank, just above the level of substrate, should be employed. Using this method, the beneficial effects upon water quality of aquatic plants can also still be taken advantage of. In addition, fragile plants, otherwise ruled out, can also be used. Submersible heaters can also be concealed, in safety, behind the protective wall. To improve water flow, a canister filter or inlet or outlet pipe from an external filter should also be situated behind the protective wall.

Water quality and water sources

In addition to dissolved minerals and organic molecules, natural fresh water also contains a wide variety of microscopic living organisms, ranging from larvae and protozoans to bacteria and viruses. The majority of these organisms are non pathogenic, but some cause disease in both humans and animals. To render it fit for human consumption, water supply companies treat domestic water supplies with a disinfectant, the most widely used of which is chlorine. This is forced into the water under pressure as a gas and combines chemically with water to form, among other compounds, hypochlorous acid, which functions as a disinfectant. A small part of the chlorine remains as free chlorine which is relatively unstable in water and will readily diffuse into the air. Although the typical amounts of chlorine and chlorine compounds added to domestic water supplies are not harmful to humans they are known to cause problems with fish and gill-breathing amphibians and, potentially, could affect sensitive aquatic turtles. The degree of toxicity depends not only on the total amount of chlorine present, but also on the temperature, pH value, oxygen and organic content of the water.

Since free chlorine readily evaporates from water, it is relatively easy to drive this off during water changes by spraying the new water into the tank. Continuous agitation which mixes water and air is also recommended. A decorative waterfall or fountain can be very effective in this application.

Some water companies now use chloramines as a disinfectant. Chloramines, complex organic derivatives of chlorine, are formed from the combination of chlorine and ammonia, and are particularly effective because they are more stable than chlorine and release twice as much hypochlorous acid and do so over a longer period. Chloramines can also form naturally when chlorinated water mixes with nitrogenous compounds such as nitrate fertilisers. Unfortunately, because they are more stable than ordinary chlorine, chloramines are very much more difficult to eradicate from tank or pond water. Prolonged agitation, plus at least a 7-day standing period is recommended. Chemical chlorine removers are available from aquatic suppliers, but may not always be viable due to cost or the bulk required. One practical chemical treatment, frequently used in commercial aquaculture, involves adding 1 g of sodium thiosulphate for each 100 litres of water. This is agitated, then allowed to stand for 10 minutes. The treatment is concluded by adding 5 cc of 15% solution hydrogen peroxide and a further period of agitation.

An ideal solution is to use deep-well or spring water rather than public supplies, but this option is obviously not open to everyone. Collected rainwater can, however, prove to be a viable alternative, especially in areas of low atmospheric pollution. In metropolitan areas rainwater is often acidic; this does not necessarily rule out its use, but in these circumstances it is advisable to conduct a chemical analysis of the water to establish contamination and pH levels.

Reverse osmosis systems

If extremely pure water is required, one method of producing it relies upon the movement of water through a membrane. In such systems water is induced to move across a membrane from a polluted input to a pure output. The resulting output is of a purity comparable to distilled water and typically results in a 98-99% elimination of pollutants such as pesticide residues, phosphates and heavy metals. The drawbacks to the system are that it is very expen-

Above (left): A self-contained internal canister filter. Suitable for use with small turtles or in conjunction with undergravel systems for larger specimens.

Above (right): Large external canister filters. Suitable for use with larger turtles or as a container for chemical filtration media as part of a multi-filter strategy.

sive and all but the very largest systems are only capable of producing a limited output (50 litres over 24 hours is typical). For use with particularly sensitive neonate turtles however, the method has possibilities.

Small submersible filters

Filters for small systems are generally of the mechanical type. These typically consist of a cylinder of foam or similar wadding through which the water is circulated. Many are self-contained submersible canister types which include the pump motor, impeller and filtration foam in one unit. Typical flow rates range from 150 litres per hour to over 400 litres per hour. Maintenance consists of removing the foam and rinsing it under the tap. Larger models will require less frequent rinsing than smaller versions. It should be carefully noted that this type of filter merely removes suspended particulate. It does little or nothing to affect the chemical balance of the water so frequent water changes are also required if this is the sole method of filtration. Provided the water is adequately oxygenated some biological function may be also attained with cartridge filters; for this, the inclusion in the tank of an airstone driven by a separate air pump is essential. If allowed to operate in anaerobic conditions biological activity

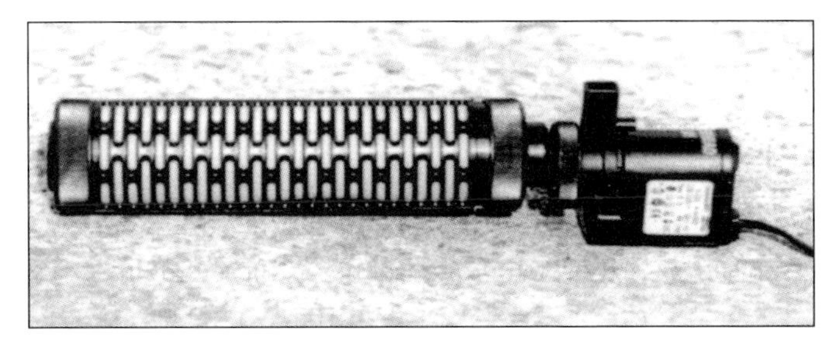

Above: A powerhead fitted with a removable accessory for fast removal of suspended particulates. This type of accessory can prove useful in small tanks.

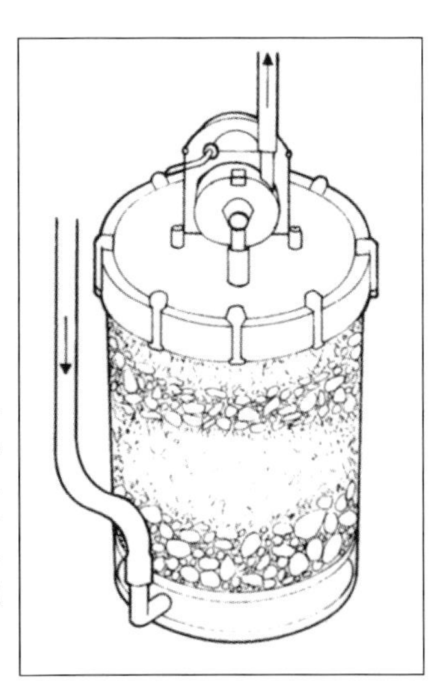

Right: Canister filters can include graduated and layered media to handle coarse particulate, fine particulate, biological and chemical functions in one unit. For effective biological filtration, it is essential that an adequate level of dissolved oxygen is present in the water.

will be very low and the filter will clog rapidly and develop an unpleasant smell. This type of filter is not really suitable for use with large animals, or high concentrations of smaller animals, as their ability to deal with large quantities of organic waste are extremely limited. These filters can, incidentally, be used successfully in conjunction with secondary biological (i.e. under-gravel) filtration. Small 'box' filters driven by air are also commonly available. These are not really adequate for use with turtles, although the better models may just suffice for hatchlings.

External filters

For larger water volumes external filters are typical. These normally consist of a large cylinder with separate layers of filter medium, varying in coarseness and function. For example, the initial (input) level may have a fine mesh to catch large particles followed by progressively finer foam and polyester filter floss layers to catch smaller particulate. This type of filter can also be fitted with activated charcoal which can assist removal of dissolved organic compounds, some proteins, lipids and certain non-ionic chemicals (such as chlorine). Activated charcoal is a very effective substance for filtration and is discussed in more detail under the heading, below, of 'chemical quality'. Zeolite is an ion-exchange material which removes ammonia and is also a useful addition to this type of filter (but see notes later). External filters are usually fed by pipes from the tank and most require positioning below the water-line to enable correct pump operation. It is usual to install them in an enclosed base beneath the tank. This type of filter is very useful for medium-sized installations where one filter can be applied to each tank. This is also useful in that it prevents cross-contamination which can occur in a shared system. Again, this type of filter can be used in conjunction with secondary biological filtration to improve overall water quality.

By clever design, it is often possible to construct a filter section beneath the land area required by many aquatic and semi-aquatic turtles; this is a great space saver and normally allows the use of a larger volume of filtration material than would otherwise be possible.

Filter types in large installations

In large installations self-contained internal or external filters are barely practicable. The animals involved may produce such large quantities of organic waste that any such system would rapidly be overwhelmed. The only answer is to progress to large commercial filters or self-built equivalents. Filters manufactured for swimming pool use are especially suited to use in large-scale turtle installations. Ideal filter mediums have proved to be diatomite and sand. An additional zeolite chamber is also recommended. Such filters are usually cleaned by back-washing.

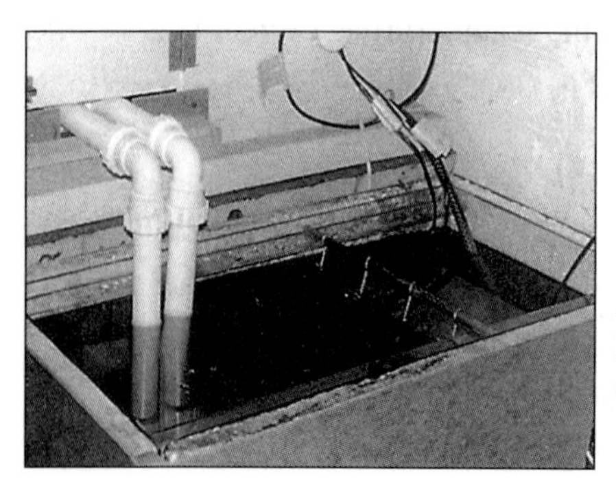

A large external filter chamber utilising hanging koi-type brushes and layered foam. Note large diameter of inlet and outlet pipes.

Another option is to adapt filters designed for use with koi. These can be particularly effective and come in a wide variety of sizes and designs. Such filters usually combine mechanical, particulate, filtration with some form of biological filtration. For large turtles, suspended brush-type koi filter chambers have proved highly effective in removing coarse particulate; these are especially quick and easy to clean. Finer particulate (and biological) filtration can be provided by means of foam-filled chambers followed by a zeolite section for final chemical filtration.

Ready-made filter chambers can be purchased from aquatic suppliers. Alternatively, many domestic water cisterns can be adapted to this purpose. Excellent filter chambers can also be constructed from marine plywood coated with G4® or similar pond sealing resin. Most of the large filters in use for the Tortoise Trust collection were made using this method.

With large systems it is usual to link individual tanks and to use a common filter system for all. This naturally increases the danger of cross-contamination with pathogens so it is virtually mandatory that any such system is fitted with ultra-violet sterilisers and that their effectiveness is checked regularly (see below).

Vegetable or plant filters

These consist of a separate, large, filter chamber or separate tank which contains a very high density of fast growing aquatic plants which are used to burn up excess nitrate and phosphate. They can be used in situations where it is not possible to introduce plants directly into the turtle's environment. One practical and easily constructed system relies upon a siphon to extract water from the turtle tank, circulates this through a second tank containing only plants, and then, assisted by a pump, returns the flow to its source. Suitable plant filter containers can be made out of plastic storage bins. Very deep containers are not effective, however, as they do not permit light penetration which is required for photosynthesis. An alternative method for smaller scale use is to employ a vertical turtle screen within the tank. I have safely grown plants behind a sheet of submerged transparent roofing material. Plant growth can be stimulated by use of special lighting, i.e. Gro-lux® tubes positioned above the vegetation.

Basic principles of biological filtration

The simplest form of biological filtration is the under gravel variety. Most are powered by an air-lift or electrically operated powerhead. Air lifts are suitable for tanks with low waste matter loads, power heads increase the flow rate through the gravel substrate and are better suited to larger tanks. One small advantage of air-lifts is that they automatically aerate the water without requiring a separate air-stone. Both can be also used in conjunction with internal or external canister filters (which remove the bulk of particulate mechanically). A biological filter functions by means of the accumulated effects of millions of living bacteria. Biological filters remove toxic nitrogenous waste products from the water. Turtles excrete urea or uric acid which is reduced rapidly to ammonia by bacterial action. The process of bacterial oxidation of ammonia is called nitrification. The nitrifying process involves two steps and each is performed by a different genus of bacteria, *Nitrosomonas* and *Nitrobacter*. These bacteria consume the nitrogenous waste products, utilise these wastes as a source of food and excrete nitrogen in an oxidised form. Oxygen is crucial for nitrification to take place, and conditions in a biological filter must be always be aerobic. This process is illustrated on page 72.

A biological filter has several essential components. There must be a suitable substrate for the bacteria to colonise. There must also be sufficient circulation through the substrate to provide oxygenated water for aerobic activity, yet water must flow through the filter medium

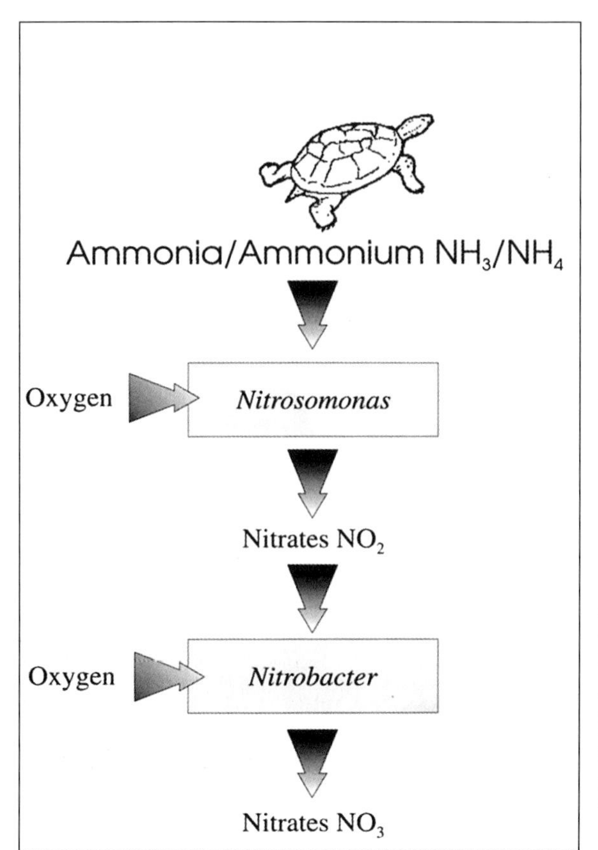

Above: A large external canister filter with graduated media visible. Provided the water is well oxygenated, this type of filter can combine effective mechanical, chemical and biological filtration functions in one compact unit.

Left: The nitrate cycle. At all stages of the process, the bacteria which digest the waste products require an input of oxygen. In anoxic tanks or systems biological filtration is ineffective. The larger the surface area offered for colonisation by nitrifying bacteria the more efficient the filter becomes. Thick gravel beds are particularly effective.

Above: An undergravel filter draws water downwards, through a deep gravel layer, where wastes are digested by bacteria. Either an air-lift operated by an air-pump, or a more powerful motorised pump (a powerhead) can be used to provide the necessary suction.

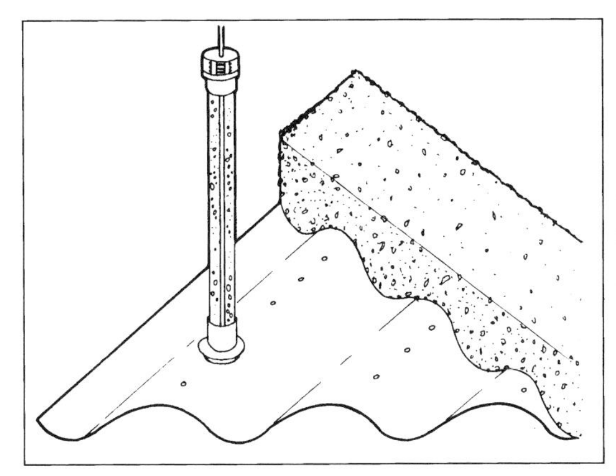

An undergravel filter made from plastic corrugated roofing sheet and a standard aquarium airlift tube. Small areas can be powered by means of an air pump, larger filters will require the use of a powerhead. This type of filter provides a large surface area for waste digestion by bacterial action. It has proved highly successful in a wide variety of turtle applications.

sufficiently slowly in order for the bacteria to be able to absorb the nitrogenous wastes. If the flow rate is too slow or ceases entirely however, the filter will become anaerobic and will begin generating ammonia instead of absorbing it. The nitrifying bacteria will then die and be replaced by species that live in an oxygen free environment. Most species of anaerobic bacteria produce toxic by-products, both inorganic (i.e. hydrogen sulphide) and organic (i.e. biotoxins). The net effect will be a smelly and often dangerous tank.

Many different materials have been used as a substrate for colonising bacteria. The most commonly used substrate in small tanks is gravel. Other substances employed for biological filter substrates include sand, pea-gravel and porous ceramics. Almost any non toxic insoluble substance that has sufficient micro-environments for the *Nitrosomonas* and *Nitrobacter* to colonise is suitable as a substrate. Larger external canister filters, properly designed and maintained, can combine both mechanical (particle) and biological filtration.

An effective under gravel filter for turtles

After some experimentation, I evolved a versatile and low-cost under-gravel filter system for the Tortoise Trust which provides a high quality of biological waste processing. It has since proved extremely reliable and effective in a wide range of tanks containing numerous medium to large-sized species. This easily constructed filter also costs approximately 25% of the price of equivalent commercial versions. It should be noted however that under gravel filtration is not usually suitable for those species which dig or forage in the tank substrate for food as the continual disturbance will severely inhibit filtration. Some turtles are also inclined to ingest gravel. This can result in fatalities. One practical solution to both problems is to cover the filtration substrate with tightly stretched nylon or wire mesh. Commercial gravel tidy nets are available from aquatic supplies to achieve the same result. I have not myself experienced either of these problems, but other keepers have, so you may decide that the precaution is justified.

The construction process is as follows:

• Obtain a sheet of plastic corrugated roofing material. Cut it carefully to size so that it is a tight fit to the inside walls of the tank.

• Every 25 mm or so, drill a 2.5 mm diameter hole along the raised surface of each corrugation

- If using a powerhead select a plastic tube to fit its inlet; if using an air lift, a 30 mm diameter transparent tube is usually satisfactory. Cut this to a suitable length to match the water depth the tank is designed for. Bore a larger hole in one corner to suit the diameter of the lift pipe and using epoxy cement glue it tightly into position as illustrated above.

- To permit improved water flow between the various corrugations, glue a series of small neoprene strips, separated by gaps along the corrugated surfaces which will be in contact with the bottom of the tank. Allow all glue to dry for at least 24 hours.

- Place in tank and cover with pea gravel to a depth of approximately 75 mm. If an inadequate depth of gravel is applied the filter will not function correctly.

- Add the powerhead or air lift tube, fill with water and rinse out thoroughly at least three times before use.

For most medium-sized turtles, this filter is so effective that it is likely no other filtration will be required. Even where additional mechanical filtration is employed, the biological functions provided by this filter will considerably improve water quality. Another method of constructing larger-scale under gravel filters, i.e. for pond use, is to bury a flexible pipe connected to a circulating pump in the substrate. One end of the pipe should be sealed and holes made at intervals throughout the length of the submerged section in order to draw water through the substrate. In larger installations a network of interconnected pipes can be used. The PVC pipes used in domestic plumbing are ideal for this purpose. To prevent inlet holes from becoming blocked by gravel, a fine mesh screen should overlay the pipes. To further improve water aeration and nitrate removal, the return flow can be routed through a vegetable or chemical, i.e. zeolite, filter and finally returned to the pond or tank by means of a spraybar, fountain or waterfall.

Setting up a biological filter

It is possible to purchase priming solutions for biological filters from tropical fish equipment suppliers; these consist of a solution containing suitable bacteria with which to start the biological process. In a new tank especially, their use can substantially reduce the time taken to build up to effective biological filtration. It is suggested that a priming solution should be used with the above design on installation to aid maturation

Oxygenation

The oxygen level of the water is by no means as directly important to turtles as it is to fish and amphibians; indirectly, however, it exerts a major influence. As we have seen, however, adequate dissolved oxygen is essential for effective biological filtration. Although it may at first seem incongruous, the addition of an airstone into every turtle tank can therefore make a real difference to overall water quality. These are usually supplied by means of a small air pump, one of which can provide sufficient air to oxygenate a large number of tanks. When selecting airstones, note that the finer the bubbles it produces the better; airstones manufactured from wood generally achieve the best results. In larger tanks and in ponds, waterfalls and fountains can also assist aeration and should be installed where possible. Some power-heads and canister filters include a venturi which draws air into the outflow and these tend to produce much better overall results than models lacking the feature. The addition of oxygenating plants to the system will also help achieve higher levels of dissolved oxygen. Maintaining good water-oxygen levels may also assist in inhibiting the growth of some anaerobic bacterial pathogens. Because of the high density of nitrifying bacteria they sustain, under-gravel biological filters have a particularly high oxygen demand and unless positive steps are taken to aerate the water can result in a serious overall oxygen inadequacy arising. Airstones or other aerating devices should therefore be used in every tank where an under gravel filter is installed.

Chemical filtration, activated carbon, resin and zeolite

As the term implies, chemical filtration media remove impurities from the water by chemical means. In practice, chemical filtration media are often used in the second chamber of a non biological filter system, the first one containing a purely mechanical medium to strain off particulate. A typical combination would be filter foam as a mechanical medium and activated carbon as a chemical filter medium. Activated carbon removes ammonia and other organic waste products from the water by a process of adsorption. This means that the adsorbed substances become loosely linked to the surface of the filter medium.

The process of activating the carbon granules, by heating them to a very high temperature, opens up millions of pores that present a large surface area for chemical adsorption. When the surface area becomes saturated by waste product chemicals the activated carbon will require replacement. Because of its limited life span activated carbon is really only suitable for smaller installations, i.e. with a capacity of not more than 500 litres or approximately 110 gallons.

In small to medium sized turtle installations, one of the best methods of employing activated carbon is to almost completely fill a large secondary external canister filter with the granulated product. One system I have regularly used relies upon an under gravel biological

A selection of filtration media suitable for incorporation into external canister filters or external filter chambers. *Top left:* Activated charcoal granuals *Top Right:* Zeolite granuals. *Bottom:* Ceramic rings which provide the maximum surface area for colonisation by nitrifying bacteria.

filter for primary filtration, but uses an external filter such as an large Eheim® or Fluval® filled 80% with activated carbon and 20% with foam at the inlet end (to assist suspended particulate removal). This combination works well provided the activated carbon is changed regularly.

A more modern alternative to activated charcoal is a resin polyfilter. This consists of a resin impregnated foam which absorbs toxic chemicals and locks them in. When exhausted, the filter block must be discarded although some can be recharged a number of times. The chief advantage over activated charcoal is that a higher level of activity is attained in a smaller package. Some resins are also specifically tailored to deal with a very selective range of toxins. This type of material is considerably more expensive than activated charcoal and, although it is very effective, tends to be of limited use in large installations due to its limited life and high cost. Various types and sizes are available and for small tanks this type of media should certainly be considered.

For larger tanks and ponds zeolite is preferred. Zeolites are hydrated silicates of calcium and aluminium, sometimes of sodium and potassium. As with most other filtration media, the larger the surface area of zeolite exposed to the water, the more effective it will be in removing waste products. While small grade granules theoretically offer a relatively large surface area, in practice they clog more easily and become gradually less efficient. The ideal grade for turtle use is that with a particle size between 5 cm (2in) and 10 cm (4in). Filter systems utilising zeolite alone need approximately 1 kg of zeolite per 5 litres (about 2.21b per gallon) of water.

One other important advantage of using zeolite in preference to activated carbon or resin is that it can be cleaned and reused. The chemical bond between zeolite and ammonia is fragile and can easily be severed by adding salted water to the used substance. As ammonia is released, the zeolite becomes effectively recharged and is ready for use again. The technique is as follows: place the used zeolite into a container, or close off the bypass valves, if fitted, and add a salt solution made up with 6 grams of salt per litre of water (approximately 1 oz. per gallon) for 24 hours. Wash the zeolite thoroughly in fresh water before using it in the filter circuit again.

Zeolite can be added in layers to an existing filter system. Although this method is often recommended (and in some systems may be the only option), in reality it is a highly inefficient way of utilising this material. By far the most effective method is to employ a separate filter chamber, or stage, containing zeolite only. This should be capable of being bypassed and isolated. It should also be fitted with a drain to allow for washing and soaking with salt water during recharging. **Caution:** the zeolite filter section must be isolated whenever medications are applied to the turtle tank. Zeolite will be permanently destroyed if substances such as malachite green, acriflavine or other disinfectants come into contact with it.

General observations

The following observations relate to almost all aquatic turtle installations and should be noted carefully as they tend to be root causes of a great many problems if overlooked.

Algae and ultra-violet sterilisation

Excess growths of algae are rarely a serious problem in indoor tanks as they require high levels of illumination in order to flourish. In outdoor ponds, however, it can prove a persistent enemy. In a well-balanced pond, algae should not in theory present a problem. However, it is very difficult to balance a pond which houses turtles and, in practice, most keepers do experience algae problems from time to time. Excess algae can also indicate high nitrate levels and suggests more frequent water changes are required. Algae levels can sometimes be reduced by introducing other aquatic plants which will compete with the algae for available nitrates (especially *Elodea* and *Ceratophyllum* species). This will also improve the aesthetic qualities of the environment and greatly enhance oxygenation. Chemical treatments which function by using an additive that causes the algae to clump together and fall to the bottom of the pond before being siphoned off produce a short-term solution and are useful in emergencies, but in the long-run are both expensive and tedious. Other chemical algaecides may be harmful to either turtles or plants. Algae can also be removed by filtration through a fine foam filter, but, as each millilitre of water can contain over 10,000 algae particles, clogging is a continual problem. It is worth noting, however, that algae is usually less of a problem in tanks and ponds which have an undergravel filter as floating plant cells are drawn into the substrate where they die and are eventually digested. The most effective all-round solution is to use an ultra-violet steriliser; these work extremely well and have the important added benefit of destroying bacteria and viruses at the same time.

In order to destroy most protozoa and fungi, a dose of 1 watt/second is required of UV-C radiation. Viruses and bacteria can be destroyed with lower exposures. The larger the particle, the higher the necessary dose. Algae often requires very high doses, but commercial pond sterilisers take this factor into account. Most manufacturers recommend that the contents of the tank or pond be circulated through the steriliser every 90 to 120 minutes.

Ultra-violet sterilisers were once very costly, but new technology has resulted in a number of highly effective models coming onto the market at very reasonable prices. They are readily available from aquatic dealers who specialise in koi and can be highly recommended to the turtle keeper. With all ultra-violet sterilisers it is extremely important to ensure that the output tubes are changed regularly and that the internal surfaces are all kept clean; failure to do so can result in severely reduced efficiency. Sterilisers also function best if the water supplied to them is pre-filtered. Follow the manufacturer's maintenance and installation instructions carefully.

Green (*Chlorophyta*) or green-blue algae (*Cyanophyta*) is unsightly, but not dangerous. Some forms of red algae (*Rhodophyta*) however, can be damaging to plants and possibly also to turtles. Its presence usually indicates that a thorough clean-out and water change is in order. This variety of algae is often introduced on aquatic plants originating in Southeast Asia and it is one of the more difficult types of algae to eliminate once established. Brown algae (*Diatomacea*) is usually encountered in well shaded waters and is particularly unsightly,

Internal view of an ultra-violet aquarium steriliser showing UV tube, starter electronics, and surrounding water collar.

coating plants, turtles and tank hardware with a thick brown slime. It should be remembered, however, that filamentous, or thread, algae is a favourite foodstuff of many turtles, especially in their juvenile phase, so this should not necessarily be discouraged. Filamentous algae is also a superb water purifier, removing large quantities of ammonia and nitrate and grows extremely rapidly. It can more than double its own mass within 24 hours in favourable conditions.

In indoor tanks, it may be worth experimenting with the addition of algae-eating fish; some turtles will consume these immediately, but others will leave them entirely alone.

Ozone and magnetic treatments

Algae cells and numerous other pathogens can also be destroyed using an ozone generator, or ozonizer. Ozone (O_3) is a highly unstable form of oxygen (O_2) which has strong disinfectant properties. In aquatic systems, ozone units are usually fitted in the return pipe from the main filter. It is important that such systems are properly designed, maintained, and monitored as ozone is highly toxic to all forms of life, including plants. Algae cells can also be affected by strong magnetic fields and a number of magnetic treatment units are now on the market. Some users report good results.

Overfeeding

The widespread practice of overfeeding aquatic turtles is a primary cause of blocked filters and poor water quality. The feeding of oily fish, which are especially problematic in this regard, is not only likely to prove harmful to the turtles, but also results in clogged filters and unpleasant smells. Feed only as necessary and avoid overfeeding. If food is left floating in the tank, then overfeeding is probably occurring. With most aquatic turtles feeding three to four times per week is perfectly adequate. Daily feeding is very rarely appropriate.

Community accommodation

In general terms, most turtles can be expected to do best if maintained in single species groups. However, in the wild there is no doubt that sympatric species occur and share the same habitat. Even so, some predate upon each other. Certain highly aggressive species, such as snapping and soft-shell turtles, rarely make good companions for other species. The experience of many keepers suggests that mixed-group tanks and ponds can be successful, but also that great care needs to be exercised in planning such arrangements. It is also very unwise to combine non-sympatric species due to disease risks. It is also unwise to mix specimens of disparate size as the larger animals may view the smaller ones as a tasty snack. Some public zoological collections feature highly diverse mixed turtle exhibits; usually, they *a)* have the space to reduce territorial aggression and to allow animals under attack to escape, or *b)* expect to lose a few vulnerable animals from time to time.

Water test kits

These are highly recommended and many versions are available from aquatic suppliers; most will test pH, ammonia, nitrite and nitrate. Electronic models are a convenient, though more expensive, alternative. Test kits can prove useful in evaluating filter efficiency and indicate accurately when water changes are required. In an ideal tank or pond, ammonia levels should remain below 0.05 mg/litre and the nitrate concentration should be below 0.3 mg/litre. The optimum level for both is zero. Other target parameters include; dissolved oxygen >6 ppm; redox potential 350 mV (using electronic meter); nitrite zero; phosphate zero. Most chemical test kits function by means of comparing colour changes caused by reagents with a supplied colour chart.

pH

The term pH means potential hydrogen ion, and represents the number of moles (gram-molecules) of hydrogen ions present in one litre of solution. The value is so small it is usually represented as the logarithm of its reciprocal and called the pH value. For example, if the concentration is 10-7 its reciprocal is 107 and the pH value is 7. The pH scale is a series of calibrations from 0 to 14. 0 represents the strongest degree of acidity and 14 represents the highest degree of alkalinity. It is important to realise that an increase or decrease of 1 point on the pH scale represents a rise or fall of 10 times actual alkalinity or acidity. A value of 7 represents a condition which is neither acid nor alkaline, and is therefore neutral. From this it is clear that any reading from 7.1 to 14 indicates an alkaline condition progressively getting stronger as it approaches 14, and any reading from 6.9 to 0 indicates an acid condition, progressively becoming more acidic as it approaches zero. In the wild, most freshwater measures between 6.5 and 8.5, with brackish water typically at the high end of this scale. In the case of fish the pH of water is often extremely important. Its importance to turtles is not fully understood, but it is evidently quite important to many South American and Asiatic river turtles which demonstrate scute disease and skin degeneration if placed in water which is too alkaline. There is also some evidence that many freshwater turtles are less susceptible to infection by pathogens if maintained in the pH range below 6.8 and that many disease organisms prefer an alkaline environment. The individual requirements of a species should be investigated if possible before introduction to a tank. Various proprietary water treatments are available to adjust water pH. One simple method of increasing pH is to scatter crushed limestone in the tank substrate. A curious, but effective, means of decreasing pH, or increasing acidity, is to add dilute tea to the water. For greater convenience, proprietary treatments are recommended. Beware of inadvertently increasing alkalinity by use of unsuitable gravel substrates. Many gravels act as pH buffers. For Amazon blackwater species a neutral, often flint, gravel should be selected.

Air temperature

Care should be taken to ensure that the air in the tank, or tank room, is not significantly cooler than the water temperature. Turtles exposed to draughts of cold air run the risk of respiratory infections, even if the water temperature is adequate. Some species require the air temperature to be several degrees above that of the water.

Salinity

Although referred to as freshwater turtles, many species actually inhabit coastal marshes where the salinity is close to marine conditions. In Turkey, for example, I once encountered *Mauremys caspica*, *Trionyx triunguis* and *Emys orbicularis* all sharing a tidal lagoon with a large *Caretta caretta*! In many other localities freshwater turtles live in tidal estuaries where conditions vary on a cyclic basis from "fresh" to "marine". There is evidence that a lack of salinity can lead to an increased incidence of skin and shell infections. Although difficult to quantify, if a turtle occurs in the wild in brackish conditions then some effort to duplicate those conditions in captivity should be made. Proprietary marine salts are readily available from tropical fish suppliers and are a convenient method of adjusting salinity. Most turtles from brackish habitats will respond well if the salinity is maintained at 25 - 35% of the level of sea water which is typically 35 parts per thousand sodium chloride and other dissolved salts. For most brackish species, therefore, dissolved salts should be maintained at a level of 8.75 to 12.25 parts per thousand. A few species may require higher levels. Salinity may be measured with a hydrometer. Readings from hydrometers reflect not only dissolved salts but also the temperature of the water and are expressed as units of specific gravity. Compensation for temperature effects is usually required. Electronic meters are also available.

Hard and soft water

These common terms reflect the level and type of soluble materials present in water, mainly the bicarbonates and sulphates of calcium and magnesium, but also chloride and nitrate salts. Bicarbonates of calcium and magnesium cause temporary hardness, but sulphates of calcium and magnesium cause permanent hardness. Bicarbonates also tend to inhibit the water from becoming acidic. Soft water, lacking bicarbonates, tends to an acidic nature. For turtles that require acidic water, avoid the inclusion of calcareous rocks, gravels, coral or broken shells in the substrate. For most freshwater turtle species, a medium hardness and neutral or only slightly acidic water is required. Certain Amazon and rain forest species are an exception to this, and require much more acidic conditions and very soft water. See also under pH.

Water changes

Regular water changes are essential in all captive maintenance systems for turtles. Even with the best possible mechanical and biological filtration water quality will gradually deteriorate. Many keepers find that changing 50% of the water weekly is adequate. Others change more frequently. A complete water change once per month with half-changes at 14 days has also proved to be an effective and practical cycle. Regular changes will reduce disease and parasitic contamination and will lengthen filter media life. Care should be taken to ensure that the temperature of fresh water approximates that of existing system water and that the change water does not contain either toxins or agents that will damage biological filter systems. It should be noted that an important side benefit of water changing is that in many aquatic species it immediately initiates sexual activity and is therefore a useful strategy to encourage captive breeding.

Evaporation and water quality

All uncovered tanks and ponds are subject to evaporative losses. Depending upon the external temperature and relative humidity, these losses can be considerable. The lost water can, of course, be easily replaced but suspended toxins will continue to present a hazard as a high level of evaporative losses will tend to concentrate these in the remaining water. It is therefore essential that tanks and ponds are not just topped up indefinitely but that a regular complete water change is also implemented. Evaporation can be reduced by fitting a tank hood wherever possible. I have found that sheets of transparent polycarbonate are ideal for this purpose, especially where tanks of non-standard dimensions are concerned. The additional benefits of a tank hood include ease of maintaining high levels of local humidity and a reduction in overall heat losses.

Top: A combined aquarium heater and thermostat unit. *Below:* A heater for use with a separate electronic thermostat. For use with turtles, only non-breakable models should be employed. Available in a range of powers from 50 to 300 watts.

Care and maintenance of biological filter systems

The nitrifying bacteria in biological filter systems, such as under-gravel filters, are very sensitive organisms. Even rinsing the tank or gravel with chlorinated tap water can instantly destroy them. Antibiotics introduced into the water for turtle treatment are even more effective at killing them. Apart from removing excess detritus from the surface the filter bed should be disturbed as little as possible. On no account introduce antibacterial agents into the water system when a biological filter exists.

Heating

In large installations, the 'warm room' technique may suffice. In most situations, however, some form of individual tank heating will be required. Ordinary submersible combined heater-thermostats, as used for tropical fish, are the most common method employed. Turtles and tropical fish are, however, very different and extreme caution needs to be exercised when using this type of heater. Firstly, the danger of breakage is very real. Even medium sized turtles are quite capable of shattering the glass envelope surrounding the heating element. This can have fatal consequences, not just for the turtle, but for any human unfortunate enough to come into contact with the electrified water. **Never** touch the water when the power to the heater, or filter, is turned on, and **always** use a protective earth leakage device to guard against electrocution. If possible, only employ shatterproof aluminium encased heaters, and if you must use glass-enveloped types ensure that they are well protected behind a safety screen (see figure, below). Submersible heaters can only be used in tanks with a reasonable depth of water. They are therefore not suitable for shallow-water heating as is required in most semi-aquatic terrariums. For shallow tanks, base heating using water resistant head pads beneath the bottom glass is a viable and safe alternative. Another option is to employ circuit

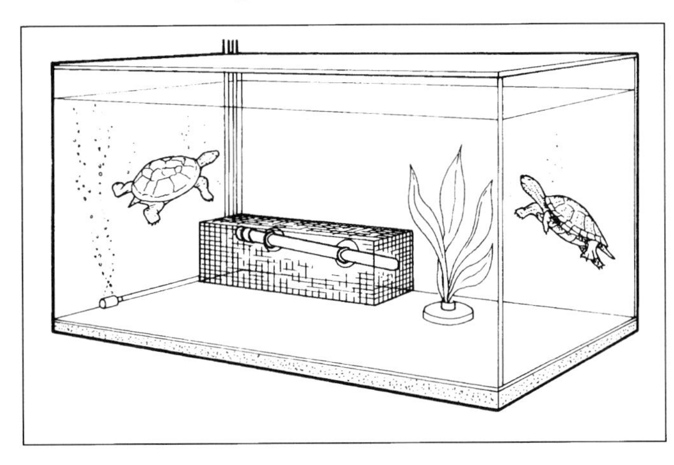

A safety screen to protect submersible heaters from damage by turtles.

heaters which are situated outside the tank in the pipeline return from the filter.

The majority of aquarium heaters sold combine a heating element and thermostat within the same unit. It must be said that my own experience with these is that the thermostat is by far the least reliable component. Leaks around the thermostat adjustment knob are another common problem. Where multiple heater-stats are to be used within the same tank it is often difficult to adjust the individual thermostats to a common temperature threshold. A better alternative to heater-stats is to use submersible heaters which do not include a built-in thermostat, and for temperature control to employ a separate electronic module. Electronic thermostats with a submersible remote probe are available for this purpose from tropical fish hobbyist suppliers; most will serve heaters up to 500 watts unaided, but a booster module can usually be added which will increase power handling to several kilowatts. This arrangement has been employed by the author on many occasions and has proved both safe and reliable.

For larger, indoor ponds, an ordinary hot-water central heating radiator can be coated with fibreglass and resin (to prevent rusting) and used as a submersible heater. Where an adequate supply of hot water exists this method can prove very effective indeed.

Do not ignore the benefits of insulation. Covering the sides and back of a glass tank in high quality insulation media can reduce heating requirements and costs by up to 40%. It also greatly increases the thermal stability of the tank. Ponds too should be insulated as well as possible. A 20 mm layer of insulating foam beneath a pond liner can drastically reduce heat losses to the ground. This is especially relevant in heated, indoor ponds. Over a period of time, the difference in running cost between an insulated and non-insulated pond will prove very substantial.

Lighting

For most aquatic turtles, the same type of lighting as used for terrestrial species will prove entirely satisfactory. Non basking species will appreciate full spectrum tubes such as Vita-lite® or Sun-Glo®, whilst basking species may prefer Chromalux® in combination with the former. Although often recommended, the claimed advantages of using high ultra-violet output black-light tubes for turtles are highly questionable; provided a balanced diet is provided, with adequate calcium and D3, high levels of ultra-violet are unnecessary. Certainly, many highly successful specialist breeders of turtles find ordinary incandescent spotlights entirely adequate for both lighting and basking purposes. My own preference is for at least some pro-

Basking facilities are extremely important for all tortoises and turtles. Here, a basking lamp is suspended over a pile of rocks in the middle of an indoor turtle pond.

Above (left) : A standard 180 gph submersible pond pump. Note foam pre-filter to prevent clogging from large particles.

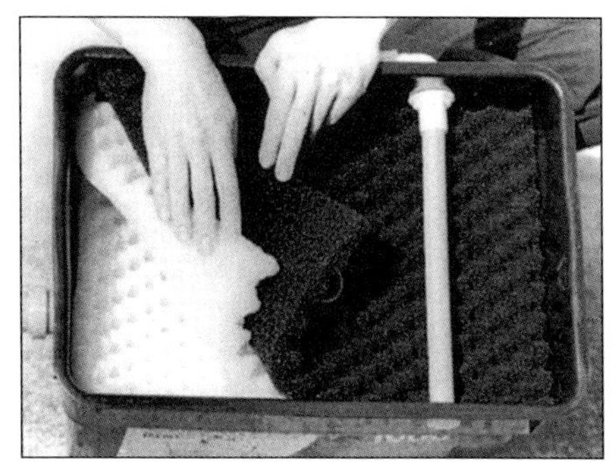

Above (right): A commercial pond filter containing layered foam media suitable for use with the pump shown opposite.Note spray-bar for water inlet.

vision of full spectrum light, however, as it appears to stimulate more natural behaviour patterns in many turtles. The benefits in this respect may be entirely psychological. I have found Vita-lite®, which is known as True-lite® in Europe, and Sun-glo®, among others, entirely satisfactory for this purpose.

Water pumps and plumbing

Although most small to medium sized filters include built-in motors and impellers, larger systems, especially those using separate filter chambers and most pond systems, employ a separate pump. Submersible pumps are by far the most popular for this purpose and are available in a wide range of sizes and throughputs (typically from 150 gph to 3000 gph). Models from the top manufacturers are both safe and reliable. In ponds and messy tanks it is advised that a pre-filter made of coarse foam should be fitted to prevent frequent clogging. I have, however, found that the very best pumps for use in large turtle tanks or ponds are those which can handle a certain amount of solid throughput; these tend to be two to three times as expensive as models which cannot cope with solids, but in my opinion are well worth the additional cost. Nothing is more tedious (or messy) than having to constantly dissemble pumps to free a jammed impeller or having to constantly rinse clean clogged inlets. All submersible pumps **must** be wired via a safety earth leakage breaker to prevent a potentially fatal electric shock in the event of a malfunction.

Pumps are usually located at the lowest level of the circuit with the outfall, following filtration and sterilisation, being gravity fed back into the pond or tank at its highest level. The height to which a pump has to transport water is referred to as the head. As the height increases so the volume of water moved is reduced. The effective head is reduced considerably by the bore, length and straightness of interconnecting hoses. Corrugated pipes should be avoided as their internal friction is much greater than smooth pipes. Connectors in pipes also seriously affect flow, so for maximum efficiency use one-piece plumbing. Keep all pipe runs as short and as straight as possible. For medium-sized pumps flexible plastic tubing between 25 mm and 35 mm is normally suitable. For very large pumps domestic PVC pipework is often used. This may exceed 50 mm in diameter.

It should be noted that if a pump is to be used with brackish water, plastic models are generally superior to those of metal construction.

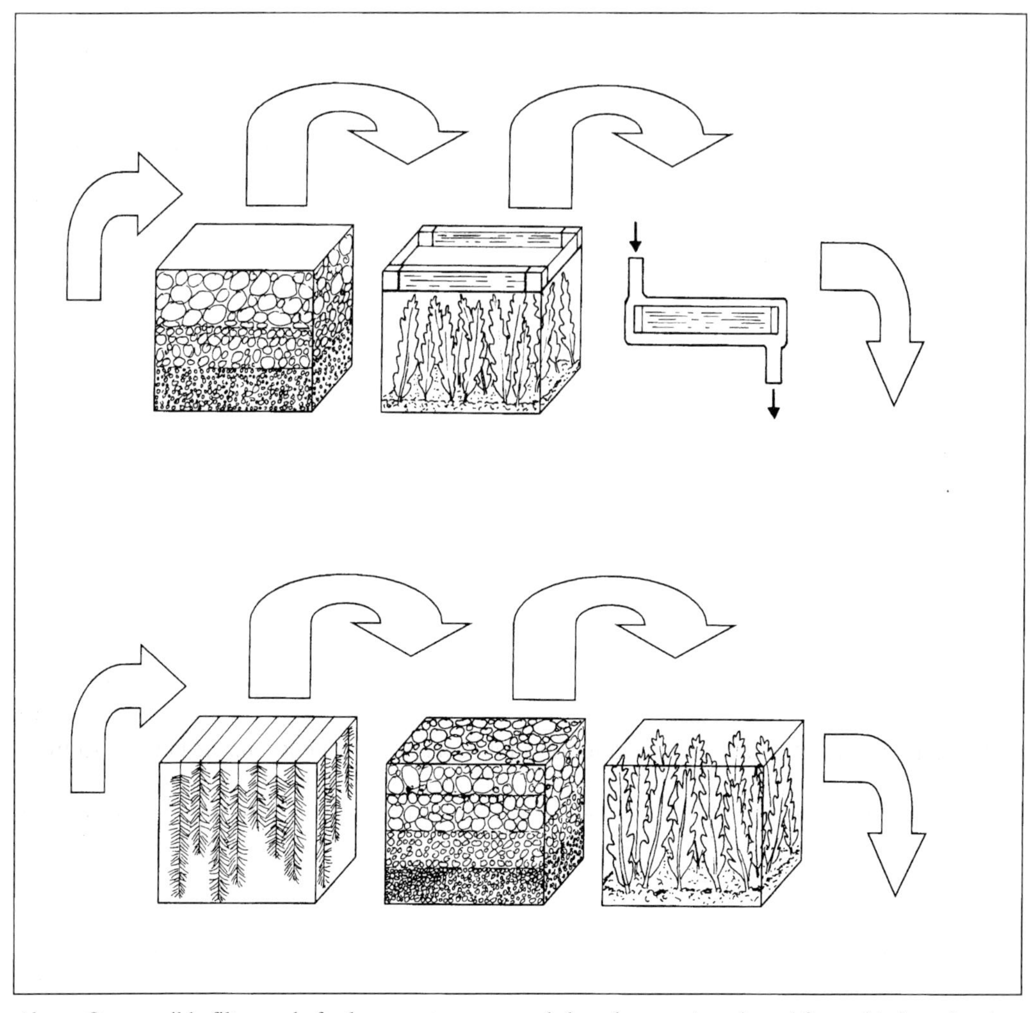

Above: One possible filter cycle for large systems or ponds based upon *a)* graduated foam, *b)* plant chamber with Gro-lux® lighting and *c)* Ultra-violet steriliser.
Below: Another possible filter cycle comprising *a)* Koi-type filter brushes, *b)* graduated foam chamber and *c)* plant chamber. Modular filter systems can be assembled in several combinations to suit particular filtration needs.

Useful products and medications

Blackwater extract

This is available commercially from tropical fish suppliers and is a convenient method of providing Amazon-blackwater type water for appropriate species. Different brands employ slightly different formulations, but most seem reasonably effective in turtle applications. Such preparations must always be used in conjunction with appropriate filtration. Many species are found either in blackwater or whitewater conditions. For example, the South American *Podocnemis erythocephalia* (Red-headed sideneck turtle) is found almost exclusively in blackwater rivers. These rivers are slow moving and contain tannin residues, hence the possible use of tea, as mentioned previously. Commercial blackwater extract closely approximates the chemical traces typical of such waters. It is entirely possible to duplicate these conditions naturally but the better commercial brands offer the benefit of greater convenience.

Marine salts

As the name implies, commercial marine salts provide a convenient formulation designed to replicate natural sea-water. They are normally used at the appropriate dilution to produce brackish conditions in turtle applications. Commercial marine salts may contain as many as 30 separate trace elements. A simpler formula, suitable for self manufacture, is as follows:

- 2, 750 g Sodium chloride
- 690 g Magnesium sulphate crystals
- 550 g Magnesium chloride crystals
- 145 g Calcium chloride crystals
- 65 g Potassium chloride
- 10 g Sodium bromide
- 0.5 g Potassium iodide
- 1.5 g Strontium chloride

The above quantities are for 100 litres of sea-water strength solution. This should be further diluted to attain brackish conditions.

Acriflavine

This is a highly useful product, usually supplied as an orange coloured stock solution, which is effective, in varying degrees, against flagellate protozoa, mycoses (fungus infections), flukes, bacteria, and some viruses. It is therefore an excellent all-round sterilising solution and is normally used at a 5-10 ppm dilution in a separate treatment tank. It is toxic to most aquatic plants and will also damage filter systems, however. Water pH is critical to effectiveness; it should only be used where the pH is near neutral. It is also photosensitive so should be stored in a dark place.

Malachite green

Usually supplied as green crystals, or as a stock solution. It is useful against protozoa and mycotic organisms. It is usually added to water in a separate treatment tank where the affected animal is dipped. Typical regimes include 1 ppm for 30 minutes duration every 24 hours for 5 days, or direct topical application to the site of fungal infection at a 25 ppm dilution for 30 seconds daily. Handle with caution and do not ingest as this product is toxic and is a suspected carcinogen.

Indian star tortoise (*Geochelone elegans*) 4/11/14

Chapter Seven

DIETARY MANAGEMENT AND NUTRITIONAL DISORDERS

Dietary related disorders represent a major cause of mortality in captive bred hatchlings and juveniles. Detailed examination of the affected living and deceased specimens reveals that a combination of recognised clinical factors are invariably present, principally acute secondary nutritional osteodystrophy resulting from an inadequate dietary calcium to phosphorus ratio. This is frequently combined with hepatic and renal dysfunction with deposits of uric acid within the renal tubules. The latter condition is most often observed in cases where artificially high protein diets have been imposed by keepers upon herbivorous species which in their native habitat would experience much lower levels of dietary protein. A high incidence of renal and hepatic diseases have also been noted for some time both in veterinary reports and necropsy surveys of long-term captive tortoises and turtles.

A survey by Rosskopf (1981) drew exclusively upon animals which had been maintained as pets. In this survey the findings were that 72.6% of mortalities exhibited severe hepatic disorders, 53% respiratory disease, principally pneumonia, 50.7% digestive tract disorders, 40.6% renal disease and 34.3% cardiac dysfunction. Other veterinary surveys have produced similar results.

The achievement of a nutritionally satisfactory captive diet for tortoises is generally more difficult than it is for aquatic turtles. For similar reasons, the dietary management of herbivorous lizards such as iguanas is generally more challenging than that of carnivorous snakes. It is a fact that with very few exceptions indeed most terrestrial tortoises are exclusively herbivorous. That this is, indeed, the case is well borne out by physiological studies which show that the tortoise's digestive system is very closely related to that of other recognised herbivores and has very little at all in common with the digestive systems of true carnivores such as snakes, cats and dogs. Biological carnivores have a rapid digestive metabolism designed for breaking down decaying animal proteins as quickly as possible and expelling the residue before toxic material can accumulate. In order to accomplish this they have short digestive tracts. Herbivores have a slower digestive metabolism better suited to steadily breaking down cellulose by gentle bacterial and enzyme action. It is worth noting also that the pancreas itself is much smaller in herbivorous testudines than it is in omnivorous or carnivorous species. Radiological studies on the alimentary tract of herbivorous testudines have revealed some quite interesting data, specifically that many weeks may be taken for food to pass completely through the gastrointestinal tract (Holt, 1978).

Nutritional disorders may be conveniently divided into two main groups consisting of:

- Diseases of excess
- Diseases of deficiency

Clinically, combinations of the two groups are common, i.e. acute carapace distortion due to lack of dietary calcium and concurrent hepatic and renal dysfunction resulting from dangerously high consumption of saturated fats and proteins.

In practice, it is possible to achieve a combination of normal growth and satisfactory osteological carapace development without incurring problems provided adequate attention is given to the specific dietary requirements of the species concerned and that sufficient levels of all essential trace elements are present (Highfield, 1988).

Animal protein and herbivorous species

The question of the provision of animal protein in the diet of captive herbivorous testudines is a contentious issue. It is sometimes argued that animal protein is appropriate in all cases or is certainly harmless even if admittedly unnatural. The present author takes the view that animal protein is properly only appropriate to carnivorous and omnivorous species and that it is harmful if provided to herbivores. As noted above there are quite distinct physiological differences between these categories of animal. There are also biochemical differences that are relevant.

Uric acid and blood urea levels are greatly elevated in herbivorous testudines fed unnatural meat based diets. Sodium urate, a salt of uric acid, which is the end result of purine metabolism is found in large quantities in meat products. Tortoises suffering from dehydration and hatchlings are at particularly high risk if placed on high protein animal foods. It is a common, and often fatal, mistake when confronted by a dehydrated and underweight tortoise to believe that increasing the protein content of voluntary or force feeds is the best way to restore health. In fact, due to the increased level of blood urea high protein foods generate, renal failure is a much more likely end result.

The saturated fat content of tinned pet foods, which are the source of animal protein most frequently relied upon by tortoise keepers, is also extremely high whereas wild herbivorous testudines would be expected to consume virtually nil saturated fat. Dried cat or dog foods in pellet form are not generally as high in fats as tinned varieties but are still far too high to be safe for consumption by most terrestrial tortoises. Many cat and dog foods also contain excessive levels of preformed vitamins A and D3 and this is yet another reason for being cautious in their use.

Hypoproteinaemia (protein deficiency)

As a primary condition, protein deficiency is normally only encountered in carnivorous or semi-carnivorous turtles which have been forced to survive (often through their owner's ignorance) on a strictly vegetable diet. It may also be found in cases of serious neglect, starvation, or generalised gross dietary mismanagement. It may also occur as a secondary condition in conjunction with sterile gut syndrome or other malabsorbtion problem. Acute cases will require treatment with specialist supportive fluid therapies which contain a combination of electrolytes, amino acids, dextrose and B complex vitamins in an easily assimilated form. One suitable product, available in the United Kingdom, is Duphalyte®. Such products may be administered orally, by stomach tube, or by means of intracoelomic or i.v. injection as directed. We have encountered hypoproteinaemia in American box turtles, African hinge-back and South American Red-foot tortoises maintained on strictly vegetarian diets.

A note on corrective vitamin and drug dosages

Throughout this text, drug dosages are given as so many milligrams (mg) per kilogram (kg). This last figure is the total bodyweight of the animal concerned and is the standard method of calculating doses and requirements. Most drugs and vitamins suitable for injection are supplied giving a figure of so many mg per millilitre concentration. Example: a drug is to be dosed at 25 mg per kg and the weight of the animal is 750 grams. The dose required is calculated by 0.75 x 25 = 18.75 mg. The drug is supplied in the form of a solution containing 100 mg per ml. In order to determine how many millilitres should be injected: 100 18.75 = 1.8 ml. If the drug was supplied at a concentration of 50 mg per ml, the amount to be given would then translate to 3.6 ml. Some dosages are described in terms of so many i.u. (international units) per kg. Provided the concentration of the formulation is known, i.e. that the concentration contains 20,000 i.u per ml, the amount required in millilitres can be calculated using the same formula. Many drugs and vitamins are supplied in a range of concentrations, usually expressed as, for example, 2.5%, 5% and 10% solutions. For example, a dose may be expressed as 3 ml per kg of a 2.5% solution. Provided the same concentration of preparation is available, no further calculations are required other than to ascertain the amount necessary for the patient: if the patient weighs 2 kg, then 6 ml should be given. If a different concentration is available, e.g. the 5% solution, then half the amount in millilitres would constitute the correct dose.

Vitamin A deficiency

Vitamin A is essential to healthy growth and development and in particular to epithelial condition. Deficiencies often manifest as metaplasia of the conjunctival epithelium, which results in swollen eyes, progressing to metaplasia of the pancreatic ducts and squamous metaplasia of the renal tubules which results in blockages of the kidneys. The external surfaces of the skin may also be raw and frequently secondary bacterial infections may also be present. There is also good reason to believe that epithelial degeneration of the lung tissues may result in respiratory problems developing and similar degeneration of the linings of the nares is certainly implicated in the aetiology of runny nose syndrome. Should breeding females become deficient avitaminosis A of the egg yolk might occur. It is believed that, in turn, this may cause abnormal development of embryos including anophthalmos, or failure to develop eyes.

Aquatic turtles and hatchlings are at special risk of developing vitamin A deficiency. High protein diets rapidly deplete neonatal stores of vitamin A and this is another reason why their use is questionable. Even for carnivorous, aquatic species, the diet provided must be within safe limits.

Treatment consists of careful topical cleansing of external damaged areas to defeat or prevent secondary bacterial infection and provision of vitamin A either orally or by injection in severe cases (up to 20,000 i.u. per kg). Oral dosing is best accomplished using ABIDEC® or similar multivitamin drops. The condition can be entirely prevented if adequate levels of the vitamin are present in the diet.

Good natural (secondary) sources of vitamin-A include all fruits and vegetables containing carotene. The carotene is then converted into true vitamin A internally. Vitamin A and vitamins D3 and E can be overdosed (hypervitaminosis A), so take care when administering pure doses. Vitamin A should only be delivered by injection under the direction of a qualified veterinary practitioner. Secondary sources cannot be overdosed as the excess is simply not converted. Vionate® contains 220,000 i.u. per kilo and at normal levels of supplementation provides sufficient levels to prevent hypovitaminosis A occurring. Hypervitaminosis A or vitamin A overdoses manifest in a manner remarkably similar to the way in which deficiencies develop with hyperkeratosis and epidermal disruption. For this reason continuous dosing with liquid vitamin drops is not recommended. The relatively low doses provided by Vionate® or similar multi-vitamin products when used as recommended are within safe tolerances. One of the best natural sources is dandelion greens which contain over 14,000 i.u of vitamin A (as beta-carotene) per 100 grams in addition to many other vital trace elements. Grated carrots are also an excellent source of beta-carotene and are well-liked by many tortoises and turtles. It is a little known fact among herpetologists, although long recognised by traditional veterinary herbalists, that carrots also possess natural worming properties. Used on a regular basis they are both safe and reasonably effective, especially for juveniles. They should not, however, be substituted for more orthodox treatments of proven effectiveness against a broad spectrum of helminths.

Vitamin B deficiency

This condition is rarely encountered in terrestrial tortoises but known to present a problem in snakes and aquatic turtles which have been fed on large quantities of frozen fish due to the presence of the enzyme thiaminase which forms in fish after death. Fish is categorically not an appropriate dietary component for terrestrial tortoises under any circumstances. Symptoms include muscle tremors, nervous type behaviour and anorexia. Treatment involves dosing with injectable thiamine hydrochloride and correcting the underlying dietary cause. The provision of a properly balanced diet to aquatic testudines will prevent the problem arising. Aquatic turtles whose diet includes fish should always be provided with a concurrent vitamin B1 supplement.

Vitamin D3 deficiency

This condition is frequently encountered in conjunction with secondary nutritional osteodystrophy. A suitable multivitamin supplement that contains 15,000 i.u. D3 per kilo, for example Vionate®, applied at approximately 4% weight to food will prevent the problem. The use of Vita-lite® or similar FSL fluorescent tubes, or better, exposure to natural unfiltered sunlight, also aids vitamin D3 production and utilisation.

It is worth reporting the results of some practical experiments undertaken on this topic by the author and some colleagues. We were interested to discover just how critical ultra-violet light exposure was to tortoises. With one group of juveniles, we allowed very little ultra-violet or natural light exposure (they were mostly reared under incandescent lighting). With another group, we allowed extensive ultra-violet and full spectrum exposure. The first group was provided with our standard tortoise diet (i.e. low protein, high fibre) supplemented with both calcium and D3. The second group was provided only with calcium. No soft-shell problems were noted in the first group. The second group eventually did begin to show some symptoms. This was eventually traced to the ultra-violet tubes reducing their output with age. These problems were identified quickly and corrective action was taken: the tubes were replaced and oral supplementation as for the first group began. Although not conclusive, this does suggest that it is probably safest to include at least some oral D3 combined with calcium in the dietary and management regime. Over-reliance upon D3 synthesis from light may not always prove safe. Studies in other reptiles also tend to confirm that a combination of oral supplementation and natural synthesis is probably the best option.

If relying upon full spectrum and low UV-B output lamps, then careful research should be undertaken to determine the wavelength and intensity of output of different brands which may be available. In order for realistic levels of D3 to be produced, tortoises and turtles may need to be in very close proximity to the lamp. This may not be practicable or, indeed, advisable. True-lite® or Vita-lite® tubes are rarely adequate sources of UV-B if this is to be the sole source of vitamin D3. There is an approximately 50% loss in UV efficiency for every 30 cm the lights are raised above the substrate. A more powerful lamp suitable for reptile use is the Westinghouse® FS20 20 watt sunlamp. When using high-output UV-B lamps, however, it is important that animals are not allowed to get too close to the source. As a rule, a minimum distance of at least 60 cm is suggested. As discussed above, however, the most satisfactory solution seems to be that of using a combination of good quality combined calcium and D3 oral supplement and full spectrum lighting to provide additional UV-B and psychological benefits. This is the method adopted as routine in all of the Tortoise Trust captive breeding projects and results have been consistently excellent for many years.

In addition to the obvious carapace distortions associated with calcium and vitamin D3 deficiency, other symptoms may be encountered. These include swollen mouths, soft jaws, limb swelling and locomotion difficulties. This set of symptoms is easy to confuse with articular gout and septic arthritis, which manifests in an almost identical manner. An investigation into any suspect animal's history may be of assistance. X-ray diagnosis may also prove fruitful.

Along with vitamin A and vitamin E, hypervitaminosis D (i.e. overdosing) is also a possibility which, should it occur, results in metastatic mineralisation of the soft tissues. Pure vitamin D should therefore not be administered (except in cases of specific deficiency syndrome and then under veterinary supervision). The use of multi-vitamin products which include D3 in balanced amounts with calcium is not dangerous and will not result in excessive doses being absorbed provided they are used as directed. All of the fat-soluble vitamins, A, D and E, are potentially dangerous and should be used with care. It should be noted that many cat and dog foods contain excessive quantities of vitamin D, certainly for tortoises, but also for many turtles, so such products should be provided infrequently, even for carnivorous and semi-carnivorous species.

Vitamin C

Vitamin C deficiency may, possibly, be implicated in many conditions, especially stomatitis and a generalised susceptibility to bacterial infection although specific deficiency diseases have not, as yet, been conclusively demonstrated in testudines. Deficiency is easily combated by good dietary management. The feeding of really fresh foods is of paramount importance. A lettuce, for example, typically loses 50% of its vitamin C within 30 minutes of being harvested.

Vitamin E

Vitamin E is a vital antioxidant. Deficiencies are usually seen in aquatic turtles which have been maintained on oily, fat-rich diets and may manifest as muscular dystrophy. Terrapins which are fed on oily fish, such as white bait are at particular risk. Therapy should include a combination of Vitamin E and selenium, a trace element which is synergistic. Evidence obtained from other animals, especially birds, suggests that even marginal vitamin E deficiencies may result in reproductive problems and contribute to the non viability of eggs.

Miscellaneous trace elements

The role played by mineral trace elements in the diet is not fully understood, even in the case of human nutrition. However, it is becoming clearer that their role is much more important than was once assumed. A considerable amount of research has been directed towards increasing our understanding of these trace elements, much of it concerning their effects on farm animals. To date little work has been carried out specifically with respect to reptiles due to their lack of economic importance. It would seem reasonable to assume however that their effects on mammals and reptiles are not dissimilar. There are many different trace elements and it is not possible to detail each one here. However, the most important include:

Iodine deficiency and hypothyroidism

This condition can result from two causes. Either a simple lack of iodine in the diet or from the practice of feeding too many goitrogenic vegetables especially the brassicas, which includes cabbage, kale and sprouts etc. Symptoms include lethargy, fibrous goitre, and myxoedema of the subcutaneous tissues. Preventative measures consist of daily provision of iodine in the form of vitamin-mineral preparations containing at least 30 mg per kg of iodine as a trace element per day. Serious cases can sometimes be helped by administering sodium iodide either orally or via injection. The addition of selenium and zinc to the diet can also counter the effects of goitrogenic vegetables. The problem can be encountered also in wild populations especially where water supplies are naturally low in iodine. This condition is most often encountered in Galapagos or Seychelles giant tortoises, which appear to have a higher than normal demand for iodine. The condition is also seen in other reptile species from volcanic habitats, where halogen-sequestrating vegetation dominates. The addition of ground kelp (seaweed) tablets to the diet of these animals appears to be highly effective in countering the syndrome and should be adopted as a standard management technique. Adult Seychelles and Galapagos tortoises remain free of the problem if provided with one kelp tablet daily and access to goitrogenic vegetables is strictly limited.

Selenium

In excess, selenium is highly toxic. It is an essential dietary trace element, however, and has excellent anti-oxidant properties. In humans, it plays an important role in preventing degenerative diseases. It is also important in the reproductive metabolism. Selenium functions in synergy with Vitamin E. The selenium content of plant foods is often deficient because inadequate quantities of selenium are found in many soils, particularly in regions which have suffered glacial erosion (most natural habitats of tortoises have not been subject to glacial erosion). Animals from arid habitats generally have a lower selenium demand than animals from tropical environments. Frye (1981) reports a selenium and vitamin E deficiency in aquatic turtles as causing a muscular disorder. A similar disorder is well known in cattle as white muscle disease. Recent research also indicates that selenium is of critical importance to the development of birds' eggs and in avian hatching success rates. As bird and reptile eggs are very similar, it is possible that selenium could prove to be equally important in the captive propagation of testudines.

Zinc

Zinc is required for bone formation and development. It is also utilised in the development of the sex organs and helps mobilise vitamin A. Zinc is also an important constituent of enzymes involved in protein synthesis and the carbohydrate metabolism. It also plays an critical role in the healing process. Zinc is a recognised essential human trace element and is the most important trace element in enzyme formation.

Chromium

Chromium maintains blood sugar levels by regulating proper use of insulin. This is important to carbohydrate metabolism. Deficiencies can result in hypoglycaemia, a condition which has been reported in crocodilians.

Molybdenum

Molybdenum is a constituent of the enzyme xanthine oxidase and has an important role in the oxidation of purine to uric acid. As such, it is of particular interest when considering reptilian biochemistry.

Cobalt

Cobalt is critical to the vitamin B12 metabolism in all grazing herbivores. Gut microflora manufacture fatty acids from ingested plant material and depend upon the presence of cobalt for this process. Deficiencies are well known in cattle and sheep. Symptoms of deficiency in these animals include anaemia and repeated intestinal problems including scour and flagellates etc.

Iron

Iron is a component of haemoglobin. Deficiencies result in anaemia. This condition is unlikely to occur in herbivorous tortoises as green-leaf material is usually rich in iron. Carnivorous species are more at risk

Manganese

Manganese aids the metabolism of carbohydrates and proteins. It also plays a role in the thyroid metabolism. Deficiencies are known to cause bone-growth defects in some animals. It is suspected that this element could be of more importance than previously realised to tortoises and turtles.

Most acute trace element deficiencies will occur in those animals reared on severely limited and generally deficient diets. i.e. lettuce as the only greenstuff. However, border-line deficiency states may occur in animals without obvious symptoms or easily attributable cause, i.e. soil deficiencies in the grazing area. Proving direct links between any given disease condition and specific trace elements is extremely difficult. It would appear prudent, therefore, to pre-empt the possibility by ensuring that a good quality multi-mineral and vitamin supplement is used routinely. The constituents of commercial preparations should be checked carefully to ensure that they contain an adequate range of essential trace-elements. It is entirely possible that many apparently mysterious reproductive failures could be linked to trace element deficiencies and the critical nature of their metabolic function should not be underestimated.

Plant estrogens and effects on reproduction

Virtually no work has yet been carried out on the possible effects of plant estrogens on the reproductive cycle of herbivorous tortoises and turtles. It is known, however, that plant estrogens are very important in other areas of animal husbandry. Plant estrogens are essentially a chemical defence system used by some plants to disrupt reproduction of their 'enemies', the grazing animals which feed upon them. Animals which graze on Australian clover, for example, become increasingly infertile. In California, certain plants produce phytoestrogens in dry years. When eaten by quail, these compounds inhibit reproduction and therefore reduce the number of young which would have fed upon them. The biology of these processes is extremely interesting (Bowers et. al., 1976). It is known, from studies in birds, that other effects of plant estrogens include influences upon the development of eggs and the period of diapause. This is an area of testudine-plant interaction which requires more research.

Coprophagy

Coprophagy, or dung-eating, is a behaviour noted in many terrestrial tortoise species. Droppings from small mammals are extremely rich in B group vitamins, calcium, certain bacteria involved in the gut fermentation process, amino acids and numerous other trace elements. Some tortoises also eat the droppings of other tortoises, particularly so in the case of hatchlings which frequently seek out the droppings of adults. In many cases, it is believed that this behaviour is part of the process of establishing normal commensal bacterial gut flora in juveniles. For this purpose, it is strongly recommended that only material from healthy adults of the same species should be used.

Some tortoise species which are notoriously difficult to maintain or rear in captivity, for example, *Psammobates* or *Homopus* species, may turn out be dependent upon regular ingestion of these bacteria, amino-acids and trace elements throughout their lives. Clearly, in captivity there are risks involved in this process. Only faeces from totally healthy animals, mammals or other tortoises, should be used. If the source is other tortoises, it is absolutely imperative that only droppings from the same species should be used as the bacterial content of tortoises' digestive tract varies among species. We have found that goat droppings are a good source of fibrous, relatively clean material for coprophagy where adult tortoises are concerned. We would not necessarily advise routine encouragement of this behaviour, but in some cases experimentation is undoubtedly justified. Dog and cat faeces are best avoided due to their heavy loads of potentially dangerous parasites (i.e. flukes). The faeces of herbivorous grazing animals is undoubtedly preferable as, although they may be parasitised, the parasites and other organisms in question are typically not as pathogenic as those encountered in carnivores. It should be noted that North Africa and the Middle East, the coprophagous habits of *Testudo graeca*, which principally involves consuming goat and camel dung, were one factor in the animal being prohibited from human consumption on religious grounds.

Metabolic bone disease and dietary calcium

By far the most common nutritional disorder encountered and a major cause of early mortality in captive-bred hatchlings, metabolic bone diseas is sometimes known as soft-shell syndrome. It is also known as nutritional secondary osteodystrophy.

The overall body shape may also be distorted with marked elongation observed in many cases. In acute cases, the hind legs project at an unusual angle and the tortoise may 'shuffle' rather than walk. The bones of the jaw may be soft and weak and, in hatchlings, the plastron may remain soft long after it ought to have hardened. Nervous symptoms associated with hypocalcaemia may also be noted. These symptoms may appear collectively or individually depending upon the progression and severity of the deficiency. Hatchlings are worse affected, due to their rapid growth and consequent higher calcium demand, but even adults will manifest the condition if placed on an acutely deficient or severely unbalanced diet for long enough during a growth phase.

The underlying bony tissue is porous and thickened and local swellings of the jaw and limbs are commonplace. The body, attempting to support the weakened skeleton, surrounds it with a fibrous connective tissue. The parathyroid glands recognise that there is inadequate calcium within the bloodstream and attempt to rectify the deficiency by leaching calcium from the bones, thus exacerbating the condition. As long as the diet and blood-serum level remain calcium deficient, this vicious cycle continues. Finally death occurs from acute calcium collapse.

Typical carapace deformities associated with this condition include raised scutes and a markedly flattened appearance, often with a depression in the region of the carapace situated above the pelvis (page 97). Animals thus affected may also manifest respiratory symptoms due to lack of space for lung expansion.

The condition results directly from inadequate levels of dietary calcium, excessive dietary protein, excessive dietary phosphorous and inadequate levels of vitamin D3. Generally a combination of factors is involved. Among inexperienced reptile keepers, metabolic bone disease is perhaps the major cause of animal casualties. The condition is especially prevalent in the case of tortoises, turtles and iguanas although it is encountered in practically all species when dietary management is unsatisfactory.

Tortoises fed on a lettuce only, or almost only, diet without mineral supplementation will invariably suffer from classic soft-shell syndrome. Those fed on high protein diets combined with a relative calcium deficiency will suffer from acute soft-shell syndrome plus gross pyramiding of the scutes and excessively high blood urea levels. Such animals may well go on to develop serious renal damage and other diseases associated with uric acid deposition. Aquatic turtles fed on unsupplemented processed meat products or meats without bone will also develop the problem.

The ideal ratio of calcium to phosphorous in herbivorous species is usually quoted as 2: 1 for growing reptiles, or at least 1.25: 1 for fully grown adults. Calculations based upon the chemical constituents of wild tortoise diets suggest that an actual raw intake figure of 3 or even 4 parts calcium to 1 part phosphate would be more realistic. It is important to note that there is a substantial difference between the raw intake figure and the actual, absorbed ratio. Vionate® is an excellent supplement that contains many valuable trace elements and vitamins. It is not, however, sufficiently rich in calcium to counterbalance the high phosphate levels encountered in many green vegetables. Even where it is provided liberally it is very difficult to maintain a ratio of 1:1 or 2:1 in practice and virtually impossible to exceed these levels. One answer is to supplement with additional raw calcium lactate or calcium carbonate in order to achieve a 'raw' or external ratio of between 3 to 4:1. The actual *absorbed* ratio will remain at approximately 2:1.

For carnivorous species of turtle calcium supplementation is just as important. Carnivorous and semi carnivorous species are especially prone to calcium-phosphorus imbalance, such animals receiving on average a ratio of 1 : 25 from red meat diets, or, if the diet consists of meat and fish 1 : 10, or even 1 : 16 if mainly insect based (i.e. crickets). Whereas in the wild such turtles would consume their prey complete with bones, or consume quantities of gastropods which are also encapsulated in calcium, in captivity, raw meat is

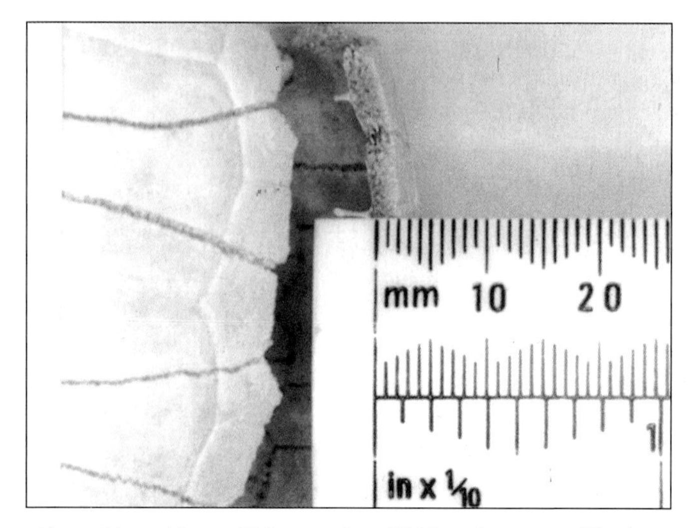

Above: Normal bone thickness of a wild *Testudo graeca*. The bone tissue here is approximately 2 mm thick and has good density. The outer carapace was free from deformity.

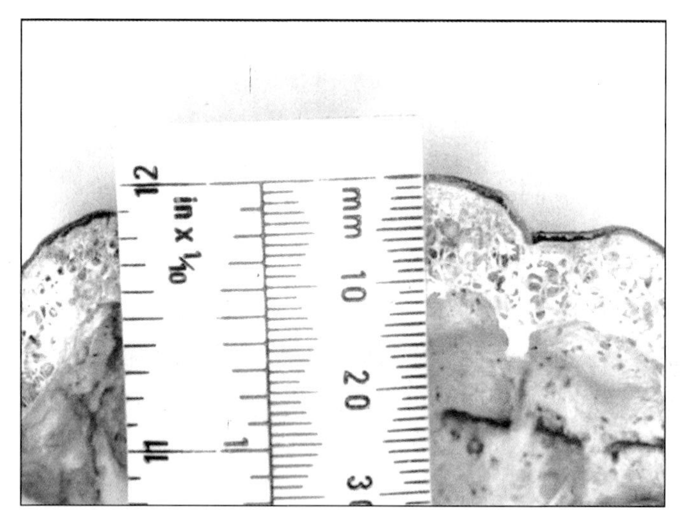

Above: Abnormal bone thickness of captive-reared *Testudo graeca* which had been fed on dog food with minimal supplementation. The bone thickness here is 12 mm, with poor density, obvious porosity and very evident deformities of the outer carapace.

Above: Captive animals maintained on high protein diets grow rapidly and mature early, but suffer a high incidence of renal dysfunction. 'Lumpiness' of the carapace is also evident in this captive-reared Chaco tortoise (*Geochelone (Chelonoidis) chilensis*)

Above: The depression visible at the rear of the carapace, together with the 'lumpy' raised scutes, are typical of a normally herbivorous tortoise (in this case, *T. hermanni*) which has been reared on a diet rich in protein but low in calcium and vitamin D3.

often provided. This contains practically zero calcium but is extremely rich is phosphorus and protein. Unless additional calcium is provided, serious deficiencies are a foregone conclusion. Meats in the form of rats, mice and whole fish are infinitely preferable in captive diets for carnivorous turtles than filleted steaks.

Many proprietary combined calcium and D3 supplements are now available and their daily use is highly recommended. In addition, it is simple enough to provide a calcium 'cake' in the tortoise enclosure or aquatic turtle terrarium. One widely used recipe suggests 1 kg of plaster of Paris plus 100 grams calcium and a quantity of D3 multi-vitamin product mixed with water and poured onto a metal tray to set. However, this particular recipe ignores the fact that plaster of Paris is hydrated calcium sulphate, a far-from-ideal source of dietary calcium and that in this form minimal calcium will actually be absorbed. The recipe can be substantially improved by including 50% finely ground calcium carbonate in the form of mixed oyster shells and cuttle fish bone. When dry, break into lumps and scatter in the tortoise enclosures and aquarium water. Most terrestrial tortoises and aquatic turtles will nibble on this as required. In the wild, many large tortoises, including leopard tortoises, are known to gnaw on bones or consume calcium-rich hyena faeces. A product which is not presently commercially available!

At the same time it is important that strongly negative Ca:P food items, and those rich in oxalic acid, are totally excluded from the diet. All dietary constituents should be selected so that the overall dietary calcium to phosphorus ratio, prior to supplementation, is at worst neutral and if at all possible positive. A reference table of commonly available foodstuffs is provided in Appendix One.

Some specialist suppliers of reptile vitamin and mineral supplements now offer products which have been carefully formulated to provide a much better match to the specific dietary requirements of reptiles than the standard supplements, such as Vionate®, which were originally formulated for general purpose use. One such supplier, in Britain, is Vetark Products whose Nutrobal® high calcium supplement is especially suitable for tortoises and turtles. In the United States, Rep-Cal® is similarly recommended as a phosphorus-free source of calcium and D3.

Our own experience of rearing hatchlings of a variety of species, both temperate and tropical, herbivorous and omnivorous, aquatic and terrestrial, has proven beyond any doubt that this destructive condition can be entirely prevented if a balanced vitamin-mineral supplement is provided to all hatchlings and growing tortoises. Our preference is to use both Vionate®, a multi-vitamin and mineral preparation, which we administer at approximately 4% of food weight daily plus Nutrobal® or Rep-Cal®. It is important to note that only fresh stocks which have been kept in an airtight container are satisfactory. Outdated stocks or supplies which have been kept in bags rather than sealed containers have drastically reduced effectiveness due to oxidisation of volatile vitamins.

It is frequently assumed that a tortoise's calcium demand is relatively stable and constant; in fact this is not so. It fluctuates quite considerably and is much higher in females during egg production and in both sexes during any period of rapid growth than it is in periods of low growth or in old age. It is therefore our practice to provide all breeding females with additional sources of calcium to aid egg production.

Good natural sources of calcium for herbivores include apricots, figs, fig leaves, dandelions, chicory and parsley. It should be noted that whilst members of the *Chenopodiacea* family, such as spinach and beet greens, might appear on the surface to offer a good source of calcium, this is bound up with oxalic acid, a substance which forms insoluble calcium oxalate and is thus of limited value to the tortoise. The feeding of excessive quantities of such plants will severely inhibit the ability of the tortoise to metabolise available calcium so should be avoided. Tortoises which are fed on large quantities of spinach may develop calcium deficiency even though a supplement is being provided.

Meat-eating turtles can be provided with calcium tablets sandwiched into their feed. Alternatively, use a dried food, such as koi or cat pellets, which are soaked in water together with added multi-vitamin and mineral supplements in a bowl and then allowed to partially dry again before feeding. This will prevent the added minerals being immediately washed away on contact with the water of the tank. It should be noted that many commercially available 'turtle diets' are seriously calcium deficient. Read ingredient labels carefully and avoid reliance upon any one staple food.

The role of supplements

It may be argued that where a 'natural' diet is provided no additional mineral or vitamin supplementation is required. The fundamental problem is a) defining exactly what the natural diet of a species is and b) the difficulty of providing it. Many species browse upon a very wide range of different plants, consuming leaves, flowers and frequently stems, roots, seeds and even soil particles in the process. Many also engage in behaviour such as snail-shell eating, coprophagia, or gnawing upon bleached animal bones. This behaviour in females often coincides with periods of egg production. The range of trace elements, proteins, oils, vitamins and other micronutritional elements thus made available is both complex and extensive. Many of these elements are also mutually interactive. Sunlight and hence UV-B exposure in the wild is also very different from that typically experienced in captivity. The plants upon which wild tortoises and turtles feed are also grown in very different conditions than most substitute plants available to keepers, thereby affecting their natural or intrinsic mineral content. Whilst it may be entirely possible to avoid the use of supplements in a free-ranging situation within the natural bioclimatic range, achieving this under captive conditions is a very different matter. From the discussion of trace element requirements given above it will be noted that even marginal deficiencies may have serious consequences. For this reason, the routine use of a safe and effective multi-mineral and vitamin supplement is, in this author's opinion, by far the best and safest option.

Treatment of existing metabolic bone disease

The treatment of this condition presents a number of problems. Bone damage and carapace deformity cannot be corrected overnight, if at all, in many cases. The standard treatment program involves oral doses of vitamin D3 at a rate of 1.0 to 4.00 iu/kg daily, in combination with calcium, which is administered parenterally by injection at a rate of 1.0 to 2.5 mg/kg daily. A new treatment originally developed for iguanas and snakes offers new hope to tortoises and turtles afflicted by this condition, however.

The new treatment is based upon a synthetic hormone designed for use in humans suffering from post-menopausal osteoporosis, Paget's disease, and hypercalcaemia. The preparation concerned is called calcitonin-salmon and it functions by reversing the parathyroid effect noted earlier. Before dosing with calcitonin-salmon it is absolutely vital that blood calcium levels are adequate, as if they are deficient the effect of the drug will be to drain all remaining supplies and in all probability cause sudden death through hypocalcaemia. Therefore, a short course of calcium and vitamin D3 injections should precede the calcitonin-salmon injection which is delivered at a rate of 1.5 i.u./kg. At the same time as the calcitonin-salmon treatment is initiated it is also advisable to begin a program of 'renal-flushing' by means of oral administration of Hartmann's solution. Sterile physiologic fluids can also be administered by i.v. drip or intracoelomic injection in acute cases. This treatment offers some hope where previously non-recovery was a near certainty. There are risks associated with the therapy, but the potential benefits may outweigh these. Treatment should, of course, be followed by a revision of the dietary habits which induced the condition. Despite initially dramatic results recorded following this therapy, the long term prognosis for affected animals must remain guarded, however.

The most unfortunate feature of metabolic bone disease is that more than 99% of cases are entirely preventable by good dietary management in the first place. It is very regrettable that it still remains the number one killer of captive-bred hatchlings.

Dietary fibre

This is frequently overlooked but in fact is extremely critical to a tortoise's and turtle's well being. A lack of sufficient dietary fibre will result in poor digestion, diarrhoea and an increased risk of colic.

An examination of faeces samples taken from wild tortoises reveals fibre contents many times greater than that typical in captive animals. Wild tortoise faeces are generally well compacted, well formed, and very high in varied grass content. This should be compared to the loose, poorly formed droppings so often seen in captive collections.

A diet rich in fibre is therefore highly desirable and attempts should be made to ensure that adequate quantities are available. This can take many forms, but lucerne (alfalfa) hay and banana leaves have proved highly effective, especially in the case of captive giant species. Note however that some high fibre items, such as bean leaves, may be high in protein and have a negative Ca:P balance. This should be investigated and, if necessary, adjustments made to the overall dietary regime to compensate.

One comparatively easy way to increase the dietary fibre intake is to provide dried green leaf or grass material. Hatchlings especially seem to enjoy this and it is generally consumed avidly. Where it is provided the resulting faeces is comparable to that of a healthy wild specimen.

Left: Solid concretions of uric acid are symptomatic of: 1) excess dietary protein 2) dehydration 3) nephritis.

Another good source of dietary fibre are the pads and fruit of *Opuntia* cacti. These form part of the natural diet of many species and can even be grown in temperate climates such as Western Europe. Experiments with these have proved very promising and tortoises take them with great relish. Incidentally, it is an added benefit that *Opuntia* cacti are usually a good source of calcium. It is also worth noting that where plants are to be grown for tortoises consumption, it can help considerably to 'load' the soil with limestone chippings. This will, in turn, enrich the calcium content of any subsequent crop. Spineless forms are advised for ease of management.

Water and dehydration

Another extremely critical area which is often completely ignored is the provision of adequate supplies of water either as drinking water or as an integral component of plant foods. The problem is again compounded if animal proteins are fed to inappropriate species.

Tortoises secrete nitrogenous waste matter as uric acid. In order to remain in solution, this requires the reptile to absorb large amounts of water. If insufficient water is available dehydration will occur. Uric acid is much more insoluble than urea and therefore dehydration, even for very short periods of time, can have extremely drastic consequences including visceral and articular gout. It should never be allowed to occur under any circumstances. If dehydration is combined with a diet dangerously high in protein the result is even more catastrophic.

Tortoises emerging from hibernation and anorectic animals are at special risk as are those maintained under conditions where ready access to water is denied. Female tortoises also require additional water during egg production. Treatment consists of rehydration preferably using specialist solutions such as compound sodium lactate (i.e. Hartmann's solution) and various proprietary oral rehydration therapies based upon sodium, potassium, magnesium and chloride. Where renal problems already exist, flushing the system with pure water or Hartmann's solution is the preferred option.

It is a common mistake of non specialists upon encountering a severely dehydrated and probably emaciated animal to begin treatment by force feeding quantities of high protein food. This is inclined to have lethal consequences. Treat dehydration first and only when that has been effectively dealt with and renal function is entirely satisfactory move on to treat the underlying emaciation. Acute dehydration can occur with surprising rapidity in hatchlings and small tortoises and keepers must always be on the alert for early signs. These include the absence of urination, loss of skin elasticity, sunken eyes, and weight loss. Such symptoms should never be ignored and must always be dealt with as a matter of urgency.

It ought to be noted that certain species, particularly *Kinixys* species, *Geochelone (Chelonoidis) carbonaria* and others require constant access to drinking and bathing water in order to urinate or defecate normally. The absence of suitable water supplies will inhibit normal behaviour and can lead to a drastic increase in retained toxin levels and consequent renal stress. This appears to be an adaptation to conserve vital fluid unless a replacement source is available. It is interesting to compare the nitrogen disposal strategies employed by various tortoises and turtles and to correlate these with habitat types as given in the table on page 102. It will be noted that there is a high degree of correlation between availability or otherwise of water in the environment and the strategy employed. Aquatic species excrete very little uric acid whilst this substance predominates in arid-habitat dwellers. These results stress the importance of correct environmental maintenance in captivity.

Uric Acid and Urea excretion correlated with habitat type

Species	Habitat	Uric acid	Ammonia	Urea	Amino acids	Other
K. subrubrum	Aquatic	0.7	24.00	22.9	10.00	40.3
Pelusios spp.	Aquatic	4.5	18.5	24.4	20.6	27.2
Emys orbicularis	Semi-aquatic	2.5	14.4	47.1	19.7	14.8
Kinixys erosa	Damp habitats	4.2	6.1	61.00	13.7	15.2
Kinixys belliana	Drier habitats	5.5	6.00	44.00	15.2	26.4
G. denticulata	Damp forest	6.7	6.00	29.1	15.6	32.1
Testudo graeca	Semi-arid	51.9	4.1	22.3	6.6	4.00
G. elegans	Semi-arid	56.1	6.2	8.5	13.1	12.00

After Moyle, 1949.

Some tortoises are reluctant to drink from standing water; in such cases spraying with a garden hose to simulate rain will often prove very effective. This technique has worked very well with many animals which otherwise have refused to drink.

Steatitis and dietary fat content

Steatitis is a common condition of captive tortoises and aquatic turtles and is a disease of excess rather than deficiency. It is found in tortoises which have been fed on high fat diets and is also widespread in turtles and terrapins fed on oily fish. Tortoises fed on tinned dog and cat food are most at risk.

Other highly dangerous substances sometimes fed to tortoises and turtles by well-intentioned, but misguided, owners include hamburgers, bread, cake, boiled eggs and cheese, the latter typically consisting of 35 grams of fat and 26 grams of protein per 100 g.

The condition is characterised by obesity and by the concretion of yellowish nodules of fat throughout the thoracic cavity and invasive build-up of fat in the liver. Jaundice is a frequent consequence. Existing cases may respond to vitamin E which has antioxidant properties as well as anabolic steroids, i.e. nandoral at 0.5mg/weekly and thyroxin (20 ug every 48 hours orally). Jaundice can also be assisted by oral dosing with the amino-acid methionine, which mobilises fat stored in the liver, at a rate of 200 mg every 48 hours for 5 doses. Adequate levels of choline in the diet together with vitamin E supplementation can also help.

Protein requirement

The protein requirements of most reptiles have not been studied in sufficient detail, and no specific figures have so far been established for herbivorous terrestrial testudines. Analysis of the native diet of *Gopherus (Xerobates) agassizi*, which in many respects is typical of arid habitat testudine herbivores, suggests that the protein content of the food intake ranges from 1% (*Opuntia* Spp.) to 5% with grasses constituting a major part of the dietary intake . A safe upper protein content limit for items which are regularly included in the diet would seem to be circa 7%, as this is about as high as is ever attained in the wild by most species, even during peak periods of food availability. An average intake level of 4% would represent a close approximation of that experienced in the natural habitat.

Despite the lack of detailed information on protein demand, it is certain that the figure is very much lower kg for kg than mammals where 0.5 g of usable protein per kg would be a typical daily requirement. It seems probable that the daily requirement of a growing tortoise is in the approximate region of 0.20 g of usable protein per kg, although this may well vary considerably according to species and metabolic rate. Against this it should be noted that even such a low quality food item as lettuce contains on average 1g of protein per 100 g, and most legumes contain well in excess of 7 grams per 100 g .

Excess dietary proteins are converted by the liver into carbohydrates and fat. The first stage is to split the protein to amino acids which are then deaminated (i.e. the NH_2 group is removed and converted into urea). It is via this mechanism that dangerously high blood urea levels are generated when herbivores are placed on protein rich diets resulting not only in hepatic problems but also in acute renal distress. It should be noted that meat and meat products are not the only way in which this problem can be caused, tortoises fed excessive quantities of beans, peas, sprouted bean-shoots and similar protein-rich vegetable matter can also suffer the same effects.

Excessive quantities of protein can also seriously impair the calcium metabolism, and in addition can lead to massively accelerated growth and early sexual maturity. This is readily observed in many captive-bred hatchlings, where 2-year-old specimens raised on high protein diets frequently weigh four to five times the weight which they could reasonably expect to attain in the wild, demonstrate abnormally advanced sexual behaviour and, almost invariably, deformed pyramid-like scutes and grossly distorted carapaces. This latter effect is even seen in cases where otherwise adequate levels of calcium and vitamin D3 have been provided. Those fed on canned animal foods also tend to display definite melanistic characteristics, with much darker than usual carapace colouring due to excessive thickening of the layers of keratin forming the scutes .

In severe cases the carapace is weak and bulging and the horny shields or scutes are raised and pyramid-like especially along the central vertebral line. Radiological examination reveals gross distortions and separation of the underlying bone as well as poor bone density.

The solution is not to provide excessive quantities of protein and to ensure that mineral-vitamin levels are carefully balanced and are available in sufficient quantities. We may summarise the ideal diet for herbivorous species as consisting of the following:

- *LOW in fats, oils and protein*
- *RICH in minerals, trace elements and vitamins*
- *HIGH in fibre*
- *ADEQUATE in water content*

Try to provide as wide a range of suitable foods as possible, not ignoring more unusual items provided they meet the above criteria. *Avoid over-reliance upon one staple foodstuff.* Tortoises can easily become addicted to lettuce or similar items with unfortunate consequences. If a tortoise or turtle is acquired which has an existing food addiction the offending item should be removed entirely from the diet until more normal habits are re-established. This may take some time. Be absolutely certain to add a suitable vitamin-mineral supplement on a regular basis.

The requirements of omnivorous and carnivorous species, principally fresh-water aquatic testudines, are obviously somewhat different, but even so try to provide an interesting and varied diet adequate in trace elements and vitamins. Be particularly careful to ensure that the calcium to phosphorous balance is maintained within safe tolerances. Tinned cat and dog foods are not the best choice for testudines even where animal proteins may justifiably be included in the diet (i.e. for box tortoises) due to their extremely high saturated fat content. Where such material is to be provided dried processed meat pellets are a much better choice. Not only are these usually already vitamin and mineral enriched, but they have a far lower fat content than tinned foods and their fibre content is also much higher. Their vitamin and mineral content can be further enhanced by dressing each serving liberally with Vionate® and calcium, Nutrobal® or a similar combined phosphorous-free calcium and vitamin D3 supplement.

Dietary efficiency, juveniles and feeding frequency

Recent biochemical studies (Kay, pers. comm) indicate that juvenile tortoises and turtles have a far more efficient digestive tract than adults. Early results suggest from 4 to 6 times more efficient. This could be one explanation why juveniles seem to grow perfectly adequately in the wild even in times of severe food shortage. It would also explain why so many juveniles grow far too quickly in captivity. Certainly, the most common problem under captive conditions is obtaining growth which is comparable to wild growth: underfeeding is rarely at issue. This is an area of testudine husbandry which has been little explored, but it has obvious implications if the objective is to replicate natural rates of growth and development. It is perfectly possible to produce growth rates in captivity which greatly exceed those of wild specimens, and provided no relative dietary deficiencies occur, such growth can be apparently free of obvious defects. In such cases, it is possible to greatly accelerate sexual maturity. It should be pointed out however, that the long-term effects of so-doing are by no means clear, and that it can take many years for osteological and reproductive problems to fully manifest in tortoises and turtles.

Proprietary tortoise and turtle foods

There is a proliferation of prepared 'tortoise diets' on the market and an ever wider range of products which claim to be suited to aquatic turtles. Most of these claim to be "complete foods" and suggest that no other food variety is required. Analysis of their contents often suggests otherwise. The better formulations may be useful to add variety to an already balanced diet, but their typical protein, fibre and mineral contentsusually leave a great deal to be desired. "Scientifically formulated" they may be, but having seen juveniles reared using them, I must express serious reservations concerning their exclusive use. Very high growth rates are typical from these products, and all of our experience suggests that this is not a desirable objective. Many of these foods are given in dry pellet form; this in no way approximates the natural dietary intake of a tortoise or turtle. Some brands also contain large quantities of artificial colourings and preservatives. The long-term effects of such diets may take years to manifest and to date there is no convincing long-term evidence of their suitability or safety. They are also extremely expensive compared to the cost of maintaining animals on a natural diet. The manufacturers counter this claim by pointing to the high cost of a supermarket purchased salad diet, but how many serious turtle or tortoise keepers rely upon a supermarket for their total feed requirements? The cost of a safe, proven herbivorous diet can be practically zero if one is prepared to grow some food items, provide a natural grazing area, and are pre-

Left: Commercially available tortoise and turtle foods vary considerably in quality. Read labels carefully. Few, if any, of these products are truly suitable as a 'complete' source of nutrition and a more varied, natural-type diet is usually preferable.

pared to spend a few minutes daily collecting wild foodstuffs. A healthy, nutritionally balanced diet need be neither expensive nor time consuming.

For aquatic turtles, by far the best of the commercially available foods are of the frozen variety. These provide a viable and, usually, well-balanced alternative to dried products and can successfully be included in most dietary regimes where convenience is a factor. A hidden advantage of frozen foods is that the deep-freeze process kills many harmful parasites. For maximum safety, foods should be frozen for at least 1 month. As with all food items, however, frozen foods should never be relied upon entirely. It is worth repeating, yet again, that variety is essential.

Suggested feeding program for herbivores

The following suggested basal diet applies to *Testudo hermanni*, *Testudo graeca*, *Testudo horsfieldi*, *Testudo marginata* and most other tortoises from similar habitats including *Geochelone pardalis* (the Leopard tortoise), *Geochelone (Chelonoidis) chilensis* (the Chaco tortoise), *Asterochelys radiata*, *G. elegans* and *G. sulcata* (the African spurred tortoise). A similar dietary profile has also been used with great success for *Geochelone (Chelonoidis) carbonaria*, the South American Red-foot tortoise, however, in this case, and in the case of the *Kinixys*, or hinge-back species, a small quantity of calcium-supplemented rehydrated dried cat food is given once or twice per week. These tortoises, although largely herbivorous, do consume some carrion and take small prey occasionally.

Mixed green-leaf vegetable base (90%+)

Dandelion; cabbage (mixed varieties); clover leaves; kale; lettuce; parsley; carrot toppings; sow thistle; coarse mixed grasses (a high percentage is recommended for tortoises which enjoy grazing such as *G. pardalis*, *G. sulcata* etc.); flower heads and other fodder plants (provide by means of "natural graze" or "edible landscaping" if at all possible).

Fruit (<10%)

Melon (red, orange and white); tomato; mango; pineapple; cauliflower; apple; pear; red and green sweet peppers; cucumber; courgette (zucchini) etc.

Mix these all together in a large bowl or bucket and apply liberal quantities of a high quality multi-mineral and vitamin supplement containing adequate levels of calcium and vitamin D3. Fruit should be used very sparingly. Over ingestion can result in high levels of sugar in the gut which can in turn lead to dangerous colic and appears to encourage proliferation of digestive tract parasites, especially flagellates, possibly as a result of increased gut motility.

This diet has been proven to provide more than adequate protein, fibre and trace elements, even for breeding females of such large and rapidly growing species such as *Geochelone pardalis* and *Geochelone sulcata.* The hatchlings are also raised on this dietary regime with really excellent results. The carapace growth is smooth and even with excellent bone development. Post hatching juvenile mortality is practically zero, the only losses being recorded in cases of congenital deformity. No dietary related fatalities whatsoever have been noted since this program was adopted as standard in our own collection, or in the collections of various zoos which have adopted it subsequently. We now have excellent reports from captive-breeders around the world who have based their dietary management upon the principles originally set out in *Keeping and Breeding Tortoises in Captivity* (Highfield, 1990), and many thousands of tortoises of all species have now been successfully reared on this basis.

Edible landscaping and seasonal variation in food availability

The diets of many herbivorous species can be usefully supplemented by providing as much near-natural graze as possible. At the Tortoise Trust we have experimented with planting wild flower seeds in tortoise pens and discovered that this produced excellent results. Mixed clovers, dandelions and alfalfa (lucerne) are important basic constituents. Specialist seed suppliers are usually able to provide a suitable mixture of edible forage plants. We also found that buckwheat, first soaked and then sown, produced a highly palatable and nutritious crop which was greatly superior to 'supermarket greens'. This method is not suitable for overcrowded tortoise pens, but if animal concentrations are low, as they should be for general disease-prevention purposes, then edible landscaping is a highly recommended system of providing a quality diet at low cost. An important advantage is that seasonal availability and variety of food will be much closer to that found in nature. In most temperate environments supporting land tortoises, food availability and variety is cyclic. There is a peak in spring, followed by a drastic reduction during the hottest parts of summer, followed by renewed activity as the autumn rains begin. The precise details do, of course, vary according to location but this pattern is fairly typical. The variety of plants consumed also shifts seasonally, with a high intakes of fresh green leaves and flower heads in spring, shifting to drought resistant succulents as temperatures rise and moist green fodder plants become unavailable. In some very hot and arid locations tortoises may cease feeding entirely during this period and may aestivate underground. In captivity it seems may keepers expect their animals to feed more or less continuously. This is not necessarily either natural or beneficial to health. Whilst it may well be true of some tropical species which experience few seasonal changes, it does not reflect the reality of conditions to which the majority of temperate species are adapted.

Pesticide residues and toxicity

It is sobering thought to reflect upon the fact that a commercial lettuce crop receives - on average - 20 separate applications of pesticide before sale and that 30 individual pesticides have officially set MRL figures (Maximum permitted Residue Levels) for this crop. Some producers are on record as stating that they use as many as 40 applications of highly toxic chemicals, the recognised effects of which include sterility, birth defects, cancer and metabolic breakdown. 101 lettuce samples were tested by a laboratory. The results revealed that

100% contained inorganic bromide residues and 63% contained other pesticide residues including carbendazim, cypermethrin, demeton-s-methyl, dimethoate, dithiocarbamates, iprodione, metalaxyl, primicarb, tolclofos-methyl and vinclozolin (Lang and Clutterbuck, 1991). The same applies to most other non-organically grown supermarket fruit and vegetables. Although such produce is, supposedly, safe for human consumption, few humans consume as high a proportion of salad greens as do most herbivorous tortoises. Such produce is by no means completely free of pesticide traces. The cumulative effects of such intake are unlikely to be beneficial. If compelled to rely upon store-bought produce for tortoise food, seek out certified organic produce. Even though it may be slightly more expensive than the alternative, it is many times safer.

Suggested diet for aquatic turtles

Although most aquatic turtles are primarily carnivorous, this does not mean that they can necessarily tolerate a diet comprised entirely of meat. Just as with land tortoises, a varied and balanced diet is essential if problems are to be avoided. It should also be noted that many species become less carnivorous with age. The percentages given below are for general guidance only. The precise meat-to-vegetable balance will necessarily vary from species to species.

Meat component (approximately 65% - 90% depending upon species)

Live feeder fish; earthworms; frozen pinkie mice; Snails and molluscs; re-hydrated dried cat food with added minerals; dried commercial trout pellets (Purina® Trout-chow is particularly recommended) and small quantity low-fat tinned dog food (less than 5% of total dietary intake).

Vegetable component (approximately 35% or less depending upon species)

Romaine lettuce; grated carrot; clover, small quantity of fruit and other items as outlined under herbivore diet.

It should be noted that some species of tropical turtle require a diet rich in fruit and that others are almost entirely herbivorous. *Do not assume that all aquatic turtles are automatically carnivorous.* Consult specific maintenance information for guidance.

Feeding aquatic turtles can create serious water hygiene problems. For this reason it is best to avoid excessively oily or fatty foods, and to avoid overfeeding. Any excess will only clog filters and degrade water quality. Most turtles, unlike tortoises, only require feeding approximately twice, or at most three times, per week.

One solution to the hygiene problem is to combine a selection of the food items mentioned above into a feeding gel. Not all turtles will accept this, although the majority seem to. A recipe which has proved successful is based upon unflavoured gelatine or agar-agar as a binding agent and includes a variable selection of meat and vegetable items together with added fibre in the form of alfalfa (lucerne) pellets. It is also very easy to add a calcium and multivitamin supplement to this combination. The resulting 'cake' can be cut into slices and frozen for later use. The advantage of this method is that the binding agent prevents the food matter from dissolving too readily and fouling the tank.

Suggested diet for semi-aquatic turtles

Box turtles and most other semi-aquatic species have a variable requirement for meat vs. vegetable matter. This demand is influenced not only by age (juveniles tend to be almost entirely carnivorous) but also by species. Most box and similar turtles should be fed on alternate days. They are true omnivores and in the wild have eclectic dietary habits. In general terms however, a varied and high quality diet for this class of turtle can be constructed using the following guidelines:

Vegetable component (50%)

Berries and strawberries; romaine and red lettuce; grated carrot; dandelion greens; cauliflower; plums; small quantity green cabbage and kale leaf; flower heads etc. from list in Appendix 3.

Meat component (50%)

Low-fat canned dog food (small quantity, less than 5% total intake); live crickets, pre-dusted with vitamin powder; small land snails and slugs (in an outdoor terrarium temperate box turtles will catch these for themselves); re-hydrated dried cat and trout pellets.

These suggested diets should form the basis of experimentation. They are nutritionally sound, but the most important thing to stress is that different tortoises and turtles will demonstrate different preferences. Provided these preferences do not degenerate into food addictions, and the preferred food items are safe from a protein, vitamin and mineral point of view, there is no harm in indulging them to some extent. Ideally, the diet should be rotated and varied as much as possible, as this most closely replicates the wide-ranging diet of most wild tortoises and turtles. There is no place in a well managed collection for a monotonous, boring and nutritionally unbalanced feeding program. Longevity and breeding success depend heavily upon excellent, not barely adequate, nutrition.

Chapter Eight

PARASITIC DISEASES

Parasites present a major hazard to tortoises and turtles and, if adequate preventative steps are not taken, significantly increase the incidence of ill health and mortality. Early detection of parasite problems are an essential part of the duties of any responsible reptile keeper. Before discussing parasitic diseases and health in general, it must be stressed that it is extremely important that qualified veterinary assistance is obtained wherever possible. The information which follows is not provided in order that the services of a veterinary surgeon may be dispensed with. It is provided to enhance keeper's understanding of common disease processes, to aid early recognition of problems and to offer guidance in situations where qualified help is not readily available.

Parasites that affect tortoises fall into two classes: ecto-parasites which are found outside the body, and endo-parasites which are found internally and include intestinal worms and protozoan organisms. Ecto-parasites such as mites and ticks are generally only found on new imports, animals obtained from reptile dealers premises, or on those that have been maintained in close proximity to other animals, such as in zoos and outside enclosures. Ticks often congregate in the soft, fleshy parts around the tops of the legs, neck and tail. All newly introduced animals should be examined carefully for any evidence of their presence.

Fortunately ticks can be removed fairly easily. They can be coated with alcohol and petroleum jelly then turned on their backs in order to loosen their grip, and the mouth parts firmly prised away. Coat the resulting puncture wound with Betadine® or similar povidone-iodine solution. If mouth parts are allowed to remain embedded quite serious abscesses may result.

Mites are more difficult to deal with but fortunately they are not as widespread on tortoises and turtles as they are on snakes and lizards, so will only very rarely be encountered. A very thorough all-over bath with Betadine® sometimes works but by far the most effective method of treatment involves low-level exposure to dichlorvos, usually supplied as Vapona® or No-Pest® insecticide strips. Frye (1991) recommends a 6 mm length of strip per 10 ft^3 of vivarium space. Exposure should be limited to two exposures of 3 hours twice per week. It should be made clear that this substance is highly toxic and that extreme care is necessary in its use. Another option for severely infested turtle enclosures, and direct application to acutely infested turtles is trichlorofon spray, an agent intended as a cattle insecticide. A 0.16% dilution has been used with good results and no apparent ill effects. An otherwise useful group of anti-parasitic agents called ivermectins are **absolutely contra-indicated** for use in tortoises and turtles as there is now ample evidence of its extreme toxicity to these animals. Death has occurred very rapidly following the use of ivermectins in testudines and for this reason all keepers and veterinarians working with tortoises and turtles should avoid its use.

Flies and maggots are also a potential problem. Flies, because in addition to causing irritation and laying eggs on wound sites, are quite capable of transmitting many other bacterial diseases and of spreading protozoan or even viral infections. Flies in the reptile house should be eliminated and any wounds where flies are likely to be attracted should be treated with antibiotic preparations which include an organophosphorus (or less toxic functional equivalent) insecticide compound to destroy any larvae. One practical solution is to fit gauze fly screens wherever possible, and to use ultra-violet electrical insect killers. We have equipped our own tropical house with several of these, and have found them to be extremely effective. Bot flies, which result in the development of a maggot under the turtle's skin, are commonly seen in box turtles and some tropical species. Early signs of bot fly infestation include subcutaneous lumps usually in close proximity to a small opening. Treatment involves physical removal of the maggot and post-operative cleansing of the cavity with Betadine® or dilute hydrogen peroxide. To enhance self-healing, any remaining traces of Betadine® should be flushed out of the wound immediately following cleansing with saline solution.

Before passing on to examine various parasites in detail it is worth pointing out that in an ideal reptile house parasite prevention would begin with the architects. Corners of cages should be smooth and easy to clean, floors non-porous, and water supplies for each cage or pen entirely independent. Ventilators should be equipped with fly traps and all cages should be completely isolated from each other. A small laboratory bench equipped with a microscope would also be a vital accessory. We have found flies to be a particular problem in tropical houses, especially those which accommodate fruit eating species.

Nematodes

Helminth or nematode ('worm') infestations are by far the most commonly encountered testudine parasite. Two major classes of helminth are involved: long, round and greyish-pink varieties known as *Ascarids* and small, white thread-like types called *Oxyurids.*

Ascarid helminths of the type *Angusticaecum* as commonly isolated from Mediterranean tortoises may measure up to 100 mm in length but generally do not cause as much irritation and discomfort to the animal as do the smaller *Oxyurid* species such as *tachygonetria* and *atractis* which typically measure less than 5 mm.

Treatment is straightforward for both types of nematode and consists of introducing by stomach tube a measured quantity of an effective and safe anthelmintic. Previously drugs such as piperazine and phenothiazine have been suggested in various publications as has L-tetramisole. Unfortunately, it is clear that these particular drugs are not actually very effective and that, in addition, piperazine can prove toxic to tortoises, particularly so if the specimen is debilitated or dehydrated. It should be carefully noted that as most cat and dog worming tablets sold in pet stores are based upon piperazine salts, they should definitely not be used for testudine treatment Another drug which is contra-indicated is thiabendazole as its hydroscopic qualities can accelerate dehydration and disrupt the electrolyte balance.

The following drugs are safe in all testudines including hatchlings and debilitated specimens. Exercise due care in the case of dehydrated animals, however. In such instances we

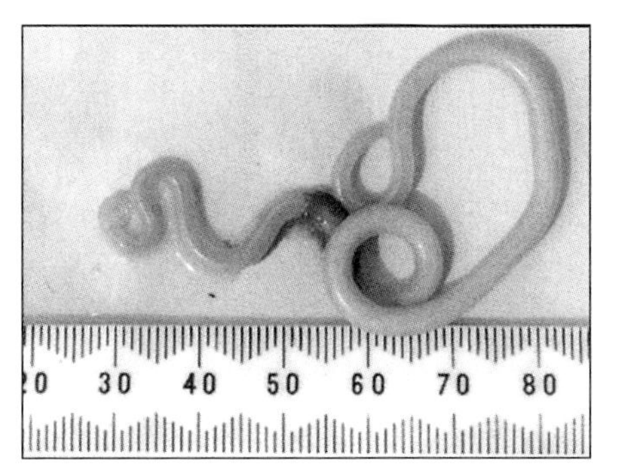

Above: Large roundworm expelled by a Leopard tortoise, *Geochelone pardalis.*

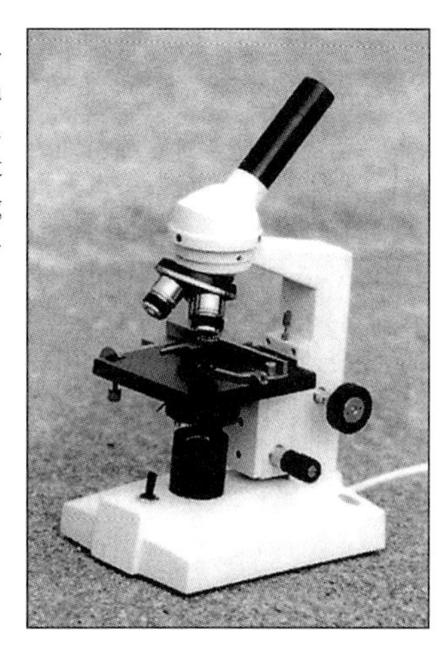

Right: A typical laboratory microscope with built-in illumination. This type of instrument is ideal for examining faecal samples for evidence of parasites.

prefer oxfendazole. Both have the major advantage that they are ovicidal, killing the parasitic ova as well as the adult worms.

FENBENDAZOLE (trade names Panacur® or Safe Guard®). The suggested dose rate is 50 mg per kilo repeated after 14 days. This equates to 3 ml per kg of the 2.5% suspension. This drug has a very wide margin of safety and has been used for many years without any reported adverse side-effects in reptiles.

OXFENDAZOLE (trade names Synathic® or Systamex®). The suggested dose rate is 65 mg per kilo with no repeat dose normally necessary, except in very high level infestations. This is equivalent to 3 ml per kg of the standard 2.265% suspension. The minimum effective dose is 1 ml/22.65 mg, even for small tortoises.

Diagnosis

Microscopic examination is by far the best method of screening for helminths. A faecal sample should be collected and placed into a test tube with a quantity of saline solution (i.e. salt). Alternative flotation solutions include saturated sugar and zinc sulphate. This should be shaken vigorously then allowed to stand for at least an hour. Faecal debris will precipitate to the bottom of the test tube and a pipette should then be used to extract a sample from the top of the solution. This should be placed on a microscope slide, preferably of the 'well' type, and examined for both ova and immature worms. Direct smears of faecal matter can also reveal the presence of worm ova.

Physical symptoms of severe helminth infestation include diarrhoea, anorexia and possible vomiting of worms. We have observed that many heavily infested animals tend to splutter small volumes of clear fluid from the mouth. On occasions, live worms may be vomited. If large-scale infestation is allowed to remain untreated, serious perforations of the intestine leading to peritonitis or even intestinal blockages can occur. Low level infestation may not be pathogenic. The ability of many helminths to enter the bile and pancreatic ducts however, can result in physical obstructions which in turn may lead to hepatic necrosis and jaundice.

Filarid helminths

Filarid helminths are transmitted by arthropod carriers such as mosquitoes and ticks. They invade the host as microfilariae, are transported in the bloodstream and then develop *in situ* to adulthood where they may cause a multiplicity of problems. They can be diagnosed by means of laboratory analyses of blood samples. Frye and Williams (1995) detail the case of a recently imported Leopard tortoise (*G. pardalis)* which developed visible helminths within the eye. Ivermectin, although very effective against this class of helminth, must not be used in treatment as it is acutely toxic in all testudines. A safe alternative therapy is levamisol given by intracoelomic injection at a dose rate of 5 mg per kg, repeated again after two weeks.

Cestodes and trematodes

Cestodes (tapeworms) are extremely rare in herbivorous testudines but may be encountered in carnivorous species and, most commonly, in aquatic turtles. The same applies to trematodes, or flukes. Some flukes infest the liver, whilst others infest the lungs or other organs. Trematode infection has also been linked to fibropapillomatous tumours in sea turtles. Lung flukes are a potentially serious problem and can result in visible respiratory distress. They may occur in some density. The aggregate mass of flukes in one recorded instance was 42% of the total lung mass of the turtle (Cox, W. A. et. al 1988).

Oxfendazole used as directed above is an effective treatment although niclosamide at 150 mg/kg has also been suggested. Praziquantel (Droncit®) at 5 to 8 mg/kg can also be used and generally is to be preferred over niclosamide, as it has a broader spectrum of effectiveness including against extra-intestinal cestodes. All of the above can be delivered by stomach tube, or, in the case of animals which are difficult to handle may be mixed in food. These particular parasites ought not to present too many problems as they require an intermediate host and this condition will rarely be met in captivity. Particular caution should be exercised, however, when feeding molluscs, shrimp and similar to turtles. These are a proven vector for many parasites. Wild caught turtles, however, may already be harbouring the organisms.

Worming difficult to handle tortoises and turtles

Although worming tortoises by means of a stomach-tube is often entirely satisfactory, in some species this means of administration can prove extremely difficult. Hinge-back tortoises (*Kinixys* species) and large Leopard (*G. pardalis*) or African Spurred tortoises (*G. sulcata*) can be particularly strong and resistant.

As an alternative, a paste preparation of fenbendazole (i.e. Panacur® paste for horses) may be applied to favourite items of food. The dose rate in such applications is 100 mg of fenbendazole per kg total bodyweight of the tortoise or turtle given over 5 days. Repeat after 2 weeks but this time for 3 days only. This dosing regime is equally applicable to Panacur® granules.

Panacur® paste for horses contains 3.5 g fenbendazole in 20 g of paste, i.e. approximately 19% concentration, or 187 mg per g. For practical purposes, a concentration of 20% can be assumed. This makes calculating the volume of paste for dosing very straightforward:

- For a 2kg tortoise: 2 x 100 mg = 200 mg = 1 g of paste total over 5 days
- For a 1.5kg tortoise: 1.5 x 100 mg = 150 mg = 750 mg of paste total over 5 days

NB: 1 g of paste is approximately equal to 1/4 teaspoon measure.

Panacur is a particularly safe drug and there is a considerable margin of safety with regard to overdosing. Obtaining a precise dose is especially difficult with fenbendazole in granular form so this margin of safety is very welcome.

As a method of routine worming difficult tortoises this system is extremely easy, results in zero stress to the animals, and has proven effectiveness. It can also be used with great success on other species, including aquatic and semi-aquatic species provided these feed out of water. In such cases the preparation can be sandwiched into a favourite morsel or used to rehydrate dried foods.

Flagellate organisms

Flagellates, often of the *Trichomonas* variety, may present a major problem in captive collections. Symptoms include diarrhoea, passage of undigested food, dehydration and anorexia. The condition is potentially serious and should be identified as early as possible. Under the microscope many very small, highly motile organisms will be observed in the fresh faecal samples.

Treatment of protozoan infection is recommended using metronidazole (Flagyl®). It has been found that the standard suspension, benzoylmetronidazole, can cause vomiting in some species. Therefore, it is suggested that standard 200 mg metronidazole tablets should be ground up and suspended in sterile water then administered by stomach tube. Several dosing schedules have been recommended from single doses at 260 mg per kilo, to 160 mg per kilo for 4 days, to 25 mg per kilo for 10 days. Treatment with dimetronidazole may also be effective in some cases, although generally metronidazole remains the preferred choice.

When flagellates are detected, one is faced with the problem of whether or not to initiate treatment. The obvious course of treating regardless is not necessarily advisable as these organisms are by no means always pathogenic. Our own approach is to obtain treatment whenever they appear to be causing a problem and to merely monitor their presence otherwise. We have found that many tortoises seem able to tolerate their presence with absolutely no ill effects and others are able to recover very quickly, without veterinary intervention, from mild attacks. If it becomes obvious that the organisms are causing a persistent nuisance, then we initiate treatment with metronidazole as described above.

One outcome of severe flagellate infections, and a problem which is compounded by the necessity of having to use metronidazole to remove them, is a condition which we term 'sterile gut syndrome', where the symbiotic gut flora are either severely depressed or in some cases eliminated entirely. Re-establishing viable colonies of such bacteria can prove difficult. Meanwhile the affected animal is completely unable to digest food and in effect starves even though it may continue to eat. Two solutions have proved effective. In milder cases, provided some bacteria remain, symbiotic flora can often be persuaded to regenerate if either live culture yoghurt or a proprietary veterinary metabolic stabiliser and culture are administered by stomach tube and the animal is kept at optimum temperatures to encourage maximum intestinal bacterial activity. In severe cases, where total sterility has occurred, a live bacterial infusion made from a healthy tortoise's faeces is the often the only effective answer. Should this latter course prove necessary, a sample of faeces should be obtained from another tortoise, screened carefully by microscopic examination for pathogens, liquidised, then administered in a fluid solution via stomach tube. The faeces of hatchling tortoises, should any be available, are especially suitable as these will have been maintained under conditions of maximum security from contamination by serious pathogens.

Dietary deficiencies or excesses are a prime cause of flagellate proliferation. An excessive intake of sugar-rich fruit is one particularly common factor. Another factor is an inadequate consumption of dietary fibre. Very frequently, even severe flagellate problems can be overcome if the keeper pays more attention to dietary management. Where tortoises are allowed to graze under near natural conditions, our experience is that serious flagellate, and nematode, problems are almost never encountered.

Finally it should be noted that where tortoises are maintained at excessively high overnight temperatures or where unrestricted access to heat lamps is provided by day-time, flagellate outbreaks are particularly commonplace; this may be due to temperature accelerated gut function. We certainly prefer to see temperate species allowed to remain cool overnight. This frequently clears the problem without additional veterinary intervention. Flagellate problems are also associated with a general loss of immune function. Tortoises maintained in mixed species groups have by far the highest incidence of persistent flagellate infestations. Keeping same species groups at non-intensive densities dramatically reduces the dangers.

Hexamitiasis

A serious flagellate infection of the renal system caused by the organism *Hexamita parva.* This condition should be treated whenever it is detected as the organism concerned is highly pathogenic resulting in either acute or chronic nephritis. Symptoms include passage of strong smelling urine, which is sometimes tinged green, and in severe cases flecked with blood. Other symptoms may include excessive drinking, anorexia and loss of weight. Treatment is with metronidazole at 50 mg/kg over 10 days. We have also eliminated these organisms using a single large dose of metronidazole at 260 mg/kg repeated after 2 weeks. If caught in the early stages, nephritis can be prevented but, if allowed to progress untreated for any length of time, the prognosis is not good. This organism is absolutely lethal to both tortoises and turtles.

The organism is commonly found in stressed animals recently obtained via trade sources and, in our own experience, it is one of the biggest single killers of newly purchased tortoises. Unfortunately, few keepers and non specialist veterinarians are aware of its symptoms, diagnosis, or treatment and, as a result, there is no doubt that many animals perish unnecessarily. Certainly it is one of the first things we now check for on being presented with a non feeding, lethargic and dehydrated animal that has recently been purchased from a dealer or passed through the hands of a large-scale collector. At the Tortoise Trust we once rescued a group of *G. pardalis* from the unhygienic premises of an exotic animal dealer which had been infected with this organism, and, even with prompt treatment, was not able to save them all. We are also aware of one instance in which 9 out of 12 Indian Star tortoises (*G. elegans*) perished during an outbreak of *Hexamita* at a zoo and another instance where a group of *G. sulcata* suffered a similar fate. Some tortoises seem particularly sensitive to the organism, and, in our experience, this includes the entire *Geochelone* genus and all tortoises of South African origin.

Affected animals should be isolated, handled using contamination procedures and have their progress carefully monitored. *Hexamita* are very small and a moderately powerful microscope (400 x magnification or greater) will be needed in order to identify them.

Balantidiosis

Balantidium is a ciliate protozoan organism of doubtful pathogenicity in tortoises. It is often found in conjunction with other organisms and may simply be opportunistic. We have detected it in *T. graeca*, *T. hermanni*, *Malacochersus tornieri* and *G. pardalis*. It has also been recorded in many other species. Although no specific treatment exists we have had 100% success using metronidazole at 260mg/kg given in a single dose. This organism should not be treated automatically, but only when it is seen in association with a veterinary problem.

Miscellaneous ciliate protozoa

Other ciliate organisms identified in tortoises include *Nyctotherus kyphodes*, and *N. teleacus* from several giant species, as well as *Geochelone (Chelonoidis) carbonaria*, *G. elegans*, *Gopherus polyphemus* and *Kinixys belliana*. Once again, the pathogenicity of these organisms is not established. It is probable that they are merely harmless commensal microflora and play a useful role in the digestion of cellulose. *Balantidium coli* causes abscesses in pigs and one of the tortoises we encountered harbouring *Balantidium testudinis* was suffering from this condition; whether or not there was a connection, however, remains unknown. Most cilliate infections will respond very quickly to a single dose of metronidazole (Flagyl®) delivered at 260mg/kg by stomach tube. This can be repeated in 10 days if not effective. As stated, unless there is good cause to believe otherwise, most *Nyctotherus* and *Balantidium* species should be regarded with equanimity and should not be automatically subject to drug therapy upon detection.

Amoebiasis

Amoebiasis is not normally a major problem tortoises and turtles, but persons who keep other reptiles ought to recognise that the organism *Entamoeba invadens* may be carried harmlessly by testudines. This organism is manifestly not harmless in snakes, where it results in a high mortality. Never allow tortoises to mix with other reptiles, i.e. snakes or lizards. The very high incidence of both parasitic and bacterial infection often seen in dealers' stocks is due almost entirely to poor hygiene and random association of mutually incompatible species. There is now evidence that, although most testudines are not in immediate danger from *Entamoeba*, there may be exceptions; giant Seychelles and Galapagos tortoises, for example, are apparently both susceptible. Symptoms include bloody diarrhoea and dehydration. Where these symptoms occur, faecal samples should be analysed immediately. Treatment is with metronidazole at 50 mg/kg orally.

Cryptosporidiosis

As with *Entamoeba invadens*, the pathogenicity of this coccidian parasite in tortoises and turtles remains unclear. It is, however, known to be highly pathogenic in lizards and snakes and is also suspected of posing a serious health hazard to humans. For this reason, contaminated animals should be handled with the utmost caution. Passive carriers are an added complication. The disease manifests in lizards and snakes as severe weight loss, mucus-laden diarrhoea and vomiting. It is highly contagious and diagnosis may prove difficult although the cysts may be visible on direct smears. Unfortunately, at the time of writing, no effective treatment is known.

Prophylactic program

Newly imported animals are typically stressed and may also harbour large quantities of potentially pathogenic parasites. This combination undoubtedly contributes to the high overall mortalities often noted. Our procedure in such cases is as follows:

- Faecal smears for helminth ova and protozoa
- Fresh urine sample for microscopic screening against *Hexamita*
- Automatic prophylactic administration of Panacur® or Synathic®
- Treatment with metronidazole (Flagyl®) at 50 mg/kg if protozoans observed, repeated in 14 days
- Repeat faecal and urine screening in 1 month, then again in 3 months

Routine employment of these procedures can greatly reduce losses. It is obviously essential that newly obtained specimens should be quarantined from existing stock until the above process is complete and their health has been adequately demonstrated.

Mycoses (fungal infections)

We have encountered several cases of ulcerative shell disease resulting from fungal infections, and infections of the lungs and intestines have also been recorded in the veterinary literature. External mycoses often respond to treatment with Betadine® povidone-iodine solution, malachite green (50 ppm solution for 30 seconds daily), or the specific anti-fungal drug, nystatin, applied topically as an ointment or powder. In cases of internal infection, ketoconazole (Nizoral®) is usually the drug of choice, given orally at 10 to 25 mg/kg every 24 hours.Where aquatic turtles are affected, it is important to clean and all tank fittings, substrates and filter equipment, including pipes, valves and pumps. Affected turtles should be removed at once to isolation tanks and placed in water containing acriflavine or a proprietary anti-fungal preparation intended for tropical fish. There are a large number of suitable products on the market and most seem reasonably safe and effective in turtle applications. Follow the manufacturer's directions regarding application. Acriflavine can also be applied topically to infected sites and allowed to dry before the patient is returned to the water. It is also important to seek qualified veterinary assistance at an early stage if the problem does not clear up quickly using the above methods.

It should be noted that the practice of providing diseased or cheap, poor quality feeder fish to turtles is particularly dangerous as several common fungal diseases of fish including *Saprolegniasis*, *Calyptrelegnia* and *Achlya* can also affect turtles. One turtle keeper experienced persistent occurrences of *Saprolegniasis* ("cotton wool disease") which affected several different species of South American turtles which were maintained in apparently well-filtered and well-maintained tanks. These outbreaks only ceased when the keeper in question suspended his practice of purchasing sick and injured goldfish from a local pet store for use as feeder fish.

Most fungal organisms require dead or decaying organic matter to be present in order to thrive. The practice of leaving uneaten food in the tank provides an ideal environment for them to do so. Spores of *Saprolegnia* and other potentially pathogenic water-borne fungi also require a site of injury, such as a slight abrasion, burn, unsloughed skin or existing bacterial infection to provide them with a firm anchoring point. Healthy turtles without such sites are normally unaffected.

Much can be done to reduce the possibility of infections by all parasitic pathogens:

- Tortoises and turtles of different species should not normally be allowed to mix. Particularly, carnivorous and herbivorous species should be maintained in strict isolation.
- Keepers should pay rigorous attention to hygiene, especially regarding food handling and preparation.
- All tortoises and turtles should be checked for parasites regularly. This can easily be accomplished by placing individuals in large plastic-lined isolation areas in order to be sure of collecting adequate faeces and urine samples.
- In the case of aquatic turtles, water hygiene is especially important. The inclusion of an ultra-violet steriliser in the filtration circuit can do much to reduce the presence of water-borne parasite ova, fungal spores and other pathogens. Beware of introducing pathogens by means of contaminated food items.

The prevention and control of parasites in captive collections is often not treated as seriously as it ought to be. This is regrettable as post-mortem surveys consistently demonstrate a link between overall mortality encountered in collections and the incidence of parasitism. Parasites are not only harmful directly but indirectly as vectors for the transmission of bacterial diseases and other pathogens. Every reptile keeper should be aware of the dangers presented by parasites and should initiate regular checks and obtain immediate veterinary treatment as soon as a problem is developing in the collection.

Chapter Nine

BACTERIAL AND VIRAL DISEASES

The subject of bacterial and viral diseases in tortoises and turtles is a vast one and can only be discussed here briefly. Bacterial diseases are certainly one of the major causes of mortality in captive collections, as many published post-mortem surveys have shown. Less is known about viral diseases, but it is gradually becoming clear that they may be more common than previously suspected.

Most of the preventative measures suggested for counteracting parasitic contagion will also prove effective against the transmission of bacterial, and most viral, diseases, i.e. good hygiene and careful handling. Certainly the regular use of povidone-iodine disinfectants can make a considerable contribution. Other more common disinfecting agents may not be suitable including those based upon phenols where, unless considerable care is exercised, toxic effects may be noted. Phenols are, however, generally very effective against gram-negative bacteria and provided due caution is exercised may prove useful in some circumstances. Products based upon quaternary ammonium compounds are frequently ineffective against gram-negative pathogens, and are therefore of extremely limited use in reptile maintenance applications where such pathogens predominate.

Necrotic stomatitis

Until a few years ago this condition was almost invariably fatal unless observed in a very mild form. Today the vast majority of cases make a full recovery. We owe this dramatic turnaround in no small way to the development of much more effective antibiotics. Cultures taken from tortoises with 'mouth-rot' almost invariably reveal the presence of Gram-negative organisms, often *Pseudomonas* or *Aeromonas* species. In the very early stages, mild cases often respond to oral swabbing with Betadine® or a similar povidone-iodine solution. If the infection is well established then antibiotic therapy is vital. Therapies based upon chloramphenicol, ampicillin or tetracycline are unlikely to be successful for this condition although the oral cephalosporins have proved highly useful even in cases of aminoglycoside resistant strains. We have used oral amoxycillin with considerable success. In every case, before antibiotics are actually applied, a swab should be taken for bacteriological culture. Whilst results are awaited treatment should not be delayed but should commence immediately after the swab is taken using the most promising therapy under the particular circumstances.

In very severe cases, where osteomyelitis of the mouth or jaw has occurred (i.e. the

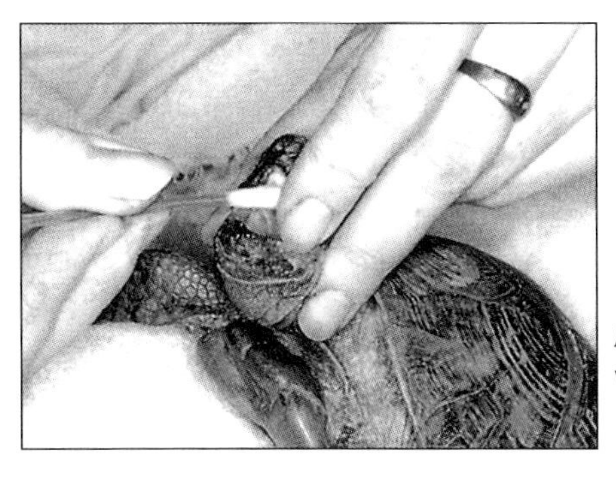

Left: Note the grip used here, when treating a tortoise with a mouth infection.

bone has become infected), the topical application of framycetin or other selected agent may be usefully supplemented with systemic therapy at 10mg/kg every 48 hours for a full course of 5 injections. This dose ought not to be exceeded due to the renal toxicity of the aminoglycoside antibiotic. The affected area should be regularly debrided, cleansed using povidone-iodine swabs, as much infected tissue as possible removed, and the animal placed under intensive care support whilst undergoing therapy.

It has recently become clear that some forms of stomatitis are the result of *Herpes*-type viral infections. These are necessarily both difficult to diagnose and to treat although some success has been recorded using specific anti-viral drugs such as Zovirax® applied topically. Other pathogens recently identified in the aetiology of this condition include beta-haemolytic *E. coli* and mycoplasmic and chlamydial organisms. In the latter instance a good response has been reported to treatment with enrofloxacin (Baytril®). Tylosin has also proved successful in some cases.

Conditions which predispose tortoises and turtles to mouth-rot include poor jaw occlusion from overgrown or damaged beaks and mouth injuries from thorns sustained during feeding. Regular beak maintenance is important and should not be ignored. A small pair of side-cutting clippers and abrasive board will suffice for all but the largest specimens. Tortoises with poor jaw occlusion are in particular danger during hibernation as the mouth becomes too dry and is very susceptible to bacterial and fungal infections.

Ocular infections and conjunctivitis

Most eye infections encountered in tortoises are comparatively easy to treat. We have observed excellent response to cloxacillin as well as to neomycin. Chloramphenicol ointment has also proved very useful. More serious infections have responded to gentamycin and tobramycin given as eye-drops.

Many ocular infections begin as a small white spot on the surface of the cornea. If untreated this can rapidly spread until the entire cornea is completely obscured and ulcerated. This condition ought not to be confused with a typical cataract, which it can closely resemble. Other ocular infections involve the surrounding tissues and can cause severe local swelling and irritation. Some cases are secondary to hypovitaminosis A, especially in hatchlings or aquatic testudines, although this is not as common as often reported.

The majority of tortoises, and especially aquatic turtles, which exhibit severely swollen eyelids will, on careful investigation, prove to be suffering from a primary bacterial infection. One should not automatically assume a vitamin A deficiency. Where the patient is an aquatic turtle, water quality should be immediately suspect. In the case of American box turtles and similar environmentally sensitive semi-terrestrials the causal factor predisposing an infection may be lack of ambient humidity. Antibacterial eye ointment (i.e. neomycin and tobramycin) or eye drops may produce a rapid improvement but can be difficult to apply. In order to be function correctly, the medication needs to be inserted so that it penetrates the inner surfaces of the membranes covering the eye. External application alone is ineffective. The treatment of aquatic turtles can be particularly awkward, as few preparations will withstand prolonged immersion in water. For the treatment of aquatic turtles therefore, systemic (injected) antibiotics are often more effective than topical treatments. For severely swollen and inflamed eyes we have found that oxytetracycline at 50 mg/kg given by intra-muscular injection usually produces a satisfactory recovery in most cases. Resistant cases may require a change of antibiotic.

In all cases, attention should be given to the patient's general environment, as many cases of conjunctivitis are the result of over-drying or contaminated water and substrate. We have found that placing affected turtles in a high humidity vivarium often speeds recovery.

Cloacitis

An inflamed or ulcerated cloacal opening often combined with an unpleasant discharge often indicates the presence of cloacitis. The condition is sometimes encountered in combination with parasite infestation, or cloacal calculus, a stone-like object formed within the cloaca. If the latter is present it should be removed. Two very effective modes of treatment include irrigating the cloaca with dilute Betadine® (povidone-iodine) or 0.75% chlorhexidine solution and the introduction of an antibiotic paste directly into the cloaca. Most cases respond very quickly.

Ear abscesses

These are extremely common (especially in American box tortoises) although we have also encountered them in almost all species of land tortoise including *Kinixys* and *Geochelone* species and in several species of aquatic turtle (including *Trachemys scripta*). The main symptom is a swelling of the tympanitic membrane and the discharge of pus into the back of the throat via the eustachian tube. We have noted success on a few occasions with systemic therapy, but only in the very early stages. The vast majority of cases encountered will be far too advanced for this to stand any chance of success however and surgical excision under a local anaesthetic is by far the best course of action. Good follow-up to surgery is vital, and in our experience most cases do best if the site is not stitched but is allowed to drain and heal naturally

Note that environmental factors and general hygiene standards are often implicated in the occurrence of this condition. In the case of American box turtles of the genus *Terrapene*, excessively high vivarium temperatures and inadequate humidity levels can certainly contribute to the problem. In the case of aquatic turtles water hygiene is often implicated.

Ulcerative shell disease (terrestrial tortoises)

USD, SCUD or shell-rot is an unpleasant condition which can take two forms, one dry the other wet. The former appears to be not of bacterial origin at all, but a mycoses or fungal infection. See the notes on this earlier. The wet form is normally caused by gram-negative bacteria invading an existing lesion and is typified by a fluid discharge, often foul smelling and tinged with blood, which seeps from between the scutes of the carapace. This condition requires urgent veterinary attention, as if left untreated it will almost invariably progress to a state causing generalised septicaemia.

The condition is usually initiated by local shell damage, particularly bruising or penetration injuries. Tick infestation can also responsible. Many cases are caused by shell-ramming behaviour during mating, or by territorial combat. The region above the supracaudal scute is the most common site of infection due to these causes. Other cases are caused by rough handling during transit, or through overcrowding of trade animals.

Treatment consists of removal of affected shields and thorough cleansing with Betadine® or similar povidone-iodine solution. Exposure of the affected sub-shield area to air certainly helps as most responsible organisms are anaerobic and exposure to oxygen seems to limit their ability to replicate. A topical antibiotic ointment should also be applied in advanced cases, framycetin is generally recommended. We have also noted good results with 1% silver sulphadiazine in paste form and this appears to be very effective against some *Pseudomonas* and other gram-negative pathogens. This preparation is a topical antibacterial formulation originally developed for the treatment of severe burns in mammals.

In very advanced cases where myelitis has occurred systemic antibiotic therapy may also be required; again the antibiotic agents of choice are framycetin, tobramycin, gentamycin or amikacin at the dose rates described previously.

The organisms most frequently isolated from USD in terrestrial tortoises include *Pseudomonas*, *Citrobacter*, and *Klebsiella*. Routine sensitivity tests reveal that all are frequently highly resistant to certain antibiotics and that best sensitivity is generally shown to framycetin, tobramycin and gentamycin among the aminoglycosides and to oxytetracycline among the non-aminoglycosides. One vital aspect of this which we cannot overemphasise is the need to undertake sensitivity tests to establish exactly which organisms are present in any given case and what they are sensitive or resistant to. Treatment should not be delayed whilst tests are undertaken, but commenced using the most promising drug under the circumstances.

Ulcerative shell disease (aquatic turtles)

The most common cause of this condition in aquatics is abrasions from tank decorations or fittings, burns from heating elements, or injuries caused as a result of mating or aggression. The treatment is essentially the same as for terrestrial species, with Betadine® solution proving effective in the majority of cases. Serious cases will require systemic antibiotic treatment. Drugs of first choice include ciprofloxacin, enrofloxacin (Baytril®) or ofloxacin at 10 mg/kg. Alternatives include aminoglycosides such as tobramycin or gentamycin at 6 mg/kg. It used to be advised that affected animals should be removed overnight for dry treatment, but better results have been obtained by keeping the patient in very clean water in an isolation tank. Treating the water with acriflavine has also proved to be highly effective in many cases. Another product which has yielded good results in conjunction with antibiotic or Betadine® treatment is Stress Coat®, a product which is designed to replace the natural 'slime' coating on tropical fish. It also seems to aid healing in freshwater turtles. The addition of Stress Coat® as a routine additive to the water of sensitive species also appears to reduce the incidence of shell and skin infections. Frye (1991) points out that shrimp can carry pathogens which may result in ulcerative shell disease; caution should be exercised in relation to this dietary item.

Skin infections

These are often closely related to shell infections and are seen in both aquatic and terrestrial species. The usual symptoms include sore, wet and foul smelling skin. If untreated, this condition may progress very rapidly to septicaemia. It is advisable to take a swab for laboratory culture. This should be followed by immediate local cleansing using a povidone-iodine solution. We have obtained consistently excellent results when treating this condition in tortoises using an aerosol-based antibiotic (oxytetracycline hydrochloride) preparation intended for the treatment of foot rot in grazing mammals.

Septic arthritis and articular gout

These are particularly unpleasant conditions, often seen together, which require prompt treatment. Delay can lead to total loss of mobility and may necessitate drastic surgery including amputation. Symptoms include swelling of the limb joints, stiffness, and evident pain attending locomotion.

There is a clear link between articular gout and excessively high intakes of dietary protein. This causes elevated urea levels and thereby initiates the condition. Our data shows that the incidence of this condition is considerably higher in normally herbivorous species which have been subjected to a diet rich in animal derived proteins (i.e. dog and cat food) than those which have had a more natural diet. The condition in humans is known to have similar causes and effects. Secondary bacterial infection of the affected joint, known as septic arthritis, may also follow. A temporary reduction in urate production can be obtained by dosing with allopurinol orally at 10 to 15 mg/kg daily. This will not affect existing urate deposits, however.

The main symptom is a swelling of the legs and stiffening of the joints. Some cases respond to systemic antibiotic treatment. Success has been reported using oxytetracycline, but we have had very good results with both gentamycin and framycetin. If only one leg is affected it is sometimes best to amputate, particularly if tissue destruction is advanced. Where more than one leg is affected, amputation is not viable for humane reasons and reliance must be placed on drug therapy. X-rays are a very useful diagnostic tool when confronted by these symptoms as they can reveal the extent to which the joints and bones have been affected.

It is important not to confuse the symptoms of septic arthritis with those of dietary induced rickets-type conditions resulting from vitamin D deficiencies. In both cases the limbs may appear swollen and there may be locomotion difficulty.

Abscesses (general)

Abscesses are extremely common in all reptiles and we have encountered them very frequently indeed in testudines. The most common sites, in order of incidence recorded, are the ears, legs, nasal passages and jaw. Internally, abscesses are also often located in the liver where they are associated with clinical symptoms of acute jaundice.

Abscesses often manifest in the form of hard, subcutaneous lumps and swellings. The pus they contain is usually yellow and caseous, often a fibrous capsule is present.

Treatment is best carried out by surgical excision. In our experience, attempts to treat systemically are almost always ineffectual, save in the very small number of cases caught in the earliest stages. The entire abscess should be carefully removed, usually under a local or a general anaesthetic, and the area irrigated with antiseptics or antibiotics. Suturing may be necessary in certain instances. Often healing progresses better without suturing however, provided repeated post-operative antibacterial irrigation is undertaken.

Isolates of bacteria cultured from testudine abscesses included mainly *Pseudomonas*, *Aeromonas* and *Citrobacter*, with *Proteus*, *Serratia*, *Enterobacter* and *Klebsiella* also present in many cases. The best antibiotic sensitivity tended to be to the aminoglycosides gentamycin, framycetin and neomycin.

Respiratory diseases
In the author's experience the two major respiratory problems of bacterial origin associated with the captive maintenance of testudines are pneumonia and R.N.S or runny nose syndrome.

Pneumonia

Two forms of pneumonia have been observed: an acute form, which can manifest rapidly and without very much in the way of advance warning, leading to death within hours if untreated, and a chronic form which can manifest just as quickly but which then stabilises, and can persist for many weeks, months or even years. Of the two types the acute form is by far the easiest to treat as it generally responds to readily available antibiotics and even cases in a state of unconsciousness and near death can make almost miraculous recoveries when so treated. The following drugs and dosing schedules have proved satisfactory when dealing with this type of pneumonia:

- Ampicillin - 50 mg/kg, dose every 24 hours for 5 days
- Oxytetracycline - as above
- Enrofloxacin (Baytril®) - 10 mg/kg every 48 hours for 10 days
- Ciprofloxacin - 10 mg/kg every 48 hours for 10 days

The above are comparatively safe compared to many other drugs and we have certainly noted no serious adverse effects despite monitoring many administrations over the years. Ampicillin can however cause local swelling at the injection site. In general we have recorded best results with enrofloxacin, ciprofloxacin, then oxytetracycline, followed closely by ampicillin. Tylosin at 50 mg/kg also seems particularly safe and effective against mild upper respiratory tract infections, where we have experienced consistently good results. In a case of acute pneumonia, however, we would have more confidence in enrofloxacin or oxytetracycline and should no improvement be noted after a few hours on these would rapidly recommend a change to ciprofloxacin. Certainly, we normally expect to see a definite improvement within hours, rather than days, from an acute phase if the drug is going to work at all. If no improvement is noted within a relatively short time, our inclination is to move on to the next drug of choice. The most important thing when confronted with an animal suffering from an acute pneumonia is to obtain an effective blood serum level of antibiotic as quickly as possible. Keeping the animal at optimum temperatures and maintaining a good state of hydration are also very important. Increased temperatures increase metabolic rate and therefore drug take-up as well as stimulating natural immune responses.

The other form of pneumonia is observed less frequently, but is also much more resistant to treatment. Here, only the amino-glycoside antibiotics or Baytril® seems effective and then not always. Roughly 75% of cases in our experience do respond to parenteral treatment with framycetin or gentamycin at 10 mg/kg every 48 hours for 7 doses but the remaining 25% continue to show no improvement or are subject to recurrence.

X-ray examinations of the lungs of tortoises affected with this latter type of pneumonia tend to show a diffuse infection sometimes affecting one lung in its entirety. In a small number of cases where all else has failed to bring about improvement, our veterinary surgeons have drilled the carapace introducing aminoglycoside antibiotics or Baytril® directly to the affected tissues thus obtaining high densities of active agent where it is needed most. This is obviously an advanced and drastic procedure, but is certainly justified in a limited number of cases.

Results have been encouraging, with complete recovery from even the most severe and chronic forms. It is only fair to point out that by no means all cases respond and that the only mortalities we have ever suffered as a result of pneumonia have been among the small number of chronic infections we have encountered. It is perhaps worth highlighting the common symptoms of the two forms of pneumonia for the benefit of readers who might not have encountered the condition.

Acute

Gaping of the mouth is often combined with stretching of the neck and obvious respiratory embarrassment. Excess mucous may or may not be visible in the nares or mouth which may be cyanotic. There may be weakness in the legs and poor retraction. Aquatic turtles may exhibit difficulty swimming and may merely float or sink to the bottom of their tank. Dehydration may also feature. Some tortoises may exhibit hyperactivity attempting to run around sometimes seemingly blindly; this may be in an effort to boost metabolic rate or ease breathing. All such cases require antibiotic therapy as a matter of the most extreme urgency. Survival time without prompt and effective treatment is measured in hours not days.

Chronic

May be persistent low level discharge of mucous, mouth may be cyanotic, mauve from deoxygenation. Coughing and wheezing might be audible. There may be a lack of strength and poor head and limb retraction. Oropharyngeal cultures will frequently reveal the presence of resistant strains of gram-negative bacteria. Another useful diagnostic procedure in tortoises and turtles requires that the animal be lightly anaesthetised. Sterile saline is then introduced into the trachea via a catheter whilst the patient is held in an upright position. Following the introduction of saline, typically no more than 5 cc/kg, the tortoise is immediately inverted and the saline removed by aspiration. The resulting solution is then examined in the laboratory for pathogens and for the presence of white cells.

Runny nose syndrome (chronic rhinitis)

This condition can present a major problem to large-scale tortoise breeders and keepers. The aetiology is complex and often involves multiple factors. The design of testudine housing and vivaria appears to have a major impact on the incidence of the condition. Secondary bacterial infection compounds the initial factors and can lead to formation of a chronic, debilitating condition which can prove extremely difficult to eliminate. It is important to note that the bacteria involved are almost always of the gram-negative type principally *Klebsiella*, *Pseudomonas* (especially *fluorescens*) and *Citrobacter* (especially *freundi*).

Probably the best advice must be to provide any tortoise suffering with this condition with the closest possible to natural and ideal conditions of temperature and humidity. Other factors frequently implicated, or suspected of implication, in chronic rhinitis include mycoses, mycoplasma and viral agents. The organism *Pasturella testudinis* has also been isolated from affected tortoises, but as this organism is also found in many healthy specimens, its significance is not yet clear. It is possible that its presence may amplify the effects of the prime, causal organism.

In the United States, recent work (Jacobson, et. al., 1995) demonstrates that in the case of chronic upper respiratory tract disease in *Gopherus (Xerobates) agassizii* populations a mycoplasmic organism called *Mycoplasma agassizii* is responsible. It is not clear if the same, or a similar, organism is generally responsible for similar conditions observed in captive animals in other parts of the world. There are similarities in the manifestation of the disease, but also a number of significant differences.

Standard procedures for dealing with the conditionin captive animals include the use of nasal antibiotic drops, i.e. neomycin, oxytetracycline in suspension or tobramycin. These are often supplemented with antibiotic injections. The best results observed to date with conventional antibiotics have been obtained with oxytetracycline, which has consistently produced a higher clear-up rate than either framycetin or gentamycin. Of the new drugs now available, enrofloxacin (Baytril®) has proved extremely useful in the treatment of this condition. This drug, delivered by injection at 10 mg/kg every 48 hours over 10 days has demonstrated a remarkably high clear-up rate. Its success is even higher if a dilute nasal irrigation of the same antibiotic is delivered simultaneously. A particularly effective nasal flush may be formulated from 0.5 cc Baytril® injectable solution and 0.5 cc tylosin injectable (5%) solution mixed with a 25 cc sterile saline solution, delivered daily.

Other drug therapy programs of benefit in RNS and pneumonia cases include 25 mg/kg doxycycline (Vibramycin®) sometimes combined with Baytril® at 10 mg/kg or Naxcel® (a cephlaosporin) at 2 mg/kg (Rosskopf, 1990).

The condition is most often encountered in large collections or in animals which have been mixed with others of a different species. Maintaining good quarantine is vital if outbreaks are to be avoided. In the United Kingdom this condition was prevalent among many Tortoise Trust and other herpetological society members with large tortoise collections. After advice was given, and acted upon, not to mix species and to avoid the unnecessary movement of animals from one collection to another incidence of the problem fell dramatically. In our own institutional collection our policy of never mixing animals from different geographical origins and in taking extreme care over new introductions has virtually eliminated the problem. Keepers who holiday home tortoises, or who attend tortoise meetings with their animals are at particular risk. Mycoplasmic agents are certainly involved in many cases, and viruses are also suspected of some involvement in others. These pathogens are highly contagious and it cannot be stressed enough that prevention is infinitely better than cure. Passive carriers almost certainly exist and all infected, suspect or recovered tortoises must be regarded as possibly permanent carriers and should be subject to full quarantine measures.

Finally, it is worth checking, before recourse is made to drug therapies, that the cause of any persistent nasal discharge is not merely a foreign body lodged in the nares. Grass is a particularly frequent culprit. This may seem obvious, but it is surprising how often such a simple cause is overlooked. Another common cause of runny noses is vitamin A deficiency.

Septicaemia and peritonitis

Septicaemia in tortoises is not uncommon. The pathogens mainly responsible are again of the gram-negative group often *Pseudomonas* and *Aeromonas*. Symptoms of a generalised septicaemia include vomiting, lethargy and sometimes a distinct reddish flush or tinge on the plastron or under the carapace shields caused by vascular congestion and haemorrhage. A particularly revealing symptom is petechiation of the tongue and mucous membranes with many micro-haemorrhages visible in advanced cases. Some instances of septicaemia may be accompanied by acute jaundice, and affected reptiles may drink excessively.

When confronted with these symptoms, the most effective course of action usually is to administer an antibiotic by injection as quickly as possible. Good results have been obtained with framycetin and gentamycin as well as with oxytetracycline and ampicillin, although this latter is not normally a first choice for this condition.

Septicaemia may result from abscesses or as a result of other infected lesions. In female tortoises problems with eggs are often implicated. Eggs may become stuck in the pelvic region or rupture. Egg yolk can cause serious internal inflammation, and the female may then rapidly deteriorate into a state of acute egg peritonitis.

Egg retention or dystocia

Common symptoms include problems with the back legs, reluctance to walk or swim, lethargy, and all the other signs outlined above which are associated with septicaemia. An X-ray examination will confirm the presence of eggs, sometimes highly calcified. From a good quality X-ray eggs can not only be counted, but also measured, and their shell density assessed. The aetiology of the condition is complex but a variety of factors including inappropriate photo-period, non availability of a suitable laying site, aggression by other animals, temperature, obesity, rear limb injuries and dietary deficiencies are certainly implicated. One major factor appears to be the practice of hibernating female tortoises with retained eggs. Where possible, this should be avoided. One fatality reported concerned a female *Testudo graeca* which at post-mortem was found to have 14 eggs inside her; 7 were heavily calcified and were obviously produced during the previous year and had been retained, the rest were relatively fresh.

The best treatment for egg retention is undoubtedly prevention. Provision of the correct laying environment, good nutrition and low levels of stress will all contribute to eliminating the problem. Should it occur, however, immediate action is essential if the female is to be saved. This is most definitely a life-threatening condition.

Early stage cases often respond to warm water enemas, frequent warm water baths, and lubrication of the cloacal area with water-based surgical jellies. It is best to avoid petroleum-

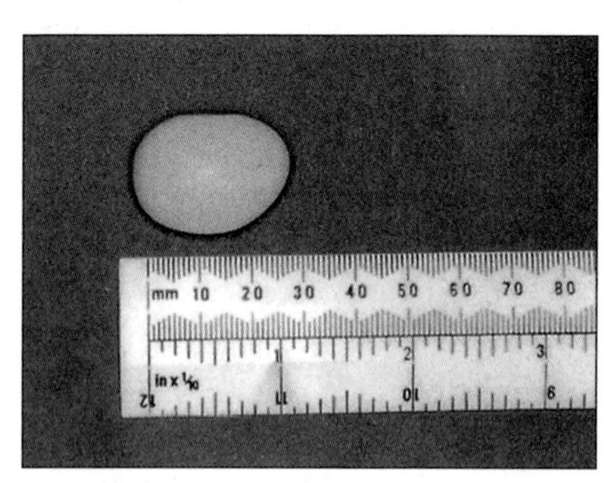

Above: A malformed and soft egg from a young female which had been subjected to a calcium-deficient diet.

Below: The 'golfball' texture of the lower egg should be compared to the normal egg, above. The lower egg has been retained and is heavily calcified.

based products. Physical manipulation of the eggs by probe has succeeded in some cases but should be regarded as a high-risk course of action. Should eggs fracture internally the danger of egg-yolk peritonitis is considerable.

Treatment of advanced cases presents certain difficulties. Where possible any underlying septicaemia should be treated first using systemic antibiotics. It may then be possible to induce laying by the use of calcium borogluconate and oxytocin injections. The calcium should precede the oxytocin by at least 12 to 24 hours. The normal dose range for oxytocin in this application is from 2 mg per kg to 10 mg per kg preceded with 10 mg per kg of an injectable solution of calcium borogluconate. We have very succesfully used a regime where a 5 day course of injectable calcium is given prior to the oxytocin. In most instances a single 10 mg per kg dose of oxytocin will prove adequate, repeated if necessary in 4 to 8 hours. It frequently helps if the uterine mucosa are lubricated or moist. Eggs are usually expelled very shortly after the oxytocin injection. Oxytocin induction can also be used routinely for 'difficult' layers and several accomplished captive breeders of aquatic turtles rely upon it virtually exclusively. It must be noted that oxytocin should always be used with caution, and only after adequate examination and assessment of the animal's condition. Improper use, as in the case of excessively large eggs, or where pelvic damage exists, can result in death. For this reason, we normally precede oxytocin treatment with a diagnostic X-ray.

For X-ray diagnosis of obstetric problems in tortoises and turtles, a dorso-ventral view is normally preferred. The precise exposure required for good results will vary according to the type of X-ray film being used. For a 750 g tortoise measuring 11.5 cm x 7.5 cm Jackson and Fasal (1981) suggest 60 Kv at 10 mAs and a focal-plane distance of 91 cm. This can be reduced to 70 cm using intensifying screens.

Surgical removal of eggs

Surgical removal via caesarean section should only be considered when all else has failed. This is a major operation with (typically) no better than a 50/50 success rate. Under a general anaesthetic the plastron is opened, eggs removed, and the section of plastron replaced with steel pin and resin reinforcements. The procedure is described in full in relevant veterinary texts. A safer, although still drastic option, involves aspirating the egg contents via hypodermic needle inserted in the femoral fossa (the area between the hind leg and the bridge). This procedure also requires that the patient is anaesthetised. The egg is then disintegrated and the shell fragments and liquid contents removed via cloaca. A prior X-ray is vital to establish the exact location and number of eggs to be removed. It should be remembered that, as stated above, egg-yolk acts as an inflammatory agent on internal tissues and thus further complications are a distinct possibility.

Viral diseases

The ecology of tortoises renders them potentially highly susceptible to viral diseases; they typically live an isolated existence in populations which are themselves isolated from others and which have probably remained isolated for thousands, and sometimes tens of thousands, of years. As such, the opportunity to develop natural resistance to a wide range of organisms is severely limited. This, of course, applies equally to bacterial pathogens.

It should be recognised that even in the case of that most mobile of animals the human being, isolated populations are at increased risk from new or alien organisms which may be introduced by visitors from populations where the same organism is endemic, but where acquired natural immunity has rendered it relatively harmless. A good example would be the common cold, which when introduced by early explorers decimated many previously isolated tribes in remote corners of the world. That example is well known, but what is not so well known is that current research indicates that even in a highly mobile and dense modern urban environment these effects are still present; epidemiologists hypothesise that some diseases including leukaemia and cancers could result from "a rare response to an unidentified mild or sub-clinical infection which is facilitated when large numbers of people come together, particularly from a variety of origins" (1).

This is of direct relevance to the management of tortoises in captivity, which are often mixed together at random, with no thought to origins, in densities many hundreds of times greater than that which they experience in the wild. It is small wonder that mortality rates in large captive colonies tend to be so high, whereas an individual pet keeper with maybe one or two tortoises, purchased from the dealer at the same time (and hence, usually, from the same geographical location) and thereafter kept in isolation in the garden can often keep those same animals in good health for decades.

Certain species show greater sensitivity to infection than others. If tortoises of North African origin are placed in an overcrowded environment in close proximity to *T. ibera* or *T. hermanni*, then the rate of opportunistic disease incidence in the North African specimens rises dramatically. Typical problems include gut parasitism of flagellate origin, respiratory, ocular and mouth infections. Death is not uncommon. There are several possibilities which could explain this, but stress and an immune system unable to cope with alien organisms must be a strongly suspected. Viral particles have regularly been isolated from the livers of affected animals at necropsy examination.

It should be understood by everyone with responsibility for captive collections that the potential for an epidemic or genetic disaster is ever present. Under absolutely no circumstances should ex-captive animals simply be released back into the wild. They could be carrying organisms which might spell death or even extinction for their species. I would also stress that animals which as part of an intended release program must **never** be exposed to non-sympatric species from other geographical areas or even maintained in close proximity to them. Complete isolation must be maintained at all times.

Viral diseases and aquatic turtles

In general, empirical evidence from captive collections suggests that aquatic testudines are less susceptible to viral diseases than terrestrial species. However, it should be noted that certain serious viral diseases do afflict marine turtles and are suspected in some freshwater turtles, so keepers should not become complacent (see, for example, Rebell, Rywlin and Haines, 1975). Specific viral diseases have, for example, been noted in *Graptemys* species (Jacobson, et. al. 1982), and in *Chrysemys picta* (Cox, et. al. 1980).

In captive or zoo collections, a much improved survival rate, not to mention breeding success rate, will be noted if non sympatric species are maintained separately and overcrowding is eliminated. To date, the following conditions have been liked to a specific viral origin in terrestrial species:

(1) Kinlen, L. 1990. The Lancet, 7th Sept. 1990.

Viral hepatitis

This contagious disease was described following mortality in *Testudo hermanni* (Heldstab and Bestetti, 1982). The present author has subsequently encountered a significant number of tortoises which have died following hepatitis-like symptoms (jaundice, disruption of digestive tract and generalised lethargy). A number of these mortalities were submitted for detailed post-mortem analysis, including electron microscopy of the liver. As with Heldstab and Bestetti's specimen (op. cit.), the livers were found to contain a large number of necrotic lesions and viral inclusion bodies were also positively identified. The virus concerned was identified as belonging to the *Herpes* group. From empirical experience, this author can conform that the disease appears to be highly contagious and capable of attaining epidemic proportions within collections. Both *T. hermanni* and *T. graeca* complex animals appear equally susceptible. No effective treatment is known. Attempts to treat affected animals with the anti-herpes drug acyclovir (Zovirax®) were ultimately unsuccessful.

Viral stomatitis

Stomatitis of viral origin may be more common than is realised, as few specimens are subjected to the detailed, and often costly, investigation required in order to detect it. In Mediterranean tortoises, it was described as early as 1988 (Cooper, Gschmeissner and Bone) in *Testudo graeca*. Three years previously, a very similar condition had been described in the Argentine Chaco tortoise (*Geochelone chilensis*) by Jacobson and others (1985). The author is aware of a number of unpublished instances of stomatitis where tissue samples have later revealed the presence of viral inclusion bodies, and where the disease has resisted all attempts at antibiotic therapy. In some cases, topical application of acyclovir ointment did result in cure. This disease is, however, both highly contagious and very difficult to treat. In most instances it is fatal, unlike common bacterial-origin stomatitis where there is a reasonably high success rate.

Viral enteritis

The literature contains two dramatic illustrations of epidemic proportion outbreaks where a viral-origin enteritic disease was determined as being implicated. Lange and others (1989) describe a population of 130 *Testudo hermanni* and *Testudo horsfieldi* where within a 3 month period 50% of the animals died. The cause was ascribed to a *herpes*-like pathogen. Oettle and others (1990) describe a similar major outbreak in a South African collection involving *Psammobates tentorius* (the Tent tortoise), *Homopus areolatus* (the Parrot-beaked tortoise), *Chersina angulata* (the Angulate tortoise) and *Geochelone pardalis* (the Leopard tortoise). In this instance, 31 tortoises died and both *Herpes* and *Paramyxovirus*-like inclusion bodies were detected in post-mortem tissue samples. Again, the author has seen virtually identical, unreported, outbreaks in the United Kingdom among captive collections and is in possession of post-mortem reports from these outbreaks where tissue samples have revealed the presence of virus inclusion bodies.

It is important to stress that viral diseases are a very serious threat indeed to the integrity of all captive collections. Once contagion has occurred, the opportunities for successful treatment are limited. Prevention does involve some inconvenience, and some small degree of additional expense; but both are insignificant compared to the inconvenience and expense involved should an epidemic take hold, to say nothing of the suffering and distress caused to the animals involved.

It is also very important to realise that an animal may be infectious and carrying a viral disease without appearing to be sick itself. Such animals are known as passive carriers. It is no use therefore simply avoiding evidently ill animals, even an outwardly healthy specimen may be carrying a disease which could be lethal to others which it contacts.

Miscellaneous diseases and conditions

The following conditions may or may not be related to bacterial infections. Sometimes they are observed individually, sometimes in combination with other diseases:

Renal dysfunction

Symptoms include oedema, pale mucous membranes and lethargy. There is usually a reluctance or inability to urinate. Weight may increase drastically due to retention of fluids. Often seen following long term anorexia, dehydration or bacterial infection.

Treatment includes flushing the renal system with compound sodium lactate or pure water. Do not administer oral rehydration therapies. Fluid should be delivered at approximately 5% of total bodyweight daily. Complete renal failure is incurable. Some forms of temporary renal failure respond to treatment as outlined above, or to systemic injection of diuretic drugs, frusemide, for example, has proved effective in testudines.

Cases of renal constipation due to concreted uric acid deposits are quite often encountered; regular baths and physiotherapy of the back legs can definitely help to release the offending blockage. In cases of persistent renal constipation due to excessive uric acid production drugs can be prescribed by which will reduce help to reduce this but in the long term strict dietary control is likely to be equally if not more effective.

Gut impactions and colic

Gut impactions may be caused by ingestion of substrate material. This can develop into generalised septicaemia. To reduce the danger substantially, offer food in a clean, substrate-free area. With juveniles, a safe substrate can be formed from alfalfa (lucerne) pellets or newspaper. Colic usually results directly from dietary mismanagement. One particularly dangerous form of colic is tympanitic colic, caused by the generation of large quantities of intestinal gas. In severe cases the gut is so distended that the lung field is invaded which inhibits respiration. Rapid death can result. The feeding of excessive quantities of carbohydrate-rich foods and sugar-rich fruit is usually responsible. Both gut impactions and tympanitic colic are readily diagnosed by means of X-ray examination. For the treatment of acute tympanitic colic Frye (1991) recommends the administration of a gas-lysing agent such as simethicone by stomach tube.

Penile prolapse

This is often secondary to another condition and in many instances occurs in the terminal phase of a serious injury or disease. Spontaneous prolapse however is treatable provided it is not merely a symptom of something more serious. The problem seems particularly common in box and aquatic turtles.

Treatment includes lubrication of the problematic organ with KY® jelly and irrigation with 0.75% chlorhexidine followed by sterile saline solution. Osmotic agents may be applied to assist reduction (glycerine and sucrose have been used with good results), serious and non-responsive cases will often require veterinary surgery. This usually involves application of a purse string suture around the cloacal aperture. This should be removed a few days later, and, hopefully, the organ will remain in place. Severely traumatised organs may require amputa-

Left: A tortoise with a severely injured leg, as a result of a rodent attack during hibernation, is provided with temporary mobility by means of a wheel attached via epoxy cement to the plastron.

tion. This is plainly a drastic solution and should only be employed as a last resort in order to save the animal's life.

Traumatic shell and limb injuries

These are usually the result of accidental damage; dropping or contact with mowers or agricultural implements are frequently to blame. Severely traumatised animals may also be seen if shipped incorrectly for trade purposes (there are international requirements governing the shipping of live animals; regrettably, these are not always enforced). Broken limbs usually respond to immobilisation. X-ray diagnosis is generally required. Jaw fractures similarly may respond to wiring and immobilisation. Carapace damage is particularly common. Minor injuries should be cleaned with very dilute Betadine® or 0.75% chlorhexidine and left open to the air to heal, but beware of fly-strike. Covering minor injuries can slow down, rather than accelerate, recovery. In areas where flies are a problem, a gauze covering can help; this will allow aeration of the site whilst offering some protection. Temporary re-enforcement to minor injuries can be provided by binding with adhesive tape. Major injuries will require intensive veterinary surgery. Wounds can be irrigated with lactated ringer's (Hartmann's) solution, followed by dressing with a dry antibiotic powder. If the injury site is fragmented, loose pieces should be removed in preparation for replacement by inert fibreglass mesh. Plastral injuries may need drilling and pinning with steel reinforcing sutures to obtain adequate strength. Major carapace loss can sometimes be repaired using fibreglass and epoxy bridges; this should not be carried out immediately, but should take place after initial stabilisation and healing. At all times allow access for drainage and inspection. It is usually best to achieve a temporary repair initially, and only proceed to a permanent repair when it is evident that the site is definitely free of any infection and natural healing is complete. This can take many months in the case of tortoises and turtles.

General care and maintenance

Tortoises and turtles in captivity require a regular visual inspection for any signs of damage or for the presence of lesions or swellings, etc. At the same time, the length of the beak and claws should also be examined. Animals which are fed on excessively soft foods may develop over-long beaks, and those which are maintained on unnaturally smooth surfaces may develop over-long long nails. Both should be trimmed to the correct length using a pair of sharp nail-cutters and then smoothed using emery board. The environmental and dietary factors responsible will require modification. The shell should be examined for signs of incipient shell-rot ('SCUD') and also for sharp edges, caused by minor traumas such as falls, which can result in abrasions to the adjacent skin. These are particularly common in the region of the nuchal shield, where they can result in severe trauma to the back of the head and the surface of the neck. A useful temporary protective measure consists of taping elasticated bandage over the area of cracked shell. If ex-pet tortoises are received which have been painted white to aid visibility, a practice which, along with drilling and tethering is thankfully no longer current, the paint should be gently removed over a period of time as it seriously interferes with the animal's ability to thermoregulate.

Accidental drowning

Drowning may occur in terrestrial tortoises and also in aquatic turtles which have become trapped under water. First aid by artificial respiration should be given immediately following draining of lungs by inverting the turtle. Artificial respiration is accomplished by moving front legs in and out regularly so that air is forced into the lungs. Veterinary assistance, which should be sought urgently, consists of administering a diuretic to remove excess fluid, provision of pure oxygen delivered by tube, and administration of a respiratory stimulant such as doxapram hydrochloride applied topically to the tongue or via occipital injection. A broad spectrum antibiotic is also recommended as a precaution against subsequent pneumonia.

Overheating

Dangerous levels of overheating most frequently occur due to thermostat malfunction or inversion under a heating element or basking lamp. A particular danger in hatchlings or adults which are static due to other veterinary problems. Symptoms include a profuse saliva discharge. Cool immediately by partly immersing in cold water. Most tortoises and turtles have a critical thermal maxima in the order of 34 - 38°C, at which temperatures death can occur rapidly.

Hepatic (liver) disease

Symptoms include acute or recurrent jaundice. Likely cause is secondary abscessing in liver following long term bacterial infection. Treatments include oral administration of the amino-acid methionine (200 mg every 48 hours) for 5 doses and in severe cases systemic injection of anabolic steroid. Total liver failure is incurable, but many cases do respond to the above. The animal should be well hydrated using compound sodium lactate or pure water. Glucose may also help.

It should be noted that very many clinical cases of liver disease result directly from incorrect dietary management, especially excessive fat intake or a diet too rich in proteins. A form of viral hepatitis has also been identified, and certainly we have encountered cases which conformed to this diagnosis. Post-mortem virus particles were also found in liver tissue. This condition is highly contagious and is most often seen in mixed species collections or following an introduction of new animals. As with rhinitis, good management practices are the best defence. For viral hepatitis no effective treatment yet exists.

Non specific anorexia

This, it must be stressed, is a symptom not a primary condition. Any animal which is "off its feed" for extended periods should be placed under close observation and carefully examined for an underlying veterinary problem. Non-feeding animals can easily become dehydrated which can exacerbate the problem. The possibility of vitamin and trace element deficiencies should be investigated. If anorexia occurs following hibernation, fluid support and force feeding may be required. The eyesight of persistently anorexic animals should always be checked carefully, as many cases turn out to be due to frost damage sustained in hibernation.

Developmental failure in juveniles

It is not uncommon to find that a certain few hatchlings fail to develop as well as their siblings. In some instances, growth may be practically zero. The same animals have a high incidence of renal failure and soft-shell problems, despite an apparently adequate diet. The precise causes of this are difficult to diagnose, and even more difficult to begin to treat. The reasons may vary from case to case so what is offered here can be no more than a generalisation based upon our own experiences. We have found that few of these animals go on to survive long-term. Our own analysis of these cases points to the possibility of a thyroid-related defect. This would explain not only the growth factor failure, but also the failure to utilise calcium properly. It may ultimately be possible to treat this condition, but at present no effective therapy has been identified. Further research is required. Another strong possibility is a trace element deficiency; selenium and manganese are the most likely elements involved. Supplementation with these may assist in some cases. In the interim, we give such hatchlings every chance and, to our surprise, a very few have survived long enough to suddenly begin developing normally. Should you be presented with such animals, however, our advice would be not to hold high expectations of survival.

Locomotion difficulties and paralysis

Locomotion difficulties, including swimming difficulties in aquatic species, are frequently encountered as a symptom of several different underlying pathologies including renal dysfunction, metabolic bone disease, serious nutritional deficiency, egg retention, egg-yolk peritonitis, articular gout and septic arthritis. This is a symptom which should not be ignored as it usually indicates that a serious underlying problem exists. Traumatic injuries can also result in locomotion difficulty and paralysis. Spinal injuries are one possibility, but fractures of the limbs, pelvic girdle and pectoral girdle should also be considered. Tortoises may also demonstrate muscle weakness following severe overheating incidents. This is due to the formation lactic acid in the tissues following the anoxia common in such situations. The lactic acid then attacks skeletal muscle cells. Treatment in such cases frequently involves corticosteroids such as dexamethasone at 0.15 mg/kg as necessary. If concurrent dehydration is present, use only a non-lactated electrolyte formulation and avoid Hartmann's solution. Non acute locomotion difficulties may often be detected by means of a careful examination of the plastron. Look for asymmetrical patterns of wear which indicate unevenness of gait. Apparent locomotion difficulties in aquatic turtles may also indicate the presence of pneumonia.

Poisoning

Poisoning in tortoises and turtles usually occurs as a result of the ingestion of poisons deliberately introduced into the environment, such as slug bait, weed killers, pesticides, mouse or rat poison or as a result of ingesting natural (plant) toxins. Carnivorous species may consume prey which has itself been poisoned. It is extremely unwise to use any toxic garden chemical or other preparation anywhere in the vicinity of tortoises or turtles. Should poisoning occur, identify the probable toxin if at all possible and seek veterinary assistance as a matter of emergency. The precise treatment required depends upon the nature of the chemical ingested. Emergency treatment may include gastric and enteric lavage, the administration of activated charcoal and kaolin, and supportive therapy including rehydration.

Poisoning by toxic plants is usually seen in pet tortoises maintained in gardens. Many common garden plants are highly toxic. These include: daffodil, euphorbia, privet, crocus, cyclamen, delphinium, foxglove, hydrangea, jasmine, lilly of the valley, lobelia, lupine, mistletoe, potato leaves, rhubarb leaves, rhododendron, wisteria and yew in addition to obvious candidates such as fly agaric mushrooms, deadly nightshade and death cap mushrooms. Comprehensive lists of poisonous plants are available via most tortoise and turtle societies.

Stress

The non-specific nature of stress makes it a difficult problem to address. However, there is no doubt that it is often at the root of many disease problems in captive collections. A stressed animal undergoes a number of biochemical changes, some of which, such as the production of steroids, suppress the natural immune system. Thus, stressed animals are many times more likely to succumb to whatever pathogens they are exposed to than healthy, non-stressed animals exposed to the same organisms. Stress can be reduced in several ways:

- By maintaining animals under as natural conditions as possible
- By providing a good diet
- By not subjecting sensitive animals to aggressive behaviour by other, more competitive animals
- By reducing overcrowding and, in the case of females, by making certain that nesting site selection is not unduly stressful

Stress in tortoises is not easy to detect, often remaining hidden until it is too late. By taking preventative steps early enough, many disease problems and fatalities can be completely avoided.

Notes on handling infectious cases

All cases of bacterial, mycotic or viral infection must be handled extremely carefully with due regard to the risk of cross infection. Use effective antiseptics liberally and do not under any circumstances allow infected, or suspect, animals to come into contact with others. Isolation facilities are absolutely essential. Wash hands between every handling and prepare food separately. Surgical gloves are useful where handling open wounds and infectious cases.

Notes on antibiotics

Mention has been made above of various antibiotic agents and dose rates. The following chart summarises these notes and provides a few more details based on several years extensive observations. It is important to note that all antibiotic drugs should only be used under the direction of a qualified veterinary surgeon.

Tylosin (50 mg/kg). Fairly safe. Good results in mild respiratory infections reported. Also active against some mycoplasma organisms.

Oxytetracycline (50 mg/kg). Fairly safe although can cause some irritation at injection site, also a tenancy to cause digestive upset. Very good to excellent results in cases of respiratory infection.

Amoxycillin (oral suspension, as per veterinary direction). A useful drug in cases of stomatitis where good results are consistently obtained. Rapid absorption into bloodstream. One of the few antibiotics where oral dosing is recommended.

Ampicillin (50 mg/kg). Can cause severe injection site irritation. Fairly safe. Reasonable to good results noted in cases of pneumonia and septicaemia.

Chloramphenicol (50 mg/kg) Good results against some gram-negative infections but principally of use against gram-positive pathogens.

Framycetin (10 mg/kg) Can prove effective against septicaemia, but typically not quite so effective against acute respiratory disease. Has also proved effective in treatment of chronic pneumonia. No side effects have been observed if safe doses employed.

Gentamycin (10 mg/kg). As above, but seems to be better than framycetin in cases of acute pneumonia.

Tobramycin (10 mg/kg). Useful in ocular and nasal infections.

Amikacin (10 mg/kg). General purpose.

Netilmycin (10 mg/kg) As above.

Doxycycline (Vibramycin®) 25 mg/kg daily. Useful in respiratory disease treatments and for treatment of resistant stomatitis where laboratory results indicate. Good activity against mycoplasma organisms.

Enrofloxacin (Baytril®) 10 mg/kg every 48 hours for 10 days. Generally very good to excellent results against chronic upper respiratory disease in tortoises.

Ciprofloxacin/ofloxaxcin 10 mg/kg every 48 hours. Good results against severe shell infections and generalised septicaemia. Also very good results against pneumonia. Ciprofloxacin has high success rate against gram-negative pathogens.

Note that aminoglycoside antibiotics should not be used in combination with frusemide or with any neuromuscular blocking drug. Where renal function is impaired, they may only be used with the most extreme caution.

All the above mentioned antibiotic drugs, except amoxycillin, are listed as per systemic subcutaneous or i.m. injection. The preferred injection site varies with the antibiotic, but normally, nephro-toxic drugs, i.e. the aminoglycosides, are injected i.m. into the front limbs and non nephro-toxic preparations are injected i.m. into the hind limbs. Tortoises on antibiotic therapy should normally be maintained at 29 - 30°C for the duration of treatment. Oral dosing is generally not recommended in tortoises as it can be difficult to calculate eventual blood serum level and the antibiotics can have a serious effect upon gut flora if delivered by this route. Where possible, i.e. in strictly local infections, a topical application is generally to be preferred, i.e. cloacitis frequently responds well to framycetin paste, i.e. a mastitis paste intended for use with cows, administered via the cloaca, and ocular infections are generally best treated with eye antibiotic ointment or drops. The only exception to the general prohibition on oral dosing is in cases of severe intestinal bacterial diseases or when eliminating *Salmonella* where no other method is practical.

Antibiotics and aquatic turtle treatment

In general, aquatic turtles on antibiotic treatment should be removed to a separate isolation tank. It is not generally realised that biological filter systems can be rapidly destroyed if antibiotics are introduced into the water. With modern antibiotics, even the slight traces released by turtles on systemic therapy will be enough to wipe out colonies of nitrifying bacteria. Where an antibiotic, or anti fungal, agent is to be added to the water itself, this is even more important. Some anti fungal preparations intended for use with tropical fish are, however, safe to use and will not damage biological filters. Certain bactericides designed for aquaculture use may also be safe, but these are rarely of value in the treatment of turtle health conditions.

Turtles on antibiotic therapy are usually best maintained in shallow water, heated to 27°C. This is normally the optimum temperature, in most aquatic species, for immune activity and antibiotic effectiveness.

It is vitally important to adequately sterilise all tanks and filter equipment which may have been exposed to an infected turtle before they are re-used. Our normal procedure is to flush the entire system with dilute povidone-iodine for at least 8 hours. Some filter materials, such as zeolite, activated carbon or chemically activated resins will need to be discarded. Biological filters will require re-starting as all nitrifying bacteria will also be destroyed during the disinfection process.

Zoonoses and general hygiene

It is important to stress that the health risks posed to human handlers by turtles are often exaggerated considerably. With adequate handling precautions and good general hygiene the risks are very limited. The organism most frequently of concern is *Salmonella*. It is true that up to 90% of some reptile populations may carry *Salmonella* as a commensal gut organism. However, the concentrations are usually extremely low, so low, in fact, that culture can prove difficult. Higher concentrations have been found in 'farmed' terrapins and several human epidemics have been traced to this cause. In such cases, the methods of housing and feeding the terrapins prior to sale have been directly implicated as a cause of the problem. Dirty, contaminated water and the feeding of uncooked contaminated meats are especially dangerous practices.

For keepers, good general hygiene practices will provide almost complete protection. Standard procedures it is highly advisable to enforce at all times include not eating or putting anything in the mouth when working with turtles, regular and thorough hand washing using hot water and a disinfectant soap after handling animals, the regular use of disinfectants such as dilute (1:20) bleach or povidone-iodine to clean feeding utensils and other apparatus and ensuring that all filter systems are in full working order. Regular maintenance is especially important when ultra-violet sterilisers are installed. Faeces and dirty water should be disposed of carefully and safely; tortoise and turtle waste is not suitable for composting as *Salmonella* organisms can survive this process. The feeding of uncooked poultry, raw eggs or meat from suspect sources to turtles is extremely dangerous and should be avoided at all costs. Another potentially zoonotic organism of concern is cryptosporidiosis. In this case, both treatment and diagnosis is far from easy and strict isolation procedures should be employed for any animal which is suspected as a carrier. *Mycobacterium* species (the group of organisms which cause leprosy) have also been isolated, in rare cases, from freshwater turtles. These organisms also represent a potentially serious hazard to human health. The presence of children, the elderly, or immune compromised persons in the vicinity of turtles is not generally advised and should in any event be monitored carefully with all necessary precautions rigorously enforced.

Part Two

Practical
Captive Breeding and Species Maintenance Profiles

Part two

Practical Captive Breeding and Species Maintenance Profiles

The first edition of this work, *Keeping and Breeding Tortoises in Captivity,* concentrated upon providing concise and practical information for those terrestrial species most likely, at that time, to be encountered by the serious hobbyist. The response to that volume has been such, however, that this edition has been expanded to include a much more comprehensive collection of information covering a wide range of truly rare and endangered species. It should be noted, however, that the movement and possession of certain of these species are controlled by state, national and international laws. A representative selection of interesting aquatic turtles also appears here for the first time. Many species that were rarely seen in private collections when *Keeping and Breeding Tortoises in Captivity* appeared are now relatively commonplace - due almost entirely to the success of private breeders in reproducing them in captivity. An excellent example of this is *Geochelone sulcata*, the African Spurred tortoise. This animal was extremely rare even in institutional collections until recently (only 13 specimens were in captivity in the Western hemisphere in 1979, according to one survey). Additional adults were imported in the 1980's and many captive breeding successes occurred. This species reproduces at a prolific rate and today numerous hobbyists possess one or more specimens. Captive bred juveniles and sub-adults are now readily available. Another example of successful captive propagation is to be found in the case of *Asterochelys* (*Geochelone) radiata*, the Madagascan Radiated tortoise, which is now being bred in substantial numbers by zoos, commercial breeders and several private individuals. Recently even *Geochelone elephantopus*, the giant Galapagos tortoise, has also been successfully bred in commercial quantities. These achievements would have been almost unthinkable only a few years ago and it is a mark of our progress in the technical aspects of captive breeding reptiles that today these results are no longer considered extraordinary. As such captive-bred offspring become available, more breeders and institutions will acquire them; at the same time, the illegal trade in wild-caught specimens will be greatly reduced. The species is propagated and its future is made more secure. This was - and remains - my main motivation for writing this book. With the expansion of this section now to include the majority of terrestrial species for which captive breeding data is available, plus a representative selection of semi-aquatic and aquatic turtles, I hope that many more species will benefit.

In the case of aquatic testudines, there are numerous genera, species and subspecies but fortunately these normally require care that is not dissimilar from their regional neighbours; it is not necessary, therefore, to provide detailed information for each and every recognised taxon. The care and breeding requirements of most freshwater aquatic testudines are remarkably similar, with temperature and behaviour patterns the only really major variables (but see occasional comments on water quality preferences). Diets, in particular, show a high degree of parity among aquatic species.

Most of the data presented is based upon actual records obtained from successful breeding groups under the direction of experienced institutional and private keepers or from field studies of the species in the wild. It must be stressed that distinct regional differences in terms of reproductive behaviour may occur within taxa and that the location and climate of the captive environment may play an even greater role. A herpetologist maintaining tropical specimens in captivity in Florida will view matters from a very different perspective than a colleague in Sweden, for example, who maintains the same species in an altogether more trying climate. The information that follows should, then, be interpreted with care, bearing in mind the many variables that undoubtedly exist.

The selection of species included, and the varying depths of detail in which they are discussed may appear, at first, somewhat eclectic. My *modus operandi* in deciding what to include drew upon the following criteria:

- Those species which are widely kept in captivity
- Those which present unusual problems
- Those which have greater captive breeding potential than is commonly realised
- Those which are very representative of a habitat class
- Those which are infrequently encountered and about which practical data is scarce

Under the heading of each species or genus I have included a short taxonomic note and description. These are necessarily very brief, although in some instances the status of the taxon or its diagnostic characters may be anything but straightforward. Readers who require further details on the various species are referred to the select bibliography which is organised by genus for ease of use.

ACANTHOCHELYS PALLIDIPECTORIS (Freiberg, 1945)

Chaco side-necked turtle

General observations: This side-necked turtle from Argentina, Paraguay and Bolivia is occasionally encountered in specialist collections. Breeding in captivity is infrequent.

Taxonomy:Formerly known as *Platemys pallidipectoris.*

Description: *Acanthochelys pallidipectoris* is a medium-sized (to 17.5 cm) side-necked turtle that varies in colouration from yellowish brown to greyish brown with dark brown borders to the scutes. The plastron is yellowish. The head has a broad yellow medial stripe bordered by a pair of greyish-brown lateral stripes. The limbs are also yellowish and are covered with large scales. The feet are webbed. The thighs bear a series of tubercles adjacent to the tail. These are more developed in males than in females. Males also possess a somewhat concave plastron and have longer and thicker tails than females of the species.

Captive environment: The natural habitats of this species include slow-moving streams, ponds and other shallow water lakes or lagoons. It is almost exclusively aquatic, venturing on to land only rarely, and then usually only to lay its eggs. In captivity, specimens have been maintained successfully in heated ponds and in surface-mounted fibreglass tanks (Horne, 1993). Alkaline water conditions are poorly tolerated and a pH of 6.5 to 6.8 is suggested. Water temperatures may range from 26 to 28°C. Air temperatures should be maintained at parity or slightly above the water temperature. Good filtration is essential as *A. pallidipectoris* is highly susceptible to bacterial and fungal shell infections. A combination of an under-gravel filter and a large external canister filter is recommended. An in-circuit UV steriliser may also prove of value. Floating aquatic plants should be included in the captive environment as these provide important shelter for what is usually a rather shy and nervous turtle. A gently sloping land area should be provided, but is unlikely to be used often. Basking rarely occurs.

Diet: The diet of this species appears to be predominantly carnivorous. In captivity, specimens will normally accept live feeder fish, tadpoles, rehydrated trout-chow and cat pellets, chopped meats and small pond snails.

Common health problems: Skin and shell infections; pneumonia if air or water temperature too low.

Breeding: Courtship can be stimulated, as is the case with many aquatic turtles, by changing the water (Horne, op. cit). Natural nesting in captivity appears difficult to achieve with this species and oxytocin induction is often necessary. The eggs measure approximately 24.8 x 23.7 mm and weigh 8.8 grams (Richard, 1991). Incubation on a high humidity substrate such as mixed peat and vermiculite hydrated 1:1 with water is suggested at a temperature of 29 - 30°C. No sex determination data is yet available for *A. pallidipectoris.*

ALDABRACHELYS (GEOCHELONE) GIGANTEA (Schweigger, 1812)

The Aldabra giant tortoise

General observations: *Aldabrachelys gigantea* is the world's largest living land tortoise, with a carapace length to 106 cm and maximum recorded weight of 120 kg. Recent captive breeding successes have resulted in a small number of hatchlings becoming available in Europe and the United States so this species is likely to be encountered more frequently in captive collections in future.

Taxonomy: Formerly referred to *Geochelone*, but recently the subgenus *Aldabrachelys* has been elevated to genus level. Bour (1982) earlier proposed a new genus, *Dipsochelys*, but this has not found general acceptance. *Aldabrachelys gigantea* is, however, sometimes referred to under Bour's preferred nomenclature, *Dipsochelys elephantina*.

Description: Unlike *G. elephantopus*, which it superficially resembles, *A. gigantea* typically possesses a nuchal scute. This character is not infallibly diagnostic, however, as Gaymer (1968) discovered 3 out of a survey of 236 tortoises on Aldabra Atoll that lacked a nuchal. The plastron is short and lacks an anal notch. The carapace and skin are uniformly grey in colour. Males are larger than females and possess thicker, longer tails.

Captive environment: Aldabra giant tortoises are relatively hardy and versatile in their captive care requirements. That said, although they may survive for long periods in sub-optimum conditions, regular breeding will only occur when conditions are closer to their ideal. Most successful captive propagation programs are located in geographical regions that offer the constant high temperatures and bright illumination they require. In the wild, *A. gigantea* is mainly found in scrubland and grassland where they attain very high population densities. Aldabra tortoises may remain active at fairly low temperatures. Feeding at 13°C is noted by Stearns (1988), but this should be considered sub-optimum and for enthusiastic feeding and to encourage the possibility of breeding, temperatures in the region of 24 - 31°C are required. Stearns (op. cit.) observed that mating normally only occurred when daytime temperatures exceeded 30°C and advises that daily access to a temperature of at least 17°C is required for a healthy appetite and to avoid respiratory disease. A large indoor tortoise house will be required in areas that experience cold winters or sub-optimum summers; to achieve this, a combination of under-floor heating (preferably using embedded hot water pipes in cement) and overhead infra-red basking sources is recommended.

Diet: A diet rich in fibre content is essential if digestive problems are to be avoided. In all respects, diet is as for *G. pardalis* and *G. sulcata*. Cactus (especially *Opuntia* species) pads and fruit are recommended, and access to a large grazing area planted with mixed grasses is also very important. When this is not available due to seasonal constraints, alfalfa (lucerne) hay is a good substitute. Juveniles require prodigious quantities of calcium and other essential trace elements to support their rapid rate of growth.

Common health problems: *Hexamita* infection; pneumonia due to cold, draughts and damp; goitre (a mineral supplement containing iodine may be required and goitrogenic vegetables should not be given in excess).

Breeding: Breeding success is more likely if males and females are temporarily separated, then reintroduced. This species seems to place importance upon territory - they do not respond well to territorial disturbances, and seem to prefer their overnight and winter accommodation to be contiguous with their feeding and nesting outdoor area. The substrate and ground profile of the breeding pen can also play a role. Mating can often be unsuccessful on hard, flat surfaces. A mixed sand-loam substrate is recommended. This should be of sufficient depth to allow for nest excavation; a depth of 500 mm will usually suffice (in the wild most nests are between 250 mm and 300 mm deep). Captive *A. gigantea* have a tendency to nest at dusk or even after darkness has fallen - beware of enclosing gravid females in overnight accommodation that lacks access to a nesting site. Potentially fatal egg retention problems may result if the breeding pen lacks a suitable nesting area, or if maintenance temperatures are too low. Some difficult females will nest if provided with a basking lamp over a nesting area after dusk. Eggs measure approximately 50 x 55 mm and have a mass of 75 g. They can be incubated on a vermiculite substrate hydrated 1:1 with water at a temperature of 30°C. Hatching typically occurs in 95 to 130 days, but may take considerably longer. Stearns (op. cit.) incubated 16 eggs at 28°C and at this temperature hatching occurred between 110 - 116 days. Hatchlings measure approximately 60 mm SCL and weigh between 40 - 47 g. By 21 months of age, growth to 13 cm and 432 grams has been noted. Stearns (op. cit.) noted scute pyramiding in some specimens and attributed this to consumption of alfalfa (lucerne) pellets which were too high in protein; a change to unprocessed alfalfa hay improved the situation. If feeding pellets, it is worth investigating protein content carefully and selecting only low protein varieties. Hatchlings are somewhat more delicate than adults and are very prone to respiratory and digestive tract problems; they should not be exposed to temperatures below 20°C and should be isolated from other species. Flagellate infections are a particular danger. The incidence is less if a diet high in fibre and low in sugar is provided as this avoids excessive gut motility, a factor that seems to predispose many species towards gastric upset.

ASTEROCHELYS (GEOCHELONE) RADIATA (Shaw, 1802)

The radiated tortoise

General observations: This extremely attractive tortoise continues to be heavily exploited within Madagascar for the decorative qualities of its shell and also for food. It is also much sought after on the international exotic pet market. Strict controls, including Appendix 1 CITES listing have reduced trade substantially in recent years. Illegal trading continues, however, as regular seizures testify. These seizures have provided the core stock of several successful external breeding programs.

Taxonomy: Formerly referred to *Geochelone*, and still considered such by many authorities. Prior to that, referred to *Testudo*. No subspecies are currently recognised.

Description: High domed carapace to approximately 38 cm and weight to 13 kg. The scutes typically feature a yellow aureole surrounded by a profound pattern of radiating yellow or orange lines on a brown or black ground. In aged specimens the accutance (edge sharpness) of pattern is reduced; in juveniles it is particularly strident. The skin of the limbs and head is pale yellow, save for a black dorsal region. The plastron has a yellow ground and features a series of black triangular markings on the abdominal, humeral, femoral and pectoral scutes.

Captive environment: Similar in all material respects to *Geochelone pardalis*. This tortoise shelters under *Opuntia* cacti and thorn bushes which are also much appreciated in captive enclosures. *A. radiata* does not respond well to cold and damp and is prone to respiratory problems if maintained in an incorrect environment.

Diet: A high fibre diet with as much natural graze as possible is recommended. Most *A. radiata* enjoy eating *Opuntia* cactus pads (the thornless varieties are usually preferred and certainly present fewer problems for handlers). Other favoured items include dried fallen leaves and mixed grasses and any red coloured fruit or flowers. Although they will take it with great enthusiasm, the temptation to feed too much fruit should be avoided as this tends to cause colic and diarrhoea. Generally, the diet should be as recommended for *G. pardalis* and *G. sulcata*.

Common health problems: *Hexamita parva*; respiratory disease; stomatitis. This species is best maintained in isolation from non-sympatric species.

Breeding: This species breeds extremely well in captivity and presents few serious captive maintenance problems. Females are highly productive and may nest up to 7 times a year, with a typical clutch comprising 6 - 8 eggs, sometimes as many as 14. These are spherical, and normally measure between 36 - 42mm in diameter. Eggs incubated at 30°C can hatch in as few as 95 days but this is very variable, with some eggs taking as long as 112 days at the same temperature. At lower temperatures incubation periods in excess of 230 days have been recorded. Increasing the incubation temperature to 31°C to 32.5°C can reduce incubation time considerably (71 days has been reported in captivity). Desirable incubation conditions are very similar to that required for *G. pardalis* and *G. sulcata*, with a medium (75 - 80%) humidity environment and a type I static air incubator consistently producing the best results. Neonates measure approximately 36 x 32 mm, weigh approximately 35 g and can initially be housed in a covered propagator lined with paper towel. Later, they do well on an alfalfa pellet substrate.

BATAGUR BASKA (Gray, 1830)

Giant Asian river terrapin

General observations: This impressive turtle is under severe pressure in the wild due to habitat destruction, over-collecting and predation of nests. It is protected under Appendix 1 of CITES. Captive breeding will play an important future role in its conservation.

Taxonomy: *Batagur* is a monotypic genus. A subspecies, *Batagur baska ranongensis* (Wirot, 1979) has been described but is not generally recognised.

Description: One of the largest emydid turtles, female *Batagur baska* attain carapace lengths of 60 cm whilst males are slightly smaller at up to 50 cm. The carapace is highly domed, more so in females than in males, is olive grey or brown in colour and the plastron is yellowish and lacks any pattern. The head is small, the nose somewhat upturned and is of the same colour as thc carapace apart from the sides, which are lighter. The back of the head is covered with small scales. The fore-limbs are enlarged, paddle-shaped and feature four strongly webbed claws.

Captive environment: *Batagur baska* is primarily an inhabitant of tidal estuaries. It requires a large and well-filtered water area with soft slopes as haul out and basking sites. The ambient humidity of the captive environment also appears to be important and humid conditions are recommended. The water temperature for this species should be maintained at approximately 28°C. A range of air temperatures from 23 - 31°C, seasonally adjusted, have proved satisfactory (Blanco, Behler and Kostel, 1990). Although an estuarine species, Davenport, Wong and East (1992) found that feeding only occurred at salinity levels of 19.8% and below and that no feeding occurred as the salinity level rose to 23%. Drinking too only occurs at low levels of salinity. The implications for captive maintenance are that a salinity level of less than 6% would appear to be best tolerated.

Diet: In the wild, the diet of this terrapin is heavily biased towards aquatic plants and overhanging vegetation, especially the leaves and fruits of mangroves. *Batagur baska* also consumes molluscs, crustaceans and fish. In captivity, most specimens will accept a mixed diet of green leaf plant material (including water hyacinth), fruit, feeder and frozen fish and prepared items such as rehydrated trout or cat pellets. Juveniles will feed upon small earthworms in addition to fruit.

Common health problems: This species is susceptible to trauma induced shell infections and is also intolerant of poor water quality.

Breeding: The onset of the breeding season, which usually takes place between October and January, is indicated by profound colour changes in male specimens. In Malaysian turtles the soft parts of the body turn black and the normally cream iris changes to bright white. It is believed that *Batagur baska* from other locations may display a different pattern of colour change. Female *Batagur baska* are capable of producing very high density clutches which range from as few as 5 to as many as 40 eggs per clutch, although some are reported to lay 50 - 60 eggs in three separate clutches (Tikader and Sharma, 1985). A sandy nesting site on a gentle slope is generally preferred. In the wild, nesting almost invariably occurs at night. The eggs are brittle-shelled, measure approximately 65 x 41 mm and weigh 65 grams. In captivity, successful incubation has been achieved on a mixed vermiculite, sand and peat substrate hydrated 1:1 with water at a temperature of 26 to 31°C. Blanco, Behler and Kostel (1990) speculate that *Batagur* may be subject to ESD and that low temperatures during incubation may result in males. It is important that a high ambient humidity is maintained throughout the period of incubation which, at the temperatures cited, takes between 80 to 100 days. The hatchlings measure approximately 60 mm long and weigh about 54 grams.

CARETTOCHELYS INSCULPTA Ramsey, 1887

The Pig-nosed turtle

General observations: An extremely rare species, it is only very recently that information on captive care and breeding has become available.

Taxonomy: The sole surviving member of the Carettochelyidae, a family of turtles common during the Tertiary period. It is the only cryptodiran turtle native to Australia.

Description: *Carettochelys insculpta* possesses a set of limbs that are unique among present-day freshwater turtles. These closely resemble those of marine turtles and are equipped with functional flippers. Its swimming motion is also closer to that of marine turtles than it is to any other freshwater turtle. *C. insculpta* is a large species, attaining up to 22.5 kg in weight and 56.3 cm in length (Georges and Rose, 1993). The carapace is grey to olive in colour and the unpatterned limbs are of a similar hue. The plastron is white or pale yellow. Its snout, from which it takes its colloquial name, is very distinctive, consisting of a blunt, fleshy proboscis bearing the nostrils.

Captive environment: The natural habitat of this unique species includes lakes, swamps, rivers (including, in Papua New Guinea, estuaries) and pools. It is often found in water between 2 and 5 metres deep and is frequently associated with sand or silt bottoms. In captivity, they can be maintained in large, smooth-sided ponds or in glass or fibreglass tanks. Underwater plant and log cover are also important, especially if more than a single specimen is to be accommodated in the same tank. *Carettochelys* are usually highly aggressive and even small specimens will attack each other. Large specimens appear particularly aggressive towards smaller specimens. Serious injuries can result. Aggressive behaviour normally ceases if visual contact is lost between two specimens. Alternatively, a plastic screen can be used to divide a tank into two separate sections (Dorrian, 1994). The water temperature should be maintained at 26 to 30°C. Good quality filtration is vital as this species is very susceptible to fungal white spot disease (*Sphagnalium* spp.). Large sand filters in combination with a UV sterilisation system are suggested. Basking has not been observed in captivity but a gently sloped exit and basking ramp should be provided as this will also serve as a nesting site. A sandy substrate is usually preferred for this purpose.

Diet: The natural diet appears heavily biased in favour of the fruit and leaves of wild fig plants (*Ficus racemosa*). Mangrove fruits are also consumed. Overall, the diet of *C. insculpta* is best described as predominantly herbivorous with a small animal protein content, mainly in the form of molluscs, insect larvae and small crustaceans. It is believed that occasionally fish may be eaten and that some carrion may also be consumed opportunistically (Georges, 1987). In captivity, a wide range of fruit is accepted including apple, paw paw, banana and orange. *Hibiscus* flowers and eel weed (*Vallisneria* spp.) are also taken with enthusiasm. In addition, some fish and rehydrated trout-chow should be provided. Although shrimp has been recommended, this must be used with caution as it is a potential vector of the very skin disorders to which this turtle is already very vulnerable.

Common health problems: Fungal and bacterial skin disorders. These are initiated and exacerbated by injuries caused during fighting or by inadequate water hygiene. Contaminated food may also be a causal factor. White spot disease may be treated by the removal of loose skin and scabs and by painting with 1% mercurochrome or acriflavine. This should be allowed to dry before the turtle is returned to the water (Georges and Rose, op. cit.). Many fungal diseases are inhibited if the water pH is maintained at or below 6.5

Breeding: The eggs of *C. insculpta* are round, hard-shelled and measure approximately 40 mm in circumference. Both clutch density and egg size appear to vary with geographical location. Clutches of between 7 to 39 eggs have been recorded. In the wild, incubation at 30°C takes between 64 to 74 days, followed by a further period of aestivation within the nest before final emergence. Sex is determined by temperature, with eggs incubated at a constant 28°C and 30°C resulting in male offspring whilst those incubated at 32°C result in females. A threshold temperature of 31.6°C is believed to apply (Georges, 1987).

CHELODINA LONGICOLLIS (Shaw, 1802)

Common Australian snake-necked turtle

General observations: A long-necked chelid turtle from Australia.

Taxonomy: Much regional variation is evident in this species, and indeed throughout the genus *Chelodina*. It is at present undergoing further study and revision.

Description: The most striking feature of *C. longicollis* is that the neck is almost as long as the carapace (which can attain 27.5 cm), giving it a most unusual appearance (but note that the neck of *C. oblonga* is longer still). The colour of the carapace is brown-black; the plastron and ventral aspect of the marginals is cream or yellow with black borders. The limbs feature light grey or brown skin on the upper surfaces but are cream to yellow on the undersides. The head is of a flattened appearance and together with the neck is similarly coloured. The eyes are usually white. The jaws are also light in colour.

Captive environment: The natural habitat of this turtle includes slow-moving streams, rivers, creeks and swamps with a wide pH range from 4.5 to 7.4 In captivity, a pH range of 6.5 to 7 is usually preferred. Water temperatures should be maintained between 22 - 24°C for normal activity; in winter temperatures can be reduced to between 5 - 8°C to provide a hibernation period although many keepers prefer to over winter as normal. A soft sandy substrate is recommended in all ponds and tanks that are to accommodate this species. Other *Chelodina* species including *C. rugosa*, *C. novaeguinae* and *C. oblonga* may be maintained under identical conditions although it should be noted that these species often do not tolerate hibernation well in captivity. Overall, most *Chelodina* species are relatively easy to maintain in captivity and established pairs breed well.

Diet: In the wild, the diet of this species consists principally of molluscs, fish, amphibians, worms and various insects. Juveniles often feed initially upon filamentous algae and very small feeder fish such as guppies in captivity. Adults will accept most prepared meats including rehydrated dried cat and koi pellets and Purina trout-chow®. This latter item has proved very successful with many turtles, and is generally recommended as part of a balanced diet.

Common health problems: Fungal diseases of the skin and carapace are common in captivity. Nichol (1985) describes persistent problems of this nature, believed to originate from the introduction of live feeder fish. An effective treatment comprised benzalkonium chloride (0.15%), carbamide (0.15%) and allantoin (0.05%) applied topically for 10 minutes. Normal treatments including malachite green and acriflavine were ineffective. Reports from several keepers suggest that the incidence of skin problems in *Chelodina* species is much reduced when water pH is maintained slightly below 6.5.

Breeding: If incubated at 28 - 30°C in a high humidity environment on a sphagnum or damp vermiculite substrate hatching can occur between 60 - 90 days. Viability is indicated by the appearance of a white spot at the top of the egg, usually within 24 hours (Nichol, op. cit.). Georges (1985) reported that *C. longicollis* do not employ a temperature determined sex mechanism. Egg retention problems are also common in this species, with many breeders resorting to the use of oxytocin on a regular basis. A typical clutch is 12 - 17 eggs although considerable variation occurs - as few as 5 or as many as 28 may be laid. Eggs may also be deposited in water which appears to seriously affect viability. A large (50 cm diameter) plastic tub filled with sand, positioned beneath a basking light and partly submerged has, however, proved an acceptable nesting site not only for *C. longicollis*, but also for *C. novaeguinae* and *C. expansa*. The hatchlings of *C. longicollis* measure approximately 25 mm SCL and require accommodation in a tank free of underwater obstructions as several keepers have reported problems with drowning. Nichol (op. cit.) reported good results with floating artificial plants, upon which juveniles sleep just beneath the surface.

CHELUS FIMBRIATUS Dumeril, 1806

Matamata

General observations: A turtle that possesses as unique a structure among aquatic species as *Malacochersus* does among terrestrial species.

Taxonomy: *Chelus* is a monotypic genus. It is noteworthy, however, that an early synonym of this turtle was *Testudo terrestris* FERMIN 1765, thus beginning the long and chequered history of this name.

Description: Thc appearance of this turtle is unmistakable, although is does bear a passing resemblance to the Alligator snapping turtle (*Macroclemys temminckii*). The head is peculiarly broad posteriorly, tapering to a point antioraly and is very flat. It also possesses a neck of considerable length and thickness. The shape of the head is so bizarre and that it is frequently difficult to locate the position of the eyes. The impression given is of an up-turned leaf. The carapace can attain in excess of 40 cm length and is usually an overall light to dark brown colour. The skin varies from brown to grey. Males have longer tails than females and feature concave plastra.

Captive environment: The natural habitat of this strange turtle includes slowly moving blackwater streams and oxbows, marshes, and forest pools. It hardly ever leaves the water and is not known to engage in basking. It spends most of its time resting quietly on the bottom. It also appears to be a very poor swimmer, and is usually found in water sufficiently shallow to permit it to extend its nares above water to breathe. It does not usually actively seek out prey, but instead lies in wait. Its unusual outline and a tendency to become covered in algae assist its camouflage in this respect. Prey is vacuumed into the mouth rather than bitten or grasped directly. Water temperatures for the Matamata should be maintained in the region of 24 - 27°C and pH should be adjusted to 6.5 - 6.8 (or lower, if necessary) as this species has a very poor reaction to alkaline water conditions. Water depth must be carefully selected to permit breathing. Juveniles are particularly poor swimmers and will drown if the water is excessively deep.

Diet: In the wild, the diet of the Matamata is believed to consist mainly of small fish and aquatic invertebrates. In captivity it will usually accept chopped fish and meats, although some keepers have stated that it expresses a strong preference for live food. Matamata that refuse to feed can sometimes be tempted with live goldfish, even when other fish are refused.

Common health problems: Skin disorders if pH out of range. Abrasions from rough tank surfaces.

Breeding: *C. fimbriatus* is rarely bred in captivity. Mating takes place only occasionally, is not often observed and may occur at night, as does most feeding activity. Male and female can, however, be maintained together in the same tank and aggression is not generally a problem. A clutch usually consists of 10 - 30 (usually 15 - 20) spherical hard-shelled eggs measuring approximately 35 mm in diameter and which weigh approximately 30 grams. Matamata eggs should be incubated lightly buried in a moist peat and vermiculite substrate as an acidic medium (pH 6 or below) is required in order to facilitate bio-erosion of the shell. Eggs incubated on a neutral substrate tend to develop full term, but the embryos often die in the egg before hatching. Even at high temperatures (31 - 32°C) *C. fimbriatus* eggs develop slowly and 200 to 270 days before hatching is not atypical. No data on the sex determination method of this species is available. Hatchling Matamata measure 40 - 45mm SCL and weigh approximately 15 g.

CHELYDRA SERPENTINA (Linnaeus, 1758)

Common Snapping turtle

General observations: A widely distributed, hardy and frequently highly aggressive turtle of formidable appearance.

Taxonomy: *Chelydra serpentina* belongs to the family *Chelydridae* of which the only other member is *Macroclemys*, the Alligator Snapping turtle. Four subspecies are currently recognised, two of which occur in the United States, the widely distributed *C. serpentina serpentina* and *C. s. osceola* (which is restricted to Florida). There are also two rarely seen South American subspecies, *C. s. rossignonii* and *C. s. acutirostris*.

Description: The carapace is tricarinate and can attain 49.4 cm SCL. The coloration of the carapace is usually a tan brown, but some very much darker specimens are seen. On older animals, the shell is often worn smooth, but on young specimens a pattern of radiating lines on each scute may be visible. The plastron is yellowish or light tan, and is much reduced. The head is enlarged and the jaws are hooked and prominent. When picked up, the snapping turtles typically gape in a threatening manner.

Captive environment: Water depth is important in the successful captive maintenance of snapping turtles. Their preference is for a water level that permits them to remain on the bottom, and yet allows them to raise their nares out of the water to breath. In the wild, snapping turtles inhabit a wide variety of aquatic habitats, from swamps to slow moving streams. *Chelydra serpentina* is also tolerant of varied water chemistry; it occurs in both acidic and alkaline conditions, and is also found in brackish water. In the wild, habitats offering a soft, muddy or sandy bottom and plentiful aquatic vegetation are generally preferred. In captivity, a large well-filtered tank or pool will be required for adult specimens. Breakable electrical heaters should **never** be used in snapper accommodation due to the obvious danger of damage and the possibility of electrocution. Surface mounted ponds have proved very satisfactory. At water temperatures of 20°C and above, *C. serpentina* is very active and will usually feed voraciously. In winter, throughout most of its natural range, it hibernates in the mud at the bottom of its pond although some individuals are known to leave the water in search of a suitable hibernaculum. The author has maintained this species for some years in Britain, and found that in an outdoor pond, hibernation usually commences in late October or November. During hibernation, at 5°C, little or no activity is observed. Activity usually recommences in March or April when water temperatures exceed 8°C. Feeding begins when temperatures exceed 15°C. Basking out of water is infrequent in *Chelydra* although some individuals appear to enjoy this more than others. The author has a large example which regulary basks out of water. Water temperatures in excess of 25°C are also not usually welcomed. Small specimens can be safely over wintered indoors in a heated tank. Snapping turtles are capable of inflicting serious injuries, and should be handled with extreme care.

Diet: *Chelydra serpentina* is by nature highly carnivorous, but also consumes some aquatic plants. Birds, snakes, frogs, toads, small mammals and numerous small aquatic creatures feature regularly on its natural menu - as do many smaller turtles. For this reason, *Chelydra* should not be maintained in mixed collections. Large *Chelydra* are also known to eat smaller specimens of their own kind. In captivity, snapping turtles will accept almost any food item placed in the water. Juveniles will accept earthworms, snails and seem to greatly enjoy trout and koi pellets.

Common health problems: None immediately evident.

Breeding: *Chelydra serpentina* lays clutches consisting of 6 to over 100 eggs, but 20 to 30 is a more typical figure. Only one clutch is normally laid per season. The eggs are spherical and measure 21 - 35 mm in diameter. Newly laid eggs are semi-pliable and feature a large air-sac. Natural incubation ranges from 55 to 130 days, but this depends greatly upon locality. Successful incubation can occur at temperatures from 20 - 31°C, with lower temperatures producing extended incubation periods. At 28°C hatching can be anticipated in 60 - 65 days. A high humidity (90%) incubation environment is recommended for this species. A 1:1

Index of Plates: Left to Right, Top to Bottom

- North African pond habitat of *Mauremys leprosa*.
- Rainforest pools are popular habitats for many species of aquatic turtle.
- A rich covering of ephemeral flowers is an important seasonal feature of this tortoise habitat in North Africa.
- Typical Mediterannean scrub habitat as favoured by *Testudo hermanni* and *T. marginata*
- Fitzroy River, N. W. Australia. Habitat for *Emydura* and *Elseya* spp. (© John Dickson)
- Semi-arid desert habitat of *Testudo graeca graeca* in southern Morocco. In marginal habitats such as this, the presence of a few key plant species, such as *Euphorbia*, is critical to the tortoises survival.

Index of Plates: Left to Right, Top to Bottom

- Vivarium accommodation featuring full-spectrum tubes and a basking lamp.
- Outdoor accommodation designed to provide a near-natural habitat for temperate species. Note protective netting to prevent escapes and reduce predator danger.
- Outdoor housing for Mediterranean tortoises with natural grazing area and overnight accommodation.
- One of the tropical houses at the Tortoise Trust. Note angled roof to maximise solar gain.
- Some species will require special micro-habitats, such as these Pancake tortoises.
- The type of substrate and plant cover provided in captivity is very important to the well-being of almost all tortoises and turtles. Here, an artificial damp 'woodland' has been constructed for this North American box turtle colony.

Index of Plates: Left to Right, Top to Bottom

- Alfalfa (Lucerne) pellets can make an effective and safe substrate for vivaria.
- This indoor African-style garden, designed to accommodate a breeding group of Leopard tortoises, is a fine example of what private keepers can achieve (© Donald Peterson).
- A surface-mounted indoor pond for Asiatic turtles. An undergravel filter maintains water quality whilst heat is provided by means of wall-mounted radiators and submerged aquarium heaters.
- Plants are important in the aquatic environment and can make a major contribution to overall water quality. They also provide shelter and enhance visual appeal.
- Easy access to and from the water is vital. Partly submerged logs will also be employed for basking.
- In outdoor ponds, well-positioned rocks will find great favour with turtles seeking prime basking sites.

Index of Plates: Left to Right, Top to Bottom

- Selecting the correct water depth is a vital part of planning any aquatic turtle accommodation. Water that is too shallow is often more hazardous than water which is deeper than necessary.
- Shallow wading ponds are required by many semi-terrestrial species (*Terrapene ornata*).
- Water quality test kits are available to assess many different variables.
- Undergravel filters have proved of the most effective means of ensuring water quality.
- Many aquatic species are highly aggressive and care needs to be taken if different species are mixed within the same accommodation. Softshell and Snapping turtles are especially problematic in this regard.
- With good design, near natural environments can be provided for aquatic turtles (Frankfurt Zoo).

Index of Plates: Left to Right, Top to Bottom

- A mating pair of Redfoot tortoises (*Geochelone carbonaria*).
- A mating pair of Egyptian tortoises (*Testudo kleinmanni*).
- A female Radiated tortoise (*Asterochelys/Geochelone radiata*) deposits her eggs (© R. D. Bartlett)
- Note expansion of the cloaca as this Egyptian tortoise deposits an egg which, in relation to her body size, is extremely large. Small species tend to have fewer, but relatively larger, eggs.
- A partly developed tortoise embryo at 5 weeks.
- Following initial 'pipping', the neonate may remain within the egg for many hours, or even days.

Index of Plates: Left to Right, Top to Bottom

- An electronic temperature probe, leading to a digital thermometer, is positioned as closely as possible to the incubating clutch.
- A soft-shelled aquatic turtle egg hatches. The yolk-sac is clearly visible. This will be more fully absorbed before the neonate finally leaves the egg.
- The egg caruncle is clearly visible on the newly-hatched turtle.
- In the wild, juveniles are highly vulnerable to predators. The camouflage of this neonate *Kinixys homeana* is well suited to a life in the fallen leaves of the forest carpet.
- At 4.5 grams, this neonate *Testudo kleinmanni* is one of the smallest species at hatching.
- Hatching *Asterochelys/Geochelone radiata,* the Radiated tortoise (© R. D. Bartlett).

Index of Plates: Left to Right, Top to Bottom

- Albino *Testudo graeca graeca.*
- Two *Testudo kleinmanni* in the process of hatching.
- Neonate *Pyxidea mouhotti* (© R. D. Bartlett)
- Nutrition is critically important to juveniles. Here, captive-bred *Testudo (graeca) ibera* are provided with a 'natural' graze area to replicate as closely as possible their wild food intake. A calcium and D3 supplement is also provided.
- A neonate *Testudo marginata* takes its first steps after leaving the egg.
- Juvenile Galapagos tortoises at the Charles Darwin Research Station on Santa Cruz.

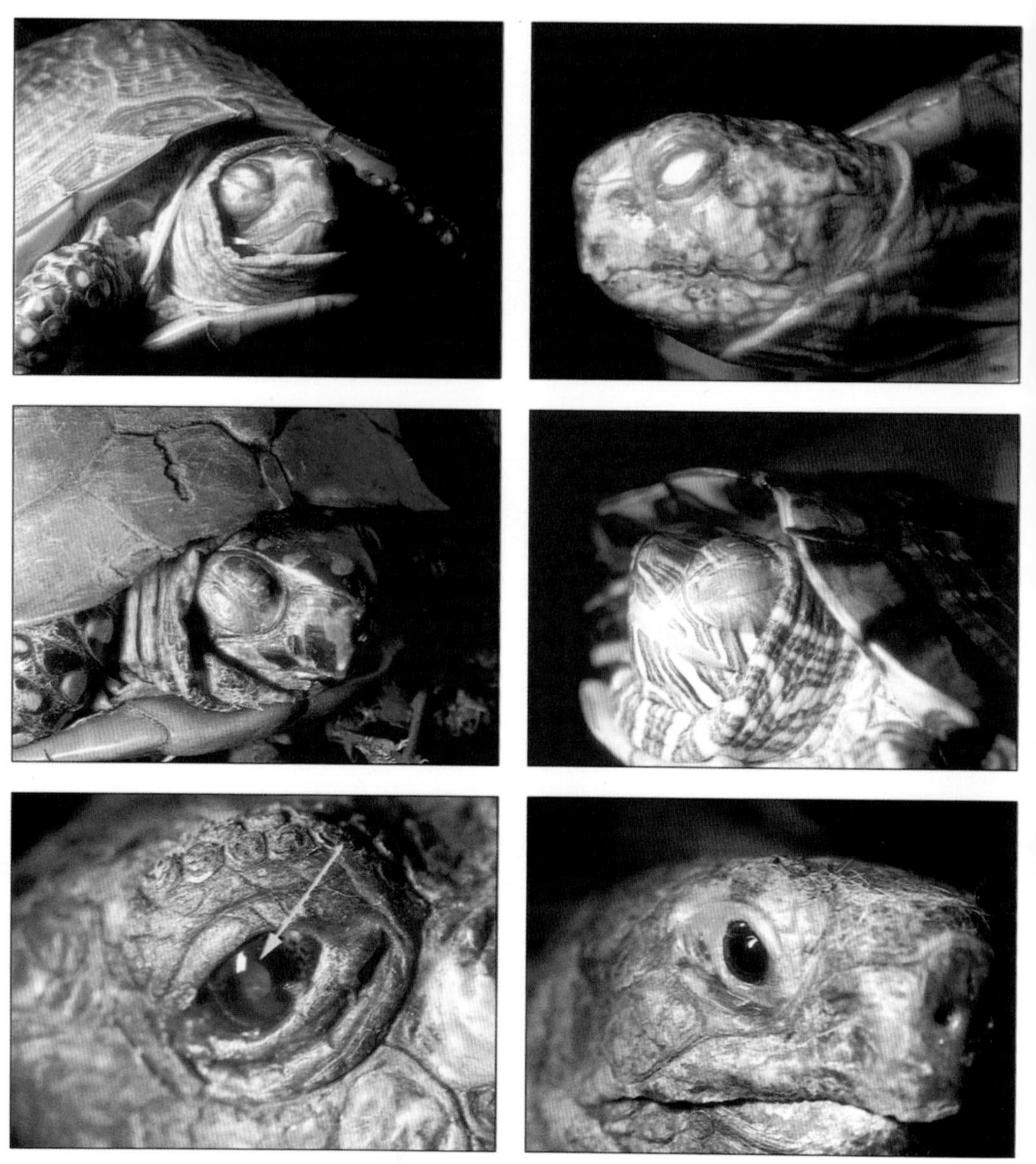

Index of Plates: Left to Right, Top to Bottom

- American box turtle with classic symptoms of swollen eyes. This condition usually responds to antibiotic therapy and improved environmental management.
- Severe eye infection in a *Testudo graeca.* A thick film of infected tissue is present.
- Swollen eyes in box turtles often occur in association with ear or mouth infections.
- In terrapins, swollen eyes are often the result of a vitamin-A deficiency or poor water hygiene.
- The opaque white disk at the rear of the lens, visible in this *Testudo graeca*, is the result of frost damage in hibernation. The tortoise is rendered blind and refuses to feed. Some cases make a full recovery, although this can take several years. Assist feeding is required in the meantime.
- The yellow tissue visible here is the result of extreme age and does not require therapy.

Index of Plates: Left to Right, Top to Bottom

- Ear abscess, American box turtle.
- Ear abscess, Red-eared slider.
- Perforated, solidified ear abscess, *Testudo graeca*. In all cases, surgical removal is required. Reptilian abscesses rarely respond to systemic therapy alone.
- Severe nasal abscess, American box turtle.
- Severe perforated nasal abscess with massive local necrosis, *Testudo graeca*.
- Perforated nasal abscess, *Testudo (g.) ibera*. A discharge of mucus was visible from a 1 mm diameter hole just above this tortoise's left nares. The nares themselves were also slightly distorted by the pressure of the abscess.

Index of Plates: Left to Right, Top to Bottom

- Without question, the most severe ear abscess we have ever encountered. This tortoise made a full recovery following surgery.
- Lesions in the upper palate as a result of a Gram-negative bacterial infection.
- Poor occlusion of the jaws can predispose a tortoise to mouth infections.
- Severe necrotic stomatitis (mouth rot).
- Thick mucus discharge associated with severe pneumonia.
- Overgrown beak, *Testudo hermanni*. Regular beak trimming may be necessary in captive situations.

Index of Plates: Left to Right, Top to Bottom

- 'Dry' shell rot or Septicaemic Cutaneous Ulcerative Disease causing severe necrosis of the bony tissue beneath the scutes.
- 'Wet' shell rot. A foul, bloody discharge is often present.
- Typical site for shell rot. Often follows injuries received during violent courtship, as in this female *Testudo hermanni*.
- Old, non-active minor lesions are often seen. These are sometimes caused by ticks which feed at the softer edges of scutes during growth phases. Provided they do not harbour active pathogens, no treatment is required.
- The region just above the supracaudal scute is the most common site for shell rot.
- Severe crushing injury. This wild tortoise was mobile and feeding despite the massive trauma which must have occurred many months previously, as healing was evident.

Index of Plates: Left to Right, Top to Bottom

- Traffic injured Red-eared slider prior to corrective therapy.
- A completed fibreglass shell repair.
- Most tortoises manage quite well following amputation of a single limb.
- A wheel attached to the plastron provides support and mobility whilst an injured limb heals.
- Massive limb trauma resulting from a rodent attack during hibernation.
- This swollen foot demands investigation. Often the result of a toe-nail becoming detached allowing infection to enter. All swellings should be fully investigated as invariably they denote a problem.

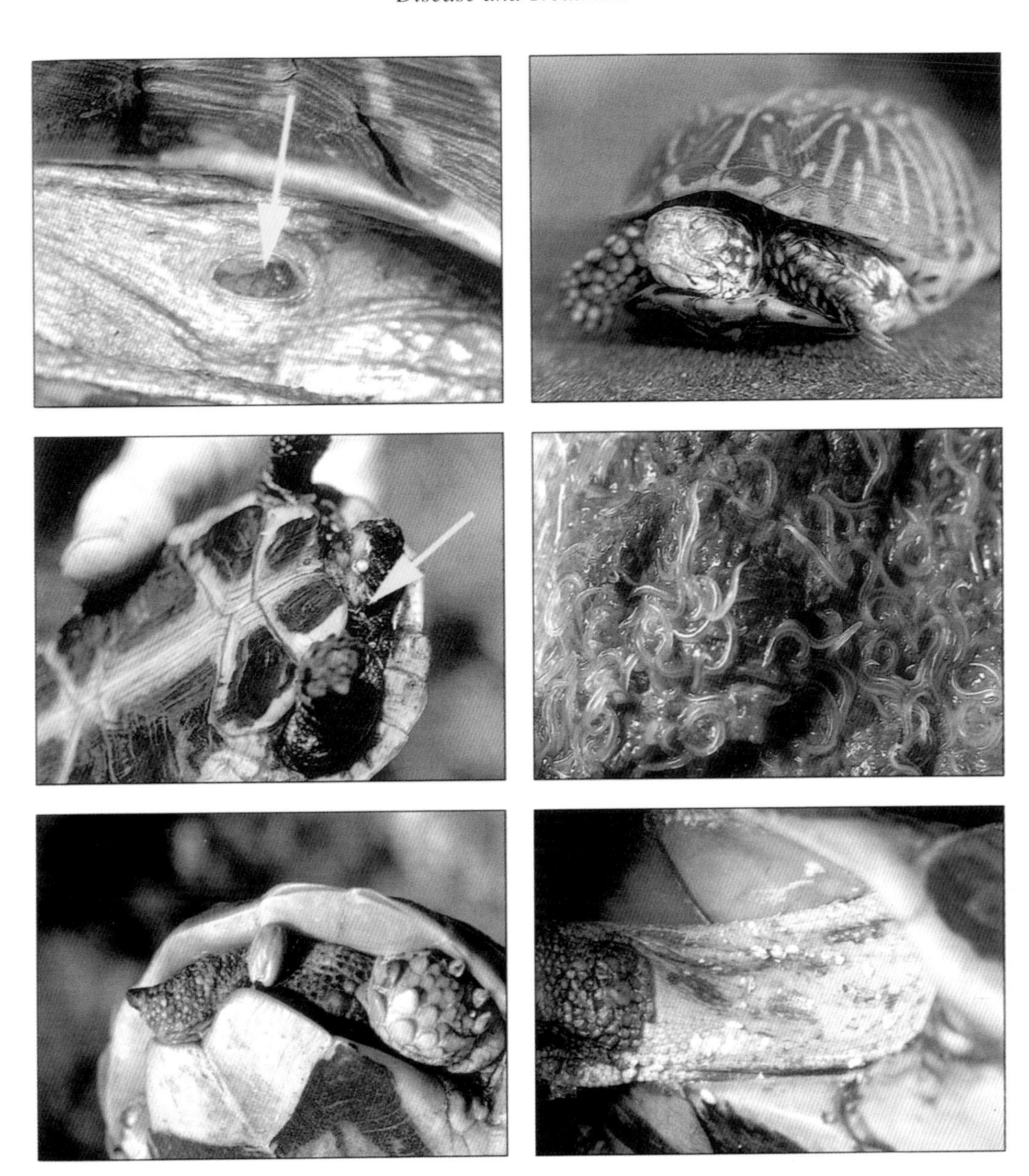

Index of Plates: Left to Right, Top to Bottom

- Bot fly larvae in an Ornate box turtle.
- A dehydrated and evidently very sick Ornate box turtle. Upon investigation, the highly pathogenic organism *Hexamita parva* was discovered in a urine sample.
- Fly strike on the infected tail region of this juvenile *Testudo hermanni hermanni*.
- Nematodes evacuated by a recently imported Pancake tortoise.
- Large ticks are often found on wild tortoises which graze in proximity to sheep, goats or cattle.
- This region of infected skin will rapidly attract the attention of flies. Animals in this condition need to be maintained behind a fly-proof screen during treatment.

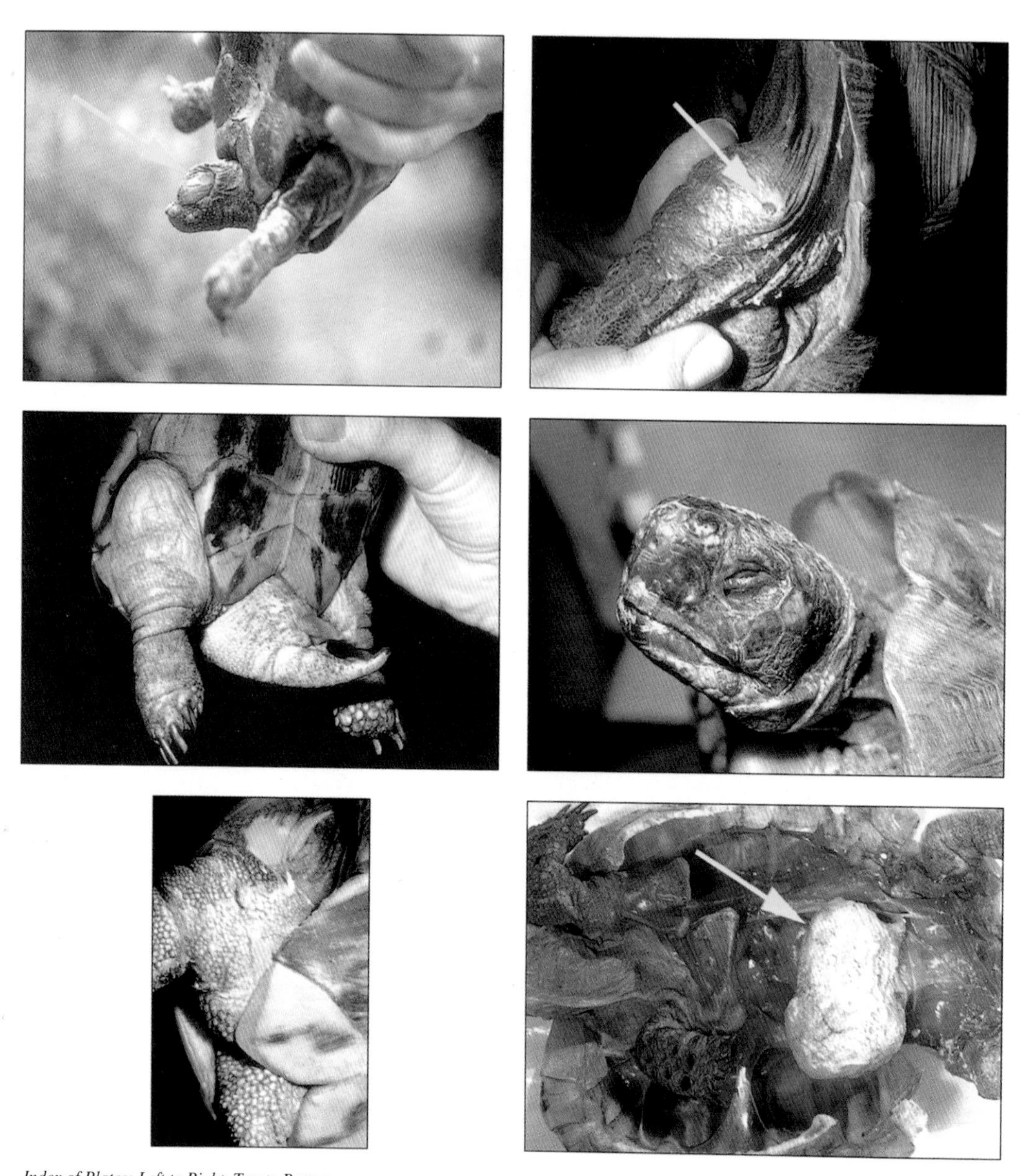

Index of Plates: Left to Right, Top to Bottom

- Cloacal abscess. Common in male tortoises.
- Subcutaneous abscess on a hind limb.
- Tortoise in terminal renal failure with acute oedema.
- Sunken eyes denote acute dehydration.
- Raw and inflamed skin, typical of acute vitamin A deficiency, can also be associated with renal and hepatic disease.
- Massive calculi in the bladder, composed of uric acid. This may result from dehydration, the feeding of a diet excessively rich in protein, the effect of nephrotoxic drugs, or nephrotoxic parasites such as *Hexamita*. The condition is usually terminal, as in this instance.

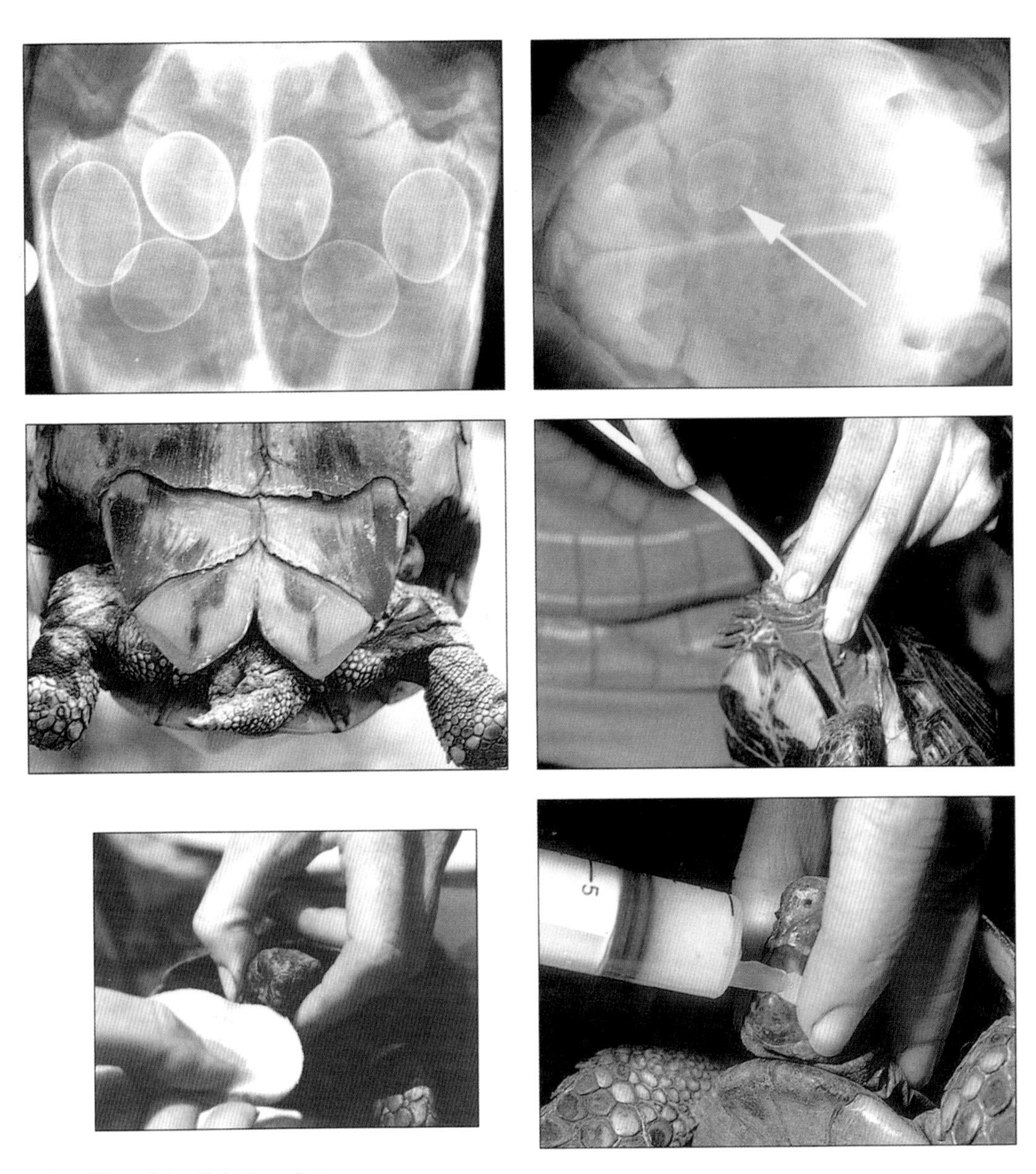

Index of Plates: Left to Right, Top to Bottom

- X-ray image of female carrying a clutch of 6 normal eggs.
- X-ray image of a female with one misshapen, broken egg. This is a serious condition requiring urgent treatment.
- Plastron of a tortoise suffering from acute septicaemia. Subcutaneous haemorrhage is very evident.
- Red marks visible beneath the scutes of the plastron may be the result of simple bruising, but can also indicate the presence of septicaemia.
- Tube-feeding and rehydration technique.
- Syringe-feeding a sick tortoise.

Index of Plates: Left to Right, Top to Bottom

- *Aldabrachelys gigantea*
- *Asterochelys (Geochelone) radiata* (© G. &. A. Beck)
- *Batagur baska* (© R. D. Bartlett)
- *Chelodina oblonga* (© John Dickson)
- *Chelodina siebenrocki* (© R. D. Bartlett)
- *Chersina angulata* (© R. D. Bartlett)

Index of Plates: Left to Right, Top to Bottom

- *Clemmys guttata*
- *Clemmys insculpta* (© R. D. Bartlett)
- *Clemmys muhlenbergii* (© R. D. Bartlett)
- *Cuora amboinensis*
- *Cuora galbifrons*
- *Emydoidea blandingii*

Index of Plates: Left to Right, Top to Bottom

- *Emydura subglobosa* (© R. D. Bartlett)
- *Furculachelys whitei* (left) and *F. nabeulensis* (right). Both fully grown adult specimens.
- *Geochelone carbonaria*
- *Geochelone chilensis*
- *Geochelone pardalis babcocki*
- *Geochelone sulcata*

Index of Plates: Left to Right, Top to Bottom

- *Geoemyda spengleri spengleri* (© R. D. Bartlett)
- *Gopherus agassizii*
- *Heosemys grandis* (albino) (© R. D. Bartlett)
- *Heosemys spinosa*
- *Homopus areolatus*
- *Hydromedusa tectifera* (© R. D. Bartlett)

Index of Plates: Left to Right, Top to Bottom

- *Indotestudo (Geochelone) elongata*
- *Indotestudo forsteni* (© Dr. Indraneil Das)
- *Kachuga tecta* (© R. D. Bartlett)
- *Kinixys belliana*
- *Kinixys erosa*
- *Kinosternon odoratus*

Index of Plates: Left to Right, Top to Bottom

- *Kinosternon bauri*
- *Malaclemys terrapin*
- *Manouria emys emys*
- *Manouria impressa*
- *Mauremys caspica*
- *Mauremys nigricans*

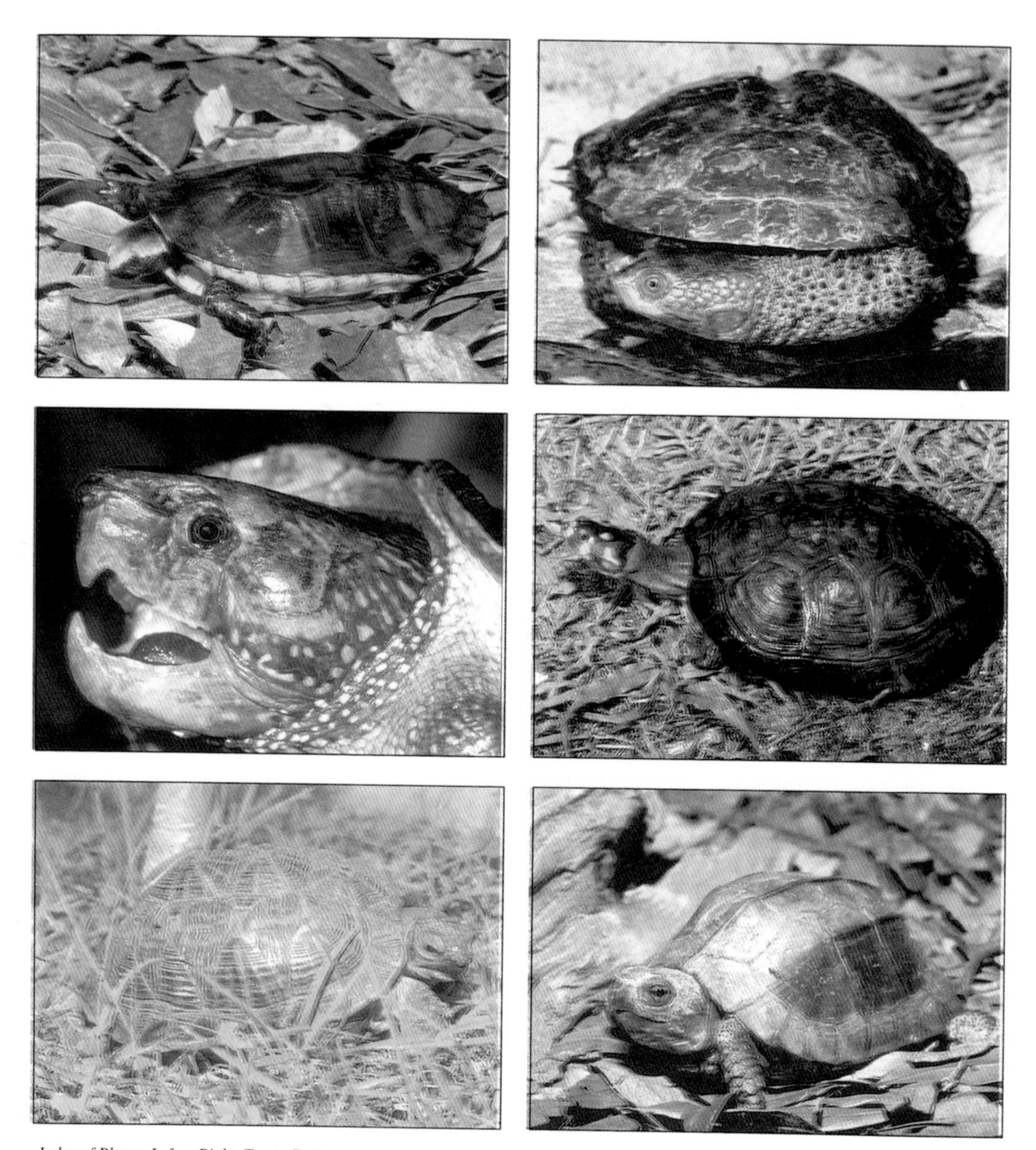

Index of Plates: Left to Right, Top to Bottom

- *Platemys platycephala* (© R. D. Bartlett)
- *Platemys spixii* (© R. D. Bartlett)
- *Platysternon megacephalum*
- *Podocnemis unifilis* (© R. D. Bartlett)
- *Psammobates tentorius veroxi* (© R. D. Bartlett)
- *Pyxidea mouhotti* (© R. D. Bartlett)

Index of Plates: Left to Right, Top to Bottom

- *Rhinoclemmys pulcherrima*
- *Siebenrockiella crassicollis* (© R. D. Bartlett)
- *Terrapene carolina triunguis*
- *Terrapene ornata*
- *Testudo (graeca) ibera*
- Proposed sub-species*Testudo (graeca) anamurensis*. Photographed at the type locality.

Index of Plates: Left to Right, Top to Bottom

- Unusual yellow variant of *Testudo (g.) ibera* race in Antakya, southern Turkey.
- *Testudo hermanni boettgeri*
- *Testudo horsfieldi*
- *Testudo marginata*
- *Testudo graeca graeca* from Type locality, Oran, Algeria.

Asterochelys (Geochelone) radiata, the Radiated tortoise. This example demonstrates clear ontogenetic evidence; the carapace pattern is dulled due to age and wear.

Chelus fimbriatus, the Matamata. A unique turtle with a body and head designed to blend in with its environment as an aid to hunting. In captivity, it is very sensitive to water pH and temperature.

Chelydra serpentina, the Common snapping turtle, demonstrates its highly aggressive nature. This turtle is best maintained in a solitary situation. Large specimens should be handled with extreme care.

Chinemys reevesii, the Reeve's or Chinese three-keeled terrapin

mixture of water and vermiculite has proved consistently successful as a substrate. Recent evidence (Miller, 1987) suggests that *C. serpentina* eggs incubated on a damp substrate produce stronger and larger hatchlings than those incubated in drier environments. *C. serpentina* determines sex by temperature, with eggs incubated at 20°C and between 23 - 24°C resulting in exclusively males, those incubated from 21 - 22°C and 25 - 28°C producing both sexes, with those incubated at 29 - 31°C resulting in exclusively female neonates.

CHERSINA ANGULATA (Schweigger, 1812)

The Angulate tortoise

General observations: The Angulate tortoise is infrequently encountered in captive collections outside southern Africa, but is relatively easy to manage and breed.

Taxonomy: *Chersina* is a monotypic genus. Although *C. angulata* display regional colour and other morphological variations, no subspecies are currently recognised.

Description: Notable features include prominently patterned marginals, the extended gular, narrow nuchal and red tinted plastron. The carapace is elongate and its ground colour is typically red-brown to brown-black. The costals and vertebrals feature a dark centre surrounded by a yellow or red-orange outer ring. Males of this species are larger than females, typically attaining 200 mm or more whilst females rarely exceed 160 mm.

Captive environment: Generally as for *G. pardalis*. During cold weather, an indoor area with adequate heating will be required. Preferred temperature for activity is the region of 22 to 25°C. Activity ceases below about 17°C or above 28°C.

Diet: Essentially herbivorous, but has been observed opportunistically feeding on carrion and also consumes snail shells (possibly as an additional source of calcium). *Chersina angulata* is also coprophagous to varying degrees both in the wild and in captivity. An appropriate captive diet is as recommended for *T. graeca*, *T. hermanni* and *G. pardalis*, etc.

Common health problems: None immediately evident.

Breeding: In the wild, courtship of *Chersina angulata* generally takes place between September and January. At this time the males become restless and mutually aggressive to an unusual degree - battles with the objective of overturning one another with their pronounced gulars are commonplace. As with *Testudo ibera*, males repeatedly butt females and bite at their legs. Females typically lay single eggs measuring approximately 35 x 38 mm and weigh 25 - 30 grams, but occasionally two are deposited simultaneously. Females may lay several nests per year; up to 7 have been recorded. The interval between clutches varies, but is usually between 28 - 45 days. Incubation is best accomplished in a static air incubator at moderate levels of humidity (60 - 65%) as employed for *T. graeca* and *G. pardalis*; if incubated at 30°C hatching typically occurs in about 90 - 100 days. The hatchlings frequently remain in the egg for several days following initial pipping. At lower temperatures the time taken is extended considerably; the eggs can still remain viable at only 21°C but at this temperature can take 12 months to hatch and embryonic mortality increases. The hatchlings measure approximately 35mm long and weigh about 14 grams.

CHINEMYS REEVESII (Gray, 1831)

Reeve's terrapin or Chinese three-keeled pond turtle

General observations: A robust emydid turtle, widely distributed in Asia and frequently maintained by enthusiast keepers.

Taxonomy: No subspecies are currently recognised, but *C. reevesii* is subject to notable geographic variation affecting both size and markings. Reeve's terrapins from Taiwan, for example, often feature more neck stripes than those seen in other populations.

Description: SCL to 24 cm, but typically much smaller (most specimens encountered are less than 150mm). Body slightly depressed, carapace features 3 well-defined median keels. The overall carapace colour is dark brown. Occasionally black specimens are encountered (Mao, 1971) but some of these may represent elderly melanistic animals. There is also a tendency for males to be more melanistic than females, but this should not be considered reliably diagnostic of gender. A more reliable dimorphic character is extended tail length and the presence of a slight plastral depression in males but not in females. The plastron is yellowish with black markings. The skin is usually olive on the limbs and tail but greyish brown with yellow stripes on the neck and head.

Captive environment: Reeve's terrapins are intelligent and popular pets in many countries. They reproduce and feed readily in captivity. A suitable water temperature range is 23.5°C to 16°C, seasonally varied. Typical active temperature range is 20 - 21°C. A basking source is essential and is best positioned above a partly submerged log or over the land area. Chromalux® lighting has proved very successful with this species. As an alternative, a normal incandescent lamp plus a full spectrum tube is recommended. For filtration, large external canister filters with foam inserts have proved sufficient. This terrapin can do well in mixed species collections and is often maintained in outdoor ponds, at least when weather permits. Naturally, it occurs in shallow streams, swamps and ponds.

Diet: Omnivorous. Aquatic plants, aquatic insects, larvae, fish and small crustacea form the bulk of the natural diet. In captivity, Reeve's turtles usually feed well and will accept a varied diet. Overfeeding should be avoided, however, as *C. reevesii* has a voracious appetite.

Common health problems: None immediately evident.

Breeding: The eggs of this species are of variable dimensions, between 33 - 44 mm long and 19 - 23 mm in diameter. Incubated at 28 - 29°C in a 90% humidity environment (on damp vermiculite) hatching typically occurs between 65 - 90 days. The juveniles measure approximately 29 mm long and weigh about 6 grams. Females may have as many of 4 clutches a year, each clutch typically comprising between 4 - 9 eggs. Large females tend to have higher clutch densities than smaller specimens. Males tend toward mutual aggressiveness and may require accommodating separately if injuries are to be avoided.

CHRYSEMYS PICTA (Schneider, 1783)

The Painted turtle

General observations: The only North American turtle that occurs from coast to coast. It is also found from Canada to Mexico.

Taxonomy: Four subspecies are currently recognised; *C. p. picta* (Eastern Painted turtle), *C. p. marginata* (Midland Painted turtle), *C. p. dorsalis* (Southern Painted turtle) and *C. p. bellii* (the Western Painted turtle).

Description: SCL to 25 cm, marginals not posteriorly serrated. Carapace olive to black with yellow or red borders to the scute sutures and additional red markings on the marginals. The skin of the neck, legs and tail is striped with red and yellow. The head carries a yellow stripe behind the eye, and the chin also features two wide yellow stripes.

Captive environment: Naturally inhabits shallow ponds, bogs, marshes and slow moving streams. This species sleeps underwater at night, resting on the bottom, and during the day can frequently be seen basking in groups on logs or upon partly submerged branches. Painted turtles hibernate under the ice in winter. Water temperature in captivity should be seasonally adjusted to replicate that in the wild. Feeding only occurs when temperatures exceed 15°C. *C. picta* will live and breed well in tanks, but outdoor ponds are much preferred. Juveniles can be successfully reared and maintained with water temperatures in the 25 - 28°C range.

Diet: Omnivorous, feeding upon aquatic plants, small fish, crustacea, insect larvae and carrion. Juveniles are considerably more carnivorous than adults.

Common health problems: None immediately evident.

Breeding: This species breeds easily in captivity. Best results are usually obtained either by hibernating animals or conditioning them by providing a torpid period during January and February where water temperatures are maintained at 10°C. Sexual maturity occurs at about 8 cm carapace length in the case of males and at 11 cm in the case of females. Eggs measure approximately 33 mm x 20 mm and weigh about 8 g. The precise dimensions may vary considerably according to subspecies or the age and size of the female. Clutch density also varies geographically, and ranges from 2 - 7 (*C. p. dorsalis*) to 20 or more (*C. p. bellii*). Most females deposit between 2 to 3 clutches per season. Incubated at 27 - 28°C on a damp vermiculite (1:1 water and substrate) at a relative humidity of 90% plus hatching can be expected in about 55 to 80 days. Early research on ESD (Environmental Sex Determination) was conducted on this species and revealed that incubation temperatures of 27°C produced all male offspring, and those of 30 - 32°C resulted in all females. Both sexes result when the eggs are incubated at either 20°C or 28°C. If incubated at a constant 28°C hatching typically occurs in 52 - 58 days. The juveniles measure approximately 27 mm SCL and in the wild, late hatchlings over winter in the nest, not emerging to feed until the following spring. *C. picta* hatchlings are known to survive subzero temperatures and cellular freezing for extended periods under natural conditions when overwintering - they are the only species so far known to possess this ability.

CLEMMYS GUTTATA (Schneider, 1792)

The Spotted turtle

General observations: A highly attractive North American emydid turtle of semi-aquatic habits.

Taxonomy: Geographic variation has been noted, but no subspecies have been proposed at the time of writing.

Description: Carapace colour black, with bright yellow spots. These spots are actually transparent holes in the black pigmentation allowing a yellow ground colour to show through. The species takes its name from their distinctive appearance. Maximum SCL to 12. 5 cm, females on average being larger than males. Colour in *C. guttata* is sexually dichromatic. Females have yellow chins and orange eyes; males have light brown chins and brown eyes.

Captive environment: These turtles are highly active at water temperatures in the region of 22°C and can be over wintered at such temperatures if desired. However, for breeding, a more natural cycle is preferable in which case a winter rest period can be given by lowering temperatures to approximately 10°C or less. Copulation has been recorded in this species at unusually low temperatures and activity may be observed even at temperatures that would induce hibernation in other species. *C. guttata* generally does well in outdoor ponds, where they will catch much of their own food for themselves and will take every opportunity to bask in the sun. A land area should be provided, and so much the better if this is well planted. In very hot weather *C. guttata* becomes inactive and may retreat to the cover offered by whatever plants the land section has to offer. In nature, *C. guttata* inhabits a wide range of shallow water environments including marshes, ponds, streams and bogs. A soft substrate is essential, as is good aquatic plant cover.

Diet: Omnivorous, but with a marked preference for animal food. Plant matter may rarely be accepted but should still be offered. Some captives will accept fruit in preference to green leaf material. Earthworms, slugs, small snails, beetles, meal worms and small fish are taken with relish.

Common health problems: None immediately evident.

Breeding: The eggs of *C. guttata* measure approximately 29mm long x 16mm diameter with a mass of 5 - 6 g. A typical clutch comprises 4 eggs, although exceptionally may number up to 8. Females may lay up to 3 clutches per season, more typically 1 or 2. Preferred nesting sites include sandy loam. Gravid females may be active after dark when egg deposition may occur. Freshly laid eggs may be indented, but these usually disappear as development commences. Incubated in damp vermiculite at a temperature of 27 - 28°C hatching can occur in 60 - 70 days. At 29 - 30°C the incubation period is typically reduced to 45 - 55 days. Eggs incubated in the temperature range 22.5°C to 27°C result in males, but those incubated at 30°C result in all female offspring. The hatchlings are approximately 28 mm in length and weigh approximately 4.5 grams. They should be housed in a terrarium giving sufficient water depth for swimming, with a ramp for easy access and exit. A high level of ambient humidity is critical to the successful rearing of *C. guttata*; a terrarium that includes a peat and sphagnum moss bog type habitat is therefore highly recommended. Juveniles are initially almost exclusively carnivorous, most accepting only small items of live prey. Sexual maturity is attained in 7 - 10 years, or as carapace length reaches 8 cm.

CLEMMYS INSCULPTA (LeConte, 1830)
The Wood turtle

General observations: The Wood turtle is popularly kept in its native United States, but is rarely seen in European collections where it is highly prized. This species has experienced serious decline in the wild and is now legally protected.

Taxonomy: Although geographical variation has been noted, to date no subspecies have been described.

Description: The Wood turtle is a medium sized emydid of 12 - 23 cm carapace length. The carapace is brown coloured and is low and broad, the individual scutes being sculptured, from which feature it derives its scientific name. The plastron is yellow with a series of dark markings at the periphery, adjacent to the marginals. The head and neck may feature red or orange coloration.

Captive environment: This turtle is semi-terrestrial and spends quite a high proportion of its time out of water, especially during wet and humid weather. This is also a very active turtle that should be provided with adequate space in both its land and aquatic habitats. An ideal captive habitat for this species would consist of a large outdoor pen, well planted, but also offering adequate unobstructed basking positions, with a well-filtered sunken pond of about 300 mm depth. It is extremely important to note that *C. insculpta* is principally associated with moving water habitats; it is rarely found in static water ponds or streams. For this reason, a high flow-rate pump and filter system is strongly recommended if its natural preferences are to be accommodated. The entire area must be completely escape-proofed as *C. insculpta* is particularly agile and is an excellent climber. Pea gravel overlaid with sphagnum moss has been found to provide an excellent substrate in *C. insculpta* (and *C. guttata*) ponds. In the wild, *C. insculpta* hibernates in winter. In captivity, a deep leaf litter pile situated on easily excavated earth makes a suitable hibernaculum. Alternatively, this turtle can be artificially hibernated in the same way as box turtles of the genus *Terrapene*. Temperatures for hibernation should be as close to 5°C as practicable. In some localities, over wintering indoors may be preferable.

Diet: Omnivorous. In the wild the diet of *C. insculpta* includes a wide variety of aquatic and terrestrial insects, snails, slugs, earthworms, tadpoles, blackberries, filamentous algae (*Chlorophyta*), sorrel, willow leaves and any available carrion. This species is believed by many to indulge in a strange behaviour known as "worm stomping" where the turtle impacts the ground with the front feet in an attempt to drive worms from cover. The Wood turtle is certainly a highly intelligent creature and watching them it is not difficult to conclude that such a feat may indeed be possible. In captivity, Wood turtles readily accept a wide range of green vegetation and fruit. Low fat dog food and reyhdrated dried cat pellets soaked in extra minerals should also be offered. In a well-planted outdoor habitat, however, *C. insculpta* should be able to obtain a high proportion of its dietary requirements by natural means. To encourage insects, worms and slugs a few slates or tiles can be laid upon the ground, watered regularly, and turned over from time to time. The turtle will quickly learn to anticipate the meal shortly to follow.

Common health problems: None immediately evident.

Breeding: Hibernation is recommended if *C. insculpta* are to breed in captivity. Mating usually follows shortly after emergence, or as water temperatures exceed 15°C. Males are mutually aggressive at this time of year, and it may be necessary to separate them from their fellows to prevent serious injuries. A second period of Autumnal mating also occurs in many areas throughout their range. Mating typically takes place in water. Normally, one clutch of between 5 - 18 (typically 7 - 9) eggs are laid per year, usually in April, May or June. A sandy loam is preferred for nest excavation. The eggs are elliptical and measure approximately 40 mm x 26 mm with a mass of about 13 g. Incubation in the wild is typically in the region of 50 - 60 days followed by a further period of between 7 and 10 days buried in the nest before final emergence. In captivity, incubation in a moderately high (80%) humidity environment at 27 - 28°C has produced consistently high hatch rates in about 45 to 50 days. It should be noted that incubation times with this species are very variable (which suggests they may be capable of diapause) - some examples have taken in excess of 10 months to leave the nest. Of critical importance is that *C. insculpta* does not employ Temperature Dependent Sex Determination, but instead relies upon chromosomes. The neonates measure approximately 34 mm in length and must be maintained in a high humidity environment. We find covered plastic plant propagators ideal - these can readily be adapted to provide both a water and land environment. As with other members of the *Clemmys* group, dehydration is an ever present danger to neonates and juveniles. Initially, hatchlings are exclusively carnivorous and most will only accept live animal food. Meal worms, small earthworms, insect larvae and small crustacea are preferred items by many. Juveniles are grey-brown in colour and lack the red or orange head and neck markings of adults. Sexual maturity is attained in about 12 to 15 years under natural conditions but may be achieved in as little as 4 to 5 years in captivity.

CLEMMYS MUHLENBERGI I (Schoepff, 1801)

The Bog turtle

General observations: Legally protected and considered threatened throughout most of its natural range due to drainage of sphagnaceous bogs and swamps. The subject of several zoo captive breeding projects and conservation plans. The rarest North American emydid. Although few keepers will actually encounter *C. muhlenbergii*, its captive maintenance and breeding is very representative of all bog and marsh dwelling turtles.

Taxonomy: No subspecies have so far been described.

Description: Average SCL 8 cm, maximum recorded size 11 cm. The carapace is light brown to red-brown-black, and each scute features a yellow centre. A dorsal keel is present. The plastron is dark brown-black with irregular lighter markings. The marginals are only slightly serrated or smooth. The most distinctive feature is an orange, red or yellow patch on temporal region of head often extending into the skin of the neck. The skin of the limbs is brown and often features red or orange spotting.

Captive environment: Most successful programs (e.g. Herman, 1990; Tyron and Hulsey, 1977) rely upon attempts to replicate natural bog-type habitats. This entails not only planting the enclosure and pond with appropriate species, but also requires great attention to substrates and ensuring a constant trickle of freshwater flow through the habitat. In the water section, a pea-gravel substrate under a 15 cm deep peat and sphagnum moss layer has proved very effective; this general concept is also ideal for other bog-dwelling species. Water depth is usually maintained in the 5 - 8 cm region above the peat and sphagnum layer. The entire habitat can be constructed within large metal or fibreglass agricultural tanks. Another option involves the use of large diameter concrete sewer pip sections, surface mounted. For maximum activity, water temperatures of approximately 23°C are suggested for indoor enclosures. In outdoor enclosures, *C. muhlenbergii* will remain active at quite low temperatures, especially on sunny days when basking is possible. In the wild, this turtle hibernates from mid-autumn to April. In dry summer weather they may aestivate.

Diet: Omnivorous. In the wild the diet of the Bog turtle includes insects, insect larvae, aquatic plants, berries and snails. In captivity, most will feed readily upon prepared foods but in a suitable enclosure (as with American box turtles) they should be able to obtain a high percentage of their dietary requirements by natural means. Supplementary feeding may be required two or three times per week as necessary and this presents an opportunity to provide a multi-vitamin and mineral additive. This species feeds both in and out of the water, although in-water feeding is much more common.

Common health problems: None immediately evident.

Breeding: Mating almost always occurs in the water, with the pair completely submerged. Eggs are usually deposited in the sphagnum layer of enclosures, with clutches comprising between 2 - 6 eggs measuring approximately 30 mm x 16 mm with a mass of 5 grams.

Incubated at an average temperature of 28°C, hatching typically occurs in approximately 40 - 50 days. Unfortunately, it is not presently known what sex determination method is employed by Bog turtles. A high humidity incubation environment is required for this species, however, and an incubation substrate of moist vermiculite and sphagnum moss has proved consistently effective. Neonates measure approximately 26 mm SCL and must be accommodated in a high humidity environment - a miniature artificial bog is recommended by most experienced breeders. This can be constructed by allowing peat and sphagnum moss to sink naturally onto a layer of pea gravel in a small aquarium (this normally takes at least 7 days) driven by an under-gravel filter and air-lift. For neonates, a water depth of 25 - 35 mm above the peat layer is recommended. Juveniles are most active, and feed with enthusiasm if maintained at ambient temperatures in the 24 - 25°C range together with additional basking facilities.

CUORA AMBOINENSIS (Daudin, 1802)

Malayan box turtle

General observations: South-east Asian box turtles of the genus *Cuora* are semi-aquatic and inhabit marshes, flooded rice paddies and slow moving streams. *C. amboinensis* is among the more terrestrial members of the genus.

Taxonomy: Three subspecies have recently been detailed (Rummler and Fritz, 1991); *Cuora amboinensis cuoro* from Java, Sumatra and Indonesia; *C. a. kamaroma* from Borneo, north-east India and Bangladesh and the nominate race *C. a. amboinensis* from the Philippines, Sulawesi and the Moluccan islands. There are marked differences in carapace shape between animals of different geographical origin. *C. a. amboinensis* from Sulawesi typically have a very round carapace; by contrast, other specimens from Indonesia have an elongate and shallow carapace.

Other members of the genus *Cuora* include *Cuora flavomarginata* from south China, *Cuora galbifrons* from Vietnam and Hainan Island, *Cuora trifasciata* from Vietnam and south China, *Cuora hainanensis* from Hainan Island, *Cuora pani* from Shaanxi in China, *Cuora yunnanensis* from Yunnan, China, *Cuora mccordi* from Kwangsi, China and *Cuora chriskarannarum* also from Yunnan in China. These species demonstrate considerable variety in coloration, markings and size. Captive maintenance is similar to *C. amboinensis,* however.

Description: Carapace to approximately 20 cm, but typically 15 - 17 cm. Ground colour dark brown to black without distinctive markings. Posterior marginals slightly flared, not serrated. Plastron colouration ranges from yellow to brown. Hinged, allowing complete closure as in American *Terrapene* species. The head is pointed, with yellow stripes on an olive-brown background. The skin of the lower jaw and chin is yellow.

Captive environment: Suggested water temperature range 24 - 26°C. Most *Cuora* species prefer shallow water and require constant access to a land area. *Cuora amboinensis* basks occasionally. It normally thrives in either aquarium tanks or indoor ponds. A relatively robust and adaptable species in captivity. Other members of the genus can be maintained in similar conditions, although some, such as *C. galbifrons*, are more terrestrial in habits. In all cases, air temperatures in the terrarium should be maintained above 28°C and the ambient humidity should also be very high. *Cuora flavomarginata* appears to be considerably more delicate than *C. amboinensis* and is very susceptible to respiratory and parasitic diseases if the environment is not maintained within the suggested guidelines.

Diet: Omnivorous, with a predilection for vegetable matter. A captive specimen maintained by the author grazes on new grass shoots, dandelion and assorted weeds which grow in the vicinity of its pond. This turtle will also take earthworms, slugs, small beetles and snails. Fruit is also accepted, as is tinned dog food - both of which are offered in small quantities. Most feeding occurs out of water. *C. trifasciata* exhibits a preference for fish and tends to feed in the water, however.

Common health problems: Pneumonia; liver disease due to parasitism and poor dietary management.

Breeding: Males are mutually highly aggressive, sometimes inflicting serious injuries, and females may also be attacked - neck biting during mating is common in all species and may result in quite unpleasant wounds. A typical clutch comprises two large eggs measuring up to 52 mm long x 30 mm (exceptionally, 33 mm) in diameter. It also appears that egg dimensions may vary seasonally from the same female. Females normally lay 3 to 4 clutches per year and eggs are normally deposited between 35 - 50 days after mating. Incubated between 28 - 30°C at 95% to 100% humidity, hatching usually occurs in 70 - 85 days. Juveniles measure approximately 43 mm in length and weigh about 15 grams, but this is subject to geographical variation with some races producing smaller eggs and hatchlings (e.g. 38 mm in length and 11

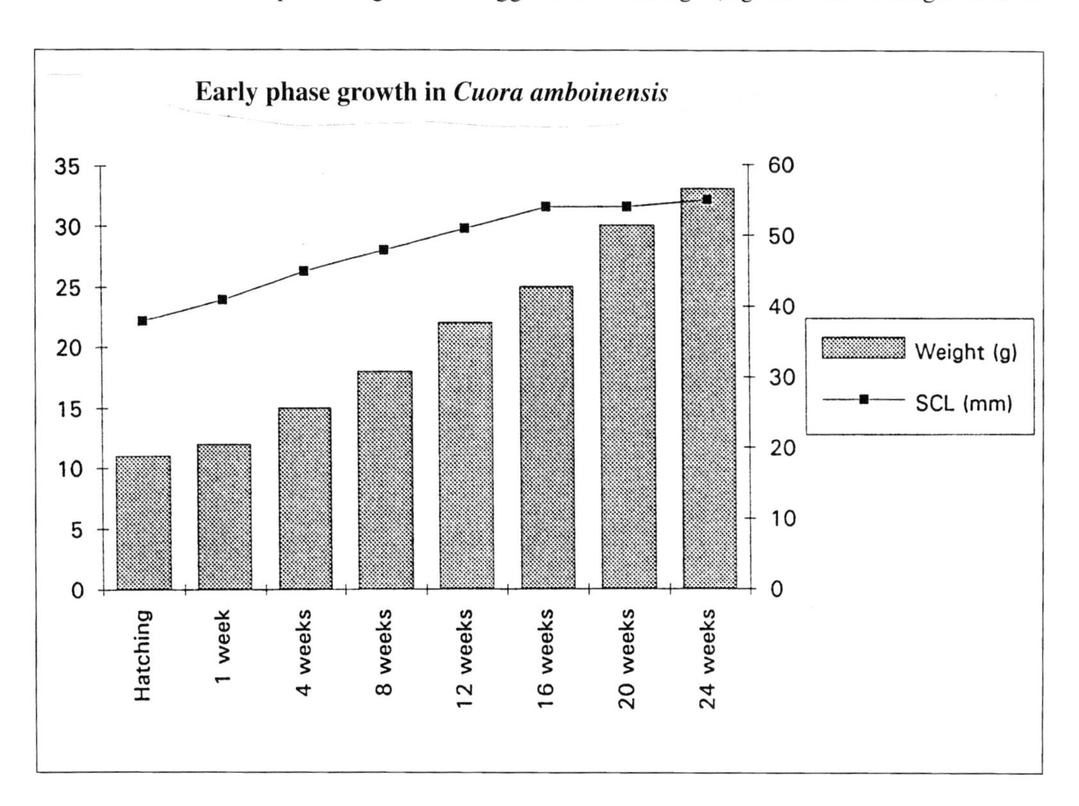

grams in weight). I am grateful to Richard Inskeep who has been keeping and breeding Amboina box turtles for many years for the following data on typical juvenile growth.Other *Cuora* species can be maintained and captive bred using very similar methods to those outlined above. For example, *C. trifasciata* (the Chinese three-striped box turtle) and *C. flavomarginata* (the Yellow-margined box turtle) although again, these are much more terrestrial in habit than *C. amboinensis*.

CYCLEMYS DENTATA (Gray, 1831)

Asian leaf turtle

General observations: This medium sized turtle derives its colloquial name from its well-camouflaged carapace which closely resembles a leaf. It is widely distributed in Asia but surprisingly little is known of its ecology. The undoubted effectiveness of its camouflage and secretive habits combine to make field studies difficult.

Taxonomy: A considerable degree of morphological variation is evident throughout this enigmatic turtle's wide range which includes Vietnam, Thailand, Myanmar, Malaysia, Cambodia, Laos, India, Bangladesh, Sumatra, Borneo, Java and the Philippines. Some authorities recognise two other species as belonging to the genus *Cyclemys*; *C. tcheponensis* and *C. tiannamensis* but these are not universally accepted (Das, 1991). It is probably best to regard *Cyclemys dentata* (as presently defined) as a complex of probable subspecies and possibly further undescribed species pending further studies and a comprehensive revision.

Description: The colouration of this turtle is extremely variable, but generally a mid to dark brown carapace with radiating lines upon the plastron. The oval carapace (to 24 cm) is depressed and flat with a distinct vertebral keel. The posterior marginals of the carapace are strongly serrated, especially so in juveniles. The limbs feature fully webbed feet and the forelimbs display a series of transverse oval scales. The head is brownish with black spots. The neck is brown-yellow with dark longitudinal streaks. Males have longer and thicker tails than females and a tendency to lighter colouration of the skin at the upper limbs, however, reliably differentiating between the sexes in this species is notoriously difficult.

Captive environment: *C. dentata* is a semi-aquatic species that inhabits hill streams up to a recorded altitude of 1,000 metres. It is also found in lowland streams, especially those bordered by forest. Juveniles and sub-adults are believed to be more aquatic in habit than adults. Tikader and Sharma (1985) state that juveniles are "absolutely" aquatic, an observation confirmed by the behaviour of a juvenile maintained in captivity by the Tortoise Trust. A land area is provided but is used very infrequently. Adult specimens are reported to utilise terrarium land areas extensively. A well-filtered shallow aquatic area is required as this species does not appear tolerant of poor water quality. An under-gravel filter operated by a powerhead with a small supplementary internal canister filter is ideal for most specimens. The author has provided *Cyclemys dentata* juveniles with entirely satisfactory accommodation based on 1 m x 50 cm plastic cement mixing tubs containing an undergravel filter and a small land area made from partly submerged plastic paint containers filled with gravel, sand and peat. A 10 cm specimen in the Tortoise Trust collection prefers a water depth of 35 mm that allows it to extend its head above water whilst resting otherwise fully submerged on the substrate. In this instance the gravel substrate is overlaid by a small quantity of submerged peat that serves to lower the pH and helps prevent the shell and skin infections to which this species can be prone. The land area for adults should be well planted and should possess a substrate such as leaf litter, peat and pine bark that will allow the inhabitants to partially bury themselves. A high humidity environment is generally preferred with temperatures in the 18 - 25°C region. If *Cyclemys dentata* is allowed to become too dry all activity will cease and eye and nose problems may also occur. A seasonal fall in temperature and an increase in ambient humidity may promote breeding activity. In captivity, *C. dentata* rapidly becomes tame and responsive to its keeper. Some basking activity has been observed, but in general, low light intensities and a gentle, all-round background heat source seems to be preferred. Provided a satisfactory level of ambient humidity (preferably over 90%) can be maintained a low wattage basking source should also be provided as an option. For this purpose ceramic-type dull-emitter heaters are ideal.

Diet: Adult *C. dentata* are omnivorous and accept a wide range of fruit, general vegetable matter and a small amount of animal protein. In nature it is known to favour fig leaves and fruit. Juveniles and sub-adults appear more carnivorous and will accept earthworms, small snails and rehydrated koi and cat pellets. Small specimens almost invariably prefer to feed in water but large adults will also feed on land.

Common health problems: Newly imported specimens may be heavily parasitised. Faecal smears should be checked for helminths and protozoan pathogens if problems are experienced. This species is also very environmentally sensitive and attention must be given to achieving the correct level of humidity, to temperature control and to water quality. Alkaline water is poorly tolerated.

Plastron, *Cylemmys dentata*

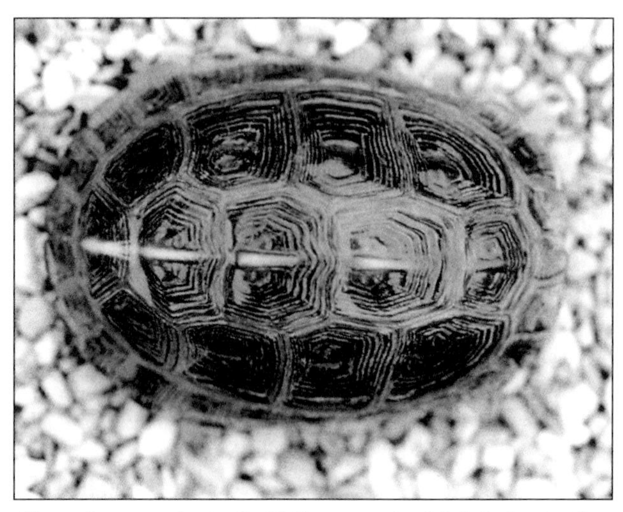

Cuora flavomarginata, the Yellow-margined Asiatic box turtle.

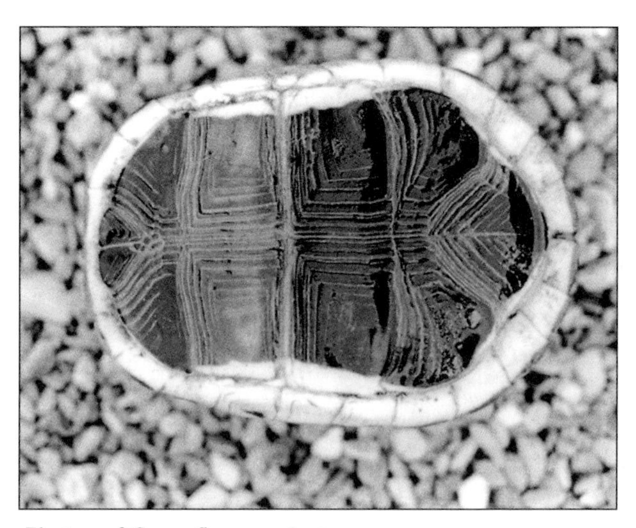

Plastron of *Cuora flavomarginata*

Breeding: *Cyclemys dentata* is infrequently bred in captivity but can prove very rewarding if a well-matched pair can be obtained as they will mate readily and lay up to 5 clutches of 2 to 4 eggs per year. These eggs are hard-shelled and typically measure 55 x 32 mm although the size of the laying female does appear to influence their exact dimensions. The eggs of *C. dentata* can be incubated in a moderately high humidity environment on a damp vermiculite and peat substrate at 30°C when hatching can be expected in 75 - 90 days. Ewart (1979) recorded the carapace length of hatchlings as 56.2 mm.

EMYDOIDEA BLANDINGII (Holbrook, 1838)

Blanding's turtle

General observations: Similar in appearance to the European pond terrapin, *Emys orbicularis.*

Taxonomy: No subspecies are currently recognised. Was once considered to belong to *Emys* on the basis of the similarities noted above. Now the sole representative of *Emydoidae.*

Description: The smooth, elongate carapace measures up to 27 cm, although the vast majority of specimens are considerably smaller. The groundcolour varies from brown to black, and is speckled with yellowish flecks and vermiculations. The throat and lower jaw are distinctly marked in bright yellow. The plastron is pale yellow with black-brown blotches and features a "semi-hinge" (located between the pectoral and abdominal scutes) which, although externally similar to that of a box turtle, does not actually close. Dimorphic characters include a longer plastron than carapace and broader body in females than males. Males also possess dark upper jaws, whilst the upper jaw of females is yellow.

Captive environment: Blanding's turtles are primarily aquatic, and most frequently inhabit marshes, slow moving rivers and streams and oxbows. Shallow and heavily vegetated water conditions are preferred. In captivity, an outdoor pond well planted with suitable aquatic and peripheral vegetation is advised where climatic conditions permit. Habitat conditions similar to those recommended for *Clemmys muhlenbergi* are ideal. If Blanding's turtles are to be maintained in aquaria, a fine gravel substrate and plentiful aquatic plants are suggested. An extensive land area is required in both cases. These turtles are most active with water temperatures in the range 18 - 21°C, but some activity continues at temperatures as low as 10°C. Aestivation often occurs when air temperatures exceed 30°C and feeding also ceases when water temperatures exceed 25°C. When water temperatures fall below 13°C *E. blandingii* usually become dormant and hibernate at the bottom of their ponds, although this species has been observed swimming beneath quite thick ice. Occasionally turtles also hibernate on land, buried in a leaf litter substrate.

Diet: Insect and amphibian larvae, molluscs, fish and aquatic plants are taken in the water. Terrestrial foraging is also common in this species when earthworms, slugs, fallen fruit, snails and beetles are consumed. In captivity, Blanding's turtle will accept koi pellets, Purina trout-chow and other prepared foods readily.

Common health problems: None immediately evident.

Breeding: Clutch density varies with the size of the laying female, but 10 - 14 eggs measuring 28 - 40 mm long by 18 - 26 mm wide is typical. Gravid females are very terrestrial in habit, and in the wild wander great distances in search of a nesting site. Normally, only a single clutch is laid each year. Sex determination is temperature dependant, with eggs incubated at 22.5 - 26.5°C resulting in 97 - 100% males, whilst those incubated at 30 - 31°C result in only females. Incubation success is greatest at mid-range temperatures (26.5 - 27.5°C). Reduced hatching rates are recorded at lower temperatures, with zero viability <22°C. The humidity throughout incubation should be high (>90%) as at lower levels of ambient humidity the eggs dehydrate and lose a substantial amount of weight. A damp vermiculite and sphagnum substrate has proved consistently successful with this species. Hatchlings typically measure 33 mm long and weigh approximately 10 g.

EMYDURA SUBGLOBOSA (Krefft, 1876)

Red-bellied short-necked turtle

General observations: Rarely encountered Australian and New Guinea short-necked turtle. Included here as it is occasionally found in trade (New Guinea examples only, as Australian export is prohibited) and as its captive care is very representative of Australasian turtles (both short-necked and side-necked) generally.

Taxonomy: No subspecies currently identified.

Description: Brown or grey carapace, to approximately 26 cm. The undersides of the marginals are red or pink. The plastron is yellow, bordered in red or pink. The head and neck are grey, with a yellow stripe running over the eye and toward the tympanic membrane. A red stripe runs from the lower jaw, which also features two yellow barbles, along the length of the neck.

Captive environment: *Emydura subglobosa* is predominantly aquatic and typically leaves the water only to bask or for the purposes of egg deposition. Basking behaviour in this species is usually enthusiastic, with many spending a considerable time under any convenient light-heat source. Chromalux® lamps are ideal for this purpose. Some captives maintained by Carl Ernst rarely basked, but this should be considered atypical behaviour. In the wild, this turtle is found mainly in rivers but is also known to inhabit ponds. The water temperature should be maintained in the region of 25 to 27°C. *Emydura* species are all susceptible to skin and shell infections if the water quality is poor, so efficient filtration is critical.

Diet: Omnivorous. Feeds upon fish, prepared meats, rehydrated trout chow and frozen foods with relish. Also takes fresh green vegetables, fruits and aquatic plants. A voracious feeder in captivity.

Common health problems: None immediately evident.

Breeding: *E. subglobosa* breeds readily in captivity. Multiple clutches of 10 or more eggs are produced and nesting typically occurs at night or early morning. A large sand bucket in a sunny location has proved a consistently acceptable nesting site for this and other Australasian turtle species. The eggs measure approximately 40 x 20 mm and are deposited rapidly in the nest. They should be incubated in a high (100%) humidity environment at a temperature of 28 - 30°C. At this temperature, hatching usually occurs in approximately 45 days. Initially, the hatchlings should be maintained in a shallow water tank (a depth of 2 cm is suggested) with a gentle slope to allow easy access and egress. Juveniles will feed upon small aquatic insects, crickets and small pieces of meat, although some will also take vegetable matter. Water temperature for both juveniles and adults can be maintained in the range 18 - 25°C. There is some evidence that maintaining water temperatures at the lower end of this spectrum encourages external basking. The breeding of other *Emydura* and Australian *Elyseya* species is similar; *Emydura macquarii* (Murray turtle) and *Elyseya latisternum* (Saw-shelled turtle) eggs can be incubated in vermiculite hydrated 1:1 with water at the same temperatures as *E. subglobosa.* Hatching also occurs within a similar time-scale. Breeding activity of these species is enhanced in an outdoor environment where local conditions permit. Freitag (pers. comm.) reported the successful incubation of eggs from a long-term captive female and F1 generation male *Emydura (Elesya) albertsii.* A colour change in fertile eggs was noted after 60 days. 40 days after hatching the juveniles measured 38 and 40 mm in length and were feeding regularly upon worms, crickets and dry cat food. They were maintained in 7 cm deep water at a constant temperature of 25°C.

EMYS ORBICULARIS (Linnaeus, 1758)

The European pond terrapin

General observations: An extremely attractive and intelligent terrapin with a wide geographical distribution. Under threat in many parts of its range due to pollution of rivers and intensive agriculture. Commonly seen in European collections, but rare in the United States.

Taxonomy: Until recently considered to consist of a single species, populations of *Emys orbicularis* demonstrate significant regional variation. New research by Uwe Fritz (1993 and 1995) has resulted in several new subspecies being proposed; *Emys orbicularis orbicularis, E. o. hellenica, E. o. luteofusca, E.o. capolongoi, E. o. lanzai, E.o. galloitalica, E.o. colchica, E.o. kurae, E. o. orientalis, E .o. occidentalis* and *E. o. fritzjuergenobsti.* These newly proposed races are not yet generally recognised and they remain controversial at the time of writing. However, the morphological evidence for them appears to be strong. Intergrades are also reported.

Description: Carapace lengths to 20 cm but most specimens are much smaller (<15 cm). Carapace coloration from light brown to black, with many fine radiating dots. The skin of the head, neck and limbs is black or brown and again bears a pattern of dots, most frequently bright yellow to white. Although not exclusively the case, males have a tendency to reddish eyes and females to yellow eyes. The tails of males are also longer than those of females. Detailed descriptions and colour illustrations of the proposed new taxa are provided by Fritz (1995) which should be consulted for specific identification.

Captive environment: For pairs and small groups a large aquarium tank filled with approximately 200mm of water is adequate. An outdoor pond is excellent where weather permits. In both instances basking facilities must be provided. This terrapin is easy to maintain, and a medium sized foam cartridge filter, possibly in conjunction with biological (under-gravel) filtration will prove satisfactory. Throughout most of its range *E. orbicularis* hibernates, but captive animals can be over wintered provided water and air temperatures are maintained between 22 - 25°C. It should be noted that *Emys orbicularis* is extremely agile. I have seen specimens climb a vertical wall. Good perimeter security is therefore essential.

Diet: Primarily carnivorous, with aquatic insects, snails, tadpoles, small frogs, salamanders and fishes high on the list of dietary preferences. Feeding may take place both in and out of the water. Juveniles take mainly insect larvae and small molluscs. In captivity, most adults will accept earthworms, meal worms, low fat tinned dog food and rehydrated trout chow dusted with multi-mineral supplements. They rapidly learn when food is to be offered and paddle anxiously in the water with heads raised - some will also respond to being called. I have seen this twice, once in a semi-captive colony in southern France and more surprisingly, in a wild population in Turkey where the terrapins had learned that tourists often threw tid-bits into a lake; the sound of a human voice was sufficient to bring dozens of them out of hiding in expectation of a meal. I have maintained this species in captivity in Britain for a number of years and find them very responsive and intelligent.

Common health problems: None immediately evident.

Breeding: Egg dimensions are somewhat variable, but typically measure 30 mm x 20 mm and weigh about 8 g. Incubation humidity is suggested at 90%. Success has been achieved with incubation temperatures from 24°C to 30°C; a wide range, compared to many species. ESD occurs, with males only in the range 24 - 28°C and 96% females at 30°C. Comprehensive research on the influence of temperature on sex in *E. orbicularis* conducted by Pieau (1971, 1975 and 1982) also demonstrated that incubation at constant temperatures in the 28 to 29°C range can result in the formation of intersexed neonates so incubation in this range should be avoided. At a mid-range temperature (25°C) hatching can be anticipated within 54 to 80 days. Neonates measure approximately 24 mm long and weigh approximately 5 grams (typical weight range 3.5 to 6 grams). The carapace of hatchlings is usually coloured dark brown with yellow lateral borders to the scutes. Water depth for hatchlings should be maintained at approximately 5 cm deep and at the same temperature as for adults. Neonates feed initially upon daphnia and insect larvae. Sexual maturity occurs at about 5 - 6 years of age in captivity or when the carapace length exceeds 100 mm.

Emys orbicularis, the European pond turtle. Male specimen. This species is subject to considerable regional variation and several new subspecies have been proposed recently.

Geochelone carbonaria, the Red-foot tortoise

A large adult *Geochelone sulcata*, the African spurred tortoise. Many are now being captive bred, but prospective keepers should be aware of the extensive space that large species such as this require.

Geochelone sulcata at 9 months of age.

GEOCHELONE CARBONARIA (Spix, 1824)
The Red-foot tortoise 5/5/14

General observations: This is one of the most common South American tortoises, with a wide distribution from Panama to northern Argentina. The descendants of introduced specimens now colonise a number of Caribbean islands, although the population of Trinidad may be a natural one. The species is named because of the bright red scales that adorn its legs in profusion.

Taxonomy: At the higher level, there is much dispute about whether this species should be attributed to *Geochelone* or whether the sub-genus *Chelonoidis* should be elevated to generic rank to include them. Thus is it not unusual to see them listed under both. With a wide and fragmented distribution, *G. carbonaria* demonstrates considerable morphological variation. This is evident not only in the carapace shape but also in colouration. However, there are no currently recognised subspecies and at present the species is considered homogenous. Even so, in view of the variation already noted caution should be exercised in captive breeding and preferably this should be restricted to specimens from similar geographical origins.

Description: A large and impressive tortoise, mature males typically measure some 300mm SCL and most of the females I have measured appear to be of similar size although much larger examples of both sexes have been reported. The principal dimorphic feature is the narrow waist of males, which according to some observers are reminiscent of an overgrown peanut. The tail of male specimens is also longer than that of females, and in males also the rear lobe of the plastron exhibits a much wider and flatter anal notch. Colour does vary according to locality of origin, with Venezuelan specimens exhibiting a yellowish plastron with a brown carapace and Argentinean specimens a darker, almost black plastron and carapace. In all cases the central areolae of the scutes are marked with yellow. The head is typically brightly marked with yellow scales, but some Venezuelan specimens possess instead a reddish-orange head.

Captive environment: Red-foot tortoises inhabit grassland savannah and drier forest habitats throughout South America. In only a few localities does it impinge upon true tropical rainforest habitats. In captivity, a moderately dry environment and temperature in the region of 21°C (night) to 27°C (day) will suit most specimens. Access to water should however be provided at all times. In most of Europe and North America Red-foot tortoises can be accommodated out of doors during the warm summer months, at least during the daytime, but in the winter and on cool nights indoor accommodation is also essential. A well-planted outdoor pen with access to a heated hut or greenhouse is probably ideal for this species which is relatively easy to manage in captivity.

Diet: In the wild these tortoises prefer fallen fruits, flowers, green leaves and will occasionally take carrion when it is encountered. In captivity caution should be exercised when offering banana as they easily become addicted to it and meat products should similarly be very strictly rationed. Over reliance upon both items can result in serious dietary problems developing. Most Red-foot tortoises will readily take melon, orange, mango, vegetable greens and grapes. A small quantity of animal protein is advised, but must not be given in excess.

Common health problems: Locomotion problems affecting hind-limbs if deprived entirely of animal protein.

Breeding: The mating ritual of Red-foot tortoises is startlingly similar in many respects to that of *T. horsfieldi*; the male advances upon the female, circles her repeatedly, extends his neck near her face whereupon he proceeds to move his head rapidly from side to side with a strange jerky motion. This is accompanied by occasional biting, shoving and ramming actions. Eventually he mounts from behind and during copulation emits an extraordinary sequence of "clucking" or "cackling" sounds. Two male tortoises will often engage in combat, and most mating activity occurs either during or just after rain. Nesting and egg laying continues all year. The Red-foot tortoises in our own collection regularly lay eggs that measure on average 45 mm long by 42 mm wide and which weigh some 35 - 50 grams. Typically a clutch consists of between 3 - 5 eggs and a female may lay 2 - 3 clutches each season. At 30 °C in a Type II incubator at moderately high humidity incubation takes on average 150 - 175 days. The hatchlings measure approximately 46 mm long, are 42 - 44 mm wide and weigh between 26 - 32 grams.

GEOCHELONE CHILENSIS (Gray, 1870)

The Chaco or Argentine tortoise

General observations: This little studied tortoise is rarely captive-bred outside its natural range and is in need of further research directed at effective captive propagation.

Taxonomy: Member of the subgenus *Chelonoidis*. Some authorities have suggested this should be elevated to generic rank but this is not generally accepted. The question of subspecies in *G. chilensis* has been vexed since Freiberg (1973) described *Geochelone donosobarrosi* and *G. petersi* from Argentina. Recent research (Buskirk, 1993) supports the view that southern Chaco tortoises, which were described as *G. donosobarrosi,* cannot be differentiated from normal *G. chilensis*. It also seems probable that *G. petersi* is similarly invalid.

Description: Maximum recorded carapace length to 433 mm, but typically not more than 260 mm. The marginals of juveniles are strongly serrated. Overall carapace colour is light to dark brown. The carapace lacks a nuchal. In respect of southern populations, Buskirk (op. cit.) and Belmonte (1991) note sexual dimorphism and dichromatism represented by apposed, pointed, antibrachial scales in females and juveniles which in the case of males are darkened and hypertrophied (enlarged). Ontogenetic changes are also apparent in *G. chilensis* with older tortoises (males especially) developing darker coloured carapaces than younger specimens. Chaco tortoises are very difficult to sex using the normal tail-length or plastral depression methods.

Captive environment: Reports that *G. chilensis* survive the often severe winters experienced in southern Argentina in open pallets seem doubtful, but unfortunately detailed information on their annual cycle is not currently available. Buskirk (Op.cit) found a number of tortoises inhabiting burrows, and notes anecdotal evidence that suggests that they may hibernate between May and September. In captivity, *G. chilensis* in Britain have demonstrated similar care requirements to *G. pardalis*. Despite the probability of hibernation in southern Argentina, northern specimens may not hibernate, and hence, it is probably wisest to over winter animals of indeterminate origin. In the wild, the habitat of *G. chilensis* comprises arid scrub with a typically sandy and rocky substrate. This substrate type is also preferred in captivity. Auffenberg comments (1969) that captive Chaco tortoises rarely live for more than two years; fortunately this has not proved to be true, and the author is aware of a number of long-term captives including some maintained by the Tortoise Trust.

Diet: As for *T. graeca* and *G. pardalis*.

Common health problems: Chaco tortoises should not be maintained in mixed enclosures with other species; viral stomatitis has been recorded in *G. chilensis* and the species has also proved susceptible to "R.N.S" and Upper Respiratory Tract Disease. *Hexamita* organisms are also known to affect this tortoise.

Breeding: The typical clutch size for this species appears to comprise two eggs that measure approximately 45 x 33 mm, however, Rottman (1969) describes a clutch of 5 eggs measuring up to 47 x 38 mm. Extremely long incubation periods seem to be the norm in the wild, with reliable reports of hatchlings not emerging from the nest for a year or more. Hatchlings typically measure 45 - 47 mm SCL and weigh 25 grams. In captivity, eggs incubated at 28 - 30°C in a medium (70%) humidity environment on a vermiculite substrate have hatched in 60 - 72 days.

GEOCHELONE DENTICULATA (Linnaeus, 1766)

The Yellow-foot or forest tortoise

General observations: These tortoises are distinguished from *G. carbonaria* principally by the bright yellow - orange (rather than red) scales of the legs. They are also light golden-brown in colour, and much larger. It is widely distributed in South America and is found in Brazil, Ecuador, Columbia, Guyana, Venezuela, Peru, Guyana and Surinam.

Taxonomy: *G. denticulata* was described earlier than *G. carbonaria* (in 1766 as opposed to 1824) and in many old accounts is to be found listed under the synonym "*Testudo tabulata*". As with *G. carbonaria* and *G. chilensis* there is dispute over its generic attribution. It does not demonstrate the marked regional variation so evident in *G. carbonaria.*

Description: Yellow-foot or Forest tortoises are considerably larger animals than Red-foot tortoises; the average mean adult SCL is 400 mm but some very much larger specimens are occasionally encountered. The record is believed to be approximately 700 mm.

Captive environment: *G. denticulata* inhabit true tropical and sub-tropical forest habitats; as such, they require higher humidity and more stable temperatures than *G. carbonaria*. Continuous access to drinking and bathing water is essential, and a frequent spray with artificial rain is also helpful in maintaining good health and normal activity. Day and night temperatures in the order of 25 - 27°C are recommended. As these are large tortoises which also demonstrate a high level of mobility and activity, any accommodation must be of adequate size. A pair can be maintained satisfactorily in an area measuring 4 m x 4 m.

Diet: Generally as for *G. carbonaria*, but with a slightly higher fruit content. Some small amount of animal protein is recommended. High fat varieties should be avoided, but rehydrated monkey-chow type products seem well suited in practice.

Common health problems: As for Red-foot tortoises.

Breeding: Although superficially similar to *G. carbonaria*, Auffenberg has pointed out that the head movement differs in *G. denticulata*, consisting of a single sweep rather than in a series of jerky motions. Male *G. denticulata* also lack the waist of *G. carbonaria*. Clutch densities have been reported as higher than *G. carbonaria*, as many as 15 on occasions, although most specimens appear to lay between 4 - 5 eggs. In the wild this tortoise does not appear to nest in the normal way, often leaving the eggs at least partially exposed. The eggs are similar in size to those of *G. carbonaria* and can be incubated under identical conditions. If anything, humidity should be a little higher. The hatchlings are very similar in both size and overall appearance to those of *G. carbonaria*; so much so that it is not easy to tell them apart. At 30°C the incubation period is usually between 140 - 160 days.

GEOCHELONE ELEGANS (Schoepff, 1794)

The Indian Star tortoise

General observations: One of the world's most distinctive tortoises, this strikingly marked animal has for many years been sought after by collectors and illegal export continues to represent a significant threat along with habitat loss and utilisation for food. It has been recorded infrequently in Pakistan, with the main area of distribution in India and Sri Lanka where population density is said to be still good.

Taxonomy: This tortoise appears to be closely related to the almost unknown *Geochelone platynota* of Burma, from which it differs principally by featuring radiating lines on the plastron and by having more rays on the costals. According to some authorities *G. elegans* has a more conical form to the vertebrals and costals than *G. platynota*, but this character is very variable even within *G. elegans* and may be related to geographical origin.

Description: The maximum recorded size of *G. elegans* is approximately 350 mm, but most specimens are considerably smaller, usually in the region of 250 mm SCL. The carapace features the radiating star pattern from whence it takes its name, a characteristic duplicated on the plastron. Each of the costal and vertebral scutes has a large, yellow central dot surrounded by a series of radiating yellow stripes.

Captive environment: *G. elegans* are found in the wild inhabiting dry, scrub forest areas, the borders of sandy deserts and even man-made wastelands. It also inhabits grassy hillsides and the borders of cultivated areas. It appears in this respect a robust and adaptable species, yet in captivity it is generally regarded as extremely sensitive and delicate. Certainly, it does not mix well with other species and is best maintained in isolated groups. In other respects, the tortoise appears to do well if kept under very similar conditions to *G. pardalis*. We have maintained this species for many years and it has not lived up to its difficult reputation. In most of western Europe and North America it can be allowed out of doors in good weather, and an enclosure that is well planted with grass, dandelion and other graze is ideal. Overnight, a heated indoor retreat will generally be required. Otherwise treat as for *G. pardalis*.

Diet: As for *G. pardalis*.

Common health problems: *Hexamita parva* urinary tract infections; pneumonia; stomatitis.

Breeding: *G. elegans* are not a particularly easy tortoise to induce to breed (or even mate) in captivity although it can be done. The most consistently successful captive breeding results have been achieved within the species natural bioclimatic range in India and Sri Lanka. Although this species habitat is typically dry, stony and thorny for most of the year, it is subject to seasonal rains or monsoons; it appears to be the on-set of this rainy season that initiates interest in mating. During this period (which occurs in India in June) the animals become especially active and feed extensively upon the new shoots of vegetation. They can often be seen marching in small groups in some areas, a lone female pursued by several males. In captivity interest in mating can sometimes be stimulated by either a natural downpour or by extensive spraying with a hose. Males rarely exhibit mutual animosity, and aggression is not often observed in this species. Females are typically larger in size than males (approximately 290 mm compared to 230 mm) and achieve sexual maturity at about 10 - 12 years of age. Males can demonstrate sexual maturity at 3 - 5 years under captive conditions. The eggs appear to be of very variable dimensions, although as in most accounts no geographical origin is disclosed for the specimens it could be that size varies with location. Most eggs measure about 42 mm x 31 mm, although records indicate a range from 38 mm to 50 mm in length and from 27 mm to 39 mm in width. Egg weight is similarly variable from 22 g to as much as 38 g. Females lay several clutches per year, typically three, but sometimes more. A normal clutch consists of 3 to 6 eggs. Incubation periods in the wild demonstrate considerable variability depending upon how late or early in the season laying occurs; data from captive specimens within the bioclimatic range indicates that it can take as little as 47 days or as long as 147 days. Artificially incubated eggs in a Type I container at 28 °C hatch in about 100 days; at 30 °C incubation takes approximately 75 days. Incubation humidity should be medium to low. The average length of hatchling *G. elegans* is 35 mm and the average weight 15 - 16 g (recorded minimum = 12 g, recorded maximum = 22 g). The hatchlings lack the distinct ray markings of the adults initially; this first becomes really evident at about 12 months of age.

GEOCHELONE PARDALIS (Bell, 1828)

The Leopard tortoise

General observations: The Leopard tortoise is the second largest African mainland tortoise (after *G. sulcata*). The largest male ever recorded measured 656 mm and weighed 43 kg. The largest recorded female measured 705 mm and attained a weight of 48.64 kg (Branch, et. al, 1990). Most are substantially smaller, but it is not unusual to find specimens of both sexes in the 350 - 450 mm length range and weighing above 15 kg. *G. pardalis* occur from Sudan and Ethiopia and extend their range throughout southern Africa. It is named because of its strikingly marked carapace which in practice constitutes an excellent camouflage.

Taxonomy: The only currently disputed area of *G. pardalis* taxonomy concerns its division into two subspecies, *G. pardalis pardalis* and *G. pardalis babcocki*. Not all authorities accept that two clearly defined geographical races occur. What is not clear, and what might be the cause of at least some of the confusion, is whether these are the only races; certainly some keepers and some field-workers I have spoken to are convinced that there may be more. Geographical size variation is certainly widespread in *G. pardalis* (Lambert, 1995). Intergrades are in any case reported which further confuses the situation. There are consistent reports of infertility between pairs that are dissimilar in appearance although which theoretically belong to the same subspecies. The best fertility is obtained from pairs that are visually very similar in terms of overall body morphology, colouration and marking.

Of the two recognised forms, *G. p. pardalis* occupies a limited range in Cape Province and in the south-western sector of the Orange Free State, whereas *G. p. babcocki* (which is sometimes known as the tropical leopard tortoise) enjoys a much wider distribution and appears to be subject to a higher degree of morphological variation than its Cape relative. It is clear from a comparison of morphological data from various countries within its range that very considerable differences in average and maximum dimensions occur; in some instances animals from one locality may be up to 300% larger than those from another. This may be due to a combination of dietary, climatic and genetic factors. There are also noticeable differences in colouration and patterning. This reinforces the need for care when selecting animals for captive propagation.

Description: Whilst juveniles of the two currently recognised subspecies are relatively easy to differentiate, the same is not always true of adults. In juveniles, *G. p. pardalis* feature two or more blackish dots in the centre of the costal and vertebral scutes whereas *G. p. babcocki* typically feature only one. In the nominate form the plastral scutes are typically blotched with margins; in *G. p. babcocki* the plastron is typically plainer and lacks the central spots. In adults *G. p. pardalis* are said to be typically flatter than *G. p. babcocki* which is highly domed as well as being considerably smaller in most cases, although this last stated character does not coincide with my own observations; I have seen some extremely large *G. p. pardalis* although as these were captive animals it was not possible to establish their geographical origin.

Captive environment: In good weather *G. pardalis* should be allowed as much access to an outdoor grazing area as possible. Shade in the form of low growing shrubs and bushes should be included to allow retreat from the mid-day sun. During cold weather and over winter, a large heated shed, greenhouse or indoor penned area is essential. This should attain daytime temperatures in excess of 20°C if normal activity is to be maintained. Sexual behaviour is most common when temperatures exceed 25°C. Spot or infra-red basking facilities are highly recommended and will be well used. Overnight temperatures should remain in excess of 10°C and preferably above 14°C. In the wild, the southern race *G. pardalis pardalis* is known to hibernate or at least to experience a winter dormancy period, often seeking retreat from the cold in other animals' discarded burrows. In captivity, most keepers prefer to keep the animals alert and feeding overwinter by means of artificial light and heat. Our own colony of *G. pardalis* overwinter in a well insulated heated shed with underfloor hot water heating and wall mounted radiators for general background heat plus several 250W infra-red basking lamps. As much natural light as possible is provided and access to outdoor grazing is also possible in periods of mild weather, even in winter. Provided the tortoises are warmed through by several hours of exposure to basking lamps and background heat, a short period outside to permit beneficial grazing on bright but cold days does not appear detrimental.

Diet: Leopard tortoises are very typical grazing herbivores; in the wild their diet consists largely of grasses and succulents such as prickly pear. Several authors refer to their consuming bones and hyena faeces for their calcium content. In captivity *G. pardalis* should be maintained on a diet very high in fibre otherwise diarrhoea and intestinal parasite problems will quickly be encountered. For some years I have maintained a colony of *G. pardalis babcocki* on a diet consisting of natural graze (grass, sowthistle, dandelion and other miscellaneous edible weeds) supplemented with cabbage and other coarse green leaf material in the winter when natural graze becomes in short supply. To supply additional fluid and variety, a few tomatoes and cucumbers are included from time to time. These are always consumed enthusiastically. Fruit is offered only very occasionally; an excess will rapidly result in digestive tract disturbances which may manifest as watery stools and possibly even as colic. A fresh supply of water should also be available at all times as most Leopard tortoises will drink regularly. This basic dietary regime is heavily supplemented with Vionate®, Rep-Cal® and Nutrobal® as these very large (and rapidly growing) tortoises have a prodigious demand for calcium.

Common health problems: *Hexamita parva* urinary tract infections; viral (*Herpes*) stomatitis. Beware of symptoms such as excessive drinking which is an early sign of *Hexamita* infection.

Breeding: Leopard tortoises, if provided with good accommodation and a well-balanced diet, can be induced to breed quite readily in captivity. Males and females can be diagnosed by a number of characters; in males the tail is longer and the hind section of the plastron is depressed (only very slightly so in the case of *G. p. babcocki*); males are also somewhat more elongate and narrower than females. In *G. p. babcocki* the males are smaller than females, whilst in *G. p. pardalis* males tend to be larger than females. For successful mating the males must always be of sufficient size to be able to mount the female properly. Males kept together will often fight, levering at each other with the gular until one or other desists in defeat. Males court females in a similar manner, with much pushing and battering with the gular. Finally, the male mounts the female and accompanies the process with a great deal of deep throated "croaking" and "grunting". Females carrying eggs may go off their food for a while immediately prior to laying, and may dig one or more trial nests in sunny areas of open ground. The nest itself usually measures about 25 cm deep and accommodates the typical clutch of 8 - 10 eggs. Again, differences in clutch size are reported between the two recognised forms with *G. p. pardalis* typically laying more eggs than G. *p. babcocki*. However, the absolute maximum recorded clutch size for *G. p. pardalis* is 18 eggs, whilst figures as high as 30 have been reported for *G. p. babcocki* which appears to contradict this. The rounded eggs of *G. p. pardalis* typically measure some 43 mm in diameter and weigh 50 grams or more whilst those of *G. p. babcocki* often are said to be smaller at approximately 35 mm with a typical weight of only 25 g. However, this does not accord with my own observations based upon Kenyan and Tanzanian specimens where the average egg size is closer to 42 mm with a weight of 45 g. The hatchlings are also claimed to differ in size, those of *G. p. babcocki* at about 38 mm in length and weighing approximately 17 g whilst those of the southern race are said to be somewhat larger at approximately 48 mm in length and up to 35 g in weight. Once again, however, I know of 46 mm hatchlings that weighed 33 g produced by a female of Kenyan origin. Females may go on to produce several clutches per season - as many as six totalling 52 eggs in all has been recorded. Incubation times in the wild are very variable, from 178 days in Zambia to 384 days in Natal. Eggs incubated artificially at 28 °C hatch in about 180 days; at 30 °C hatchlings can be expected from 130 days onwards, but most often emerge between 140 - 155 days after laying. Incubation humidity should be in the region of 80% with the eggs on slightly damp substrate. From the moment when the egg is first pierced by the hatchling, it may be many hours, or even days, before it is finally ready to leave the egg; this is true of most tortoises including all *Testudo* and *Geochelone* species. Once the immediate demand for oxygen has been met, the hatchling may remain in the egg whilst the remains of the egg-sac are absorbed. The only real danger (under normal captive circumstances) during this time is if the tortoise becomes dehydrated or if the mucous-like residue inside the egg literally glues the hatchlings mouth, nose or eyes up; mortality can occur if airways become blocked in this way. The problem is best prevented by maintaining adequate air humidity and by gently swabbing any obstructing matter away from the head and front legs using a damp cotton bud. Normally, human intervention will not be required, but it is as well to be alert to the possibility. Juveniles grow quickly, and can reach sexual maturity within 5 - 6 years in the case of males, somewhat older in the case of females which typically begin regular egg production as they attain a weight of 8 kg or more.

GEOCHELONE SULCATA (Miller, 1779)

The African spurred tortoise

General observations: The largest continental land tortoise with recorded carapace lengths to 83 cm and 105 kg (Flower, 1925). This same author also cites an 18 year old animal as measuring 750 mm and weighing 60 kg (Flower, 1933). *G. sulcata* are surpassed in size only by the giant tortoises of the Galapagos and Seychelles.

Chaco tortoise, *Geochelone (Chelonoidis) chilensis*. This example is captive-bred and demonstrates not only an abnormal vertebral scute pattern, but also 'lumpiness' due to excessive dietary protein.

Geochelone pardalis babcocki, the Leopard tortoise. In captivity, this species will require extensive indoor quarters during winter.

Texas Gopher tortoise, *Gopherus (Xerobates) berlandieri*

Heosemys spinosa, the Cog-wheel or Spiny turtle

Taxonomy: No subspecies are currently recognised. It is unclear what, if any, regional variations occur. Distribution includes much of sub-Saharan Africa, including Mauritania, Ethiopia, Sudan, Niger, Chad, Senegal and Mali.

Description: The thighs feature two or more very large and prominent tubercles. The skin is typically sandy-ivory or golden yellow-brown. The scales on the front limbs are large and imbricate. The scales on the heel may protrude. The tail lacks a caudal spur. The oval carapace is markedly flattened dorsally. The scutes are typically possess a sandy-brown ground colour with occasional darker brown borders. The plastron is typically ivory or pale horn coloured. The gulars are paired and typically forked, especially so in males. The supracaudal is usually undivided, although divided examples have been observed. The nuchal scute is absent.

Captive environment: In the wild, this tortoise inhabits arid savannahs and acacia scrub lands. In response to high temperatures and prolonged periods of drought it excavates very long burrows which it employs during aestivation. In some regions (for example, Senegal) nocturnal activity and grazing by moonlight has been observed - this may represent yet another strategy to survive in a particularly harsh environment where daytime temperatures preclude normal activity. *G. sulcata* is a relatively straightforward animal to maintain in captivity with broadly similar requirements to *G. pardalis*. A large outdoor pen will be utilised fully in fine weather, and overwintering may take place in a well insulated and heated shed.

Diet: In captivity, *G. sulcata* exhibit the same requirement for a high fibre intake as *G. pardalis*. A lack of dietary fibre, or roughage, will precipitate digestive tract disturbance, diarrhoea and an apparently much increased susceptibility to flagellate and helminth problems. The feeding of too much fruit will result in similar problems (this can also result in severe colic). Most *sulcata* will appreciate access to a natural grazing area and will feed readily upon mixed grasses and fresh alfalfa (lucerne). Some animals will also accept dried alfalfa hay. Due to their prodigious rate of growth, their demand for calcium and mineral trace elements is high. Daily supplementation should be considered mandatory. Although *sulcata* will take animal protein if offered (as will most normally herbivorous tortoises), in practice this tends to lead to excessive growth and causes carapace deformity. It should therefore be avoided. If scute pyramiding is noted, this usually indicates that either too much of the right type of food is being consumed, or, more likely, that the basal protein content of the diet is too high. It should always be remembered that *G. sulcata* is a sub-Saharan tortoise whose natural habitat is semi-desert. In such environments food is not plentiful and overfeeding in captivity is a common cause of problems with this species.

Breeding females also have a very high calcium demand due to the number of eggs and frequency of clutching (see below). The addition of ground oyster shells or cuttlefish bone to their diet is recommended in addition to routine provision of Rep-Cal®, Nutrobal® or similar combined high potency calcium and vitamin D3 supplement.

Common health problems: *Hexamita parva*; stomatitis; flagellates; pneumonia.

Breeding: The reproductive potential of *G. sulcata* is very high, with great success being reported in numerous captive breeding projects. According to Ernst and Barbour (1989) up to

17 eggs are laid at a time, however, captive specimens have regularly produced in excess of 20 (Stearns, 1989, cites one female who laid 34) and 15 should be considered an average clutch. The frequency of clutching is also high, with some females producing up to 6 clutches in a single year. The eggs are spherical, and typically measure 40 - 44 mm in diameter and normally weigh between 35 - 50 grams. Incubation successes have been noted at a wide range of temperatures, from 27°C to 32°C, although most breeders incubate in the range 28 - 30°C. Moist vermiculite and pearlite have proved consistently successful substrates for incubation. When incubated at 30°C hatching can be expected in approximately 85 to 100 days. At 28°C the incubation period is extended to 120 - 170 days. The hatchlings measure approximately 45 - 50 mm long, weigh between 25 - 30 grams, and are a uniform pale yellow-ivory colour, except for the scutes, which feature light brown sulci. Sometimes, very much darker examples are encountered. Although no specific data is yet available, it seems likely that *G. sulcata* utilises incubation temperature to determine the sex of hatchlings.

It is an essential consideration when housing breeding pairs of *G. sulcata* that an adequate depth of substrate is provided for nest excavation. The preferred medium for this species is sand infiltrated by light organic matter, e.g. fine plant roots. The excavated nests are of considerable depth, typically up to 370 mm in the case of large specimens. If an inadequate depth is provided, laying attempts may be aborted, leading to potential egg-retention problems.

GEOEMYDA SPENGLERI (Gmelin, 1789)

The Leaf turtle

General observations: Sole member of the Asian monotypic genus *Geoemyda*. Its colloquial name is derived from its serrated outline and behaviour.

Taxonomy: Two subspecies are presently recognised, *Geoemyda spengleri spengleri* and *G. s. japonica*. The subspecies are differentiated by the presence of axillary (and sometimes, inguinal) scutes in *G. s. japonica* and their absence in *G. s. spengleri*. Recent research, however, has indicated that *G. s. japonica* may be a full biological species in its own right (Yasukawa, Ota and Kikida, 1992). Distribution includes China, Vietnam, Borneo and Sumatra. *G. s. japonica occurs* only on the island of Okinawa.

Description: Carapace to 13 cm with profound marginal serration's both posteriorly and anteriorly and featuring three keels. Carapace ground colour is typically yellowish brown. Skin colour is olive brown and features a yellow post orbital stripe. The thighs feature small tubercles and the feet are only slightly webbed. The nares are small and distanced in *G. s. spengleri*, but large and closely spaced in *G. s. japonica*. The cervical scute is also larger in *G. s. spengleri* than in *G. s. japonica*.

Captive environment: This species is predominantly terrestrial, entering shallow water only very occasionally, and then usually to drink. Its natural habitat includes mesic evergreen forests where it is usually found under logs or hiding in convenient crevices. A leaf litter and crushed bark substrate has proved effective in captivity. Vivarium temperatures should normally be maintained between 18 - 24°C, although in the wild this species occurs in some areas with much lower seasonal temperatures. A drop in temperature may promote breeding activity.

Diet: Omnivorous. Captive specimens will usually accept earthworms, snails and a wide variety of fruit. In the wild, millipedes and fallen leaves are consumed.

Common health problems: None immediately evident.

Breeding: The eggs of this species are distinctly elongate at 47 mm long by 18 mm wide and have a mass of approximately 9 g. Incubation temperature appears critical, with 25 to 26°C providing the most consistent successes (although some breeders also report success at higher temperatures). Incubation humidity should be high, at 90%+. At 25°C hatching can be expected in about 70 days. The hatchlings typically measure 35 mm in length and weigh about 5 g.

GOPHERUS SPP. Rafinesque, 1832

Gopher tortoise

General observations: Because of their North American and Mexican location, Gopher tortoises have attracted considerable interest and much scientific investigation; this has resulted in their being among the best known of all land tortoises. However, also because of their proximity to humankind they are under severe pressure from collecting and from habitat destruction. All species of Gopher tortoise are now protected by law and should not be disturbed. Large numbers remain in captivity, both in private and institutional hands and therefore they attract considerable interest from prospective captive breeders. It should be noted that the obvious solution of releasing the large captive population back into the wild to replenish declining stocks is both genetically and biologically highly inadvisable. Under no circumstances should captive specimens be simply turned loose. Not only do they pose a potential genetic risk, but recent evidence suggests that they may contaminate already endangered natural populations with fatal pathogens.

Taxonomy: Until recently it was generally thought that the taxonomy of Gopher tortoises was relatively straightforward. This has proved to be very far from the truth. Four allopatric species are recognised in most recent accounts; *Gopherus agassizii* (the Desert tortoise), *Gopherus berlandieri* (the Texas tortoise), *Gopherus polyphemus* (the Florida gopher tortoise) and *Gopherus flavomarginatus* (the Mexican or Bolson tortoise) which was itself only discovered in 1888 and not fully verified until 1959. Very recently however this apparently simple picture has been completely overturned by studies that suggest that *G. agassizii* and *G. berlandieri* should be considered separately under the generic name *Xerobates*, with only *G. polyphemus* and *G. flavomarginatus* continuing under *Gopherus*. Considering that *Gopherus (Xerobates)* are probably the most intensively studied tortoises in the history of herpetology, that such discoveries are still being made says much for our knowledge of the rest! This new classification remains controversial and is not accepted by many authorities. Other authorities, however, do accept the proposals.

Further (mitochondrial DNA) results indicate that *G. (X.) agassizii* itself appears to comprise at least three genetic assemblages in discreet geographical zones as divergent from each other as *G. (X.) agassizii* is from *G. (X.) berlandieri*; clearly these tortoises have a far from simple ancestry and a great deal of work still needs to be done if their phylogeny is finally to be unravelled. It is possible that further revisions may yet be made as research progresses. Exitement ensued in 1989 when a new species of Gopher tortoise, *Xerobates lepidocephalus*, was proposed (Ottley and Velazques Solis, 1989) but this appears to be based upon misinterpretation of a normal *G. (X.) agassizii.*

Description: *Gopherus (Xerobates) agassizii* typically features a SCL to 380 mm, although most much smaller with females smaller than males. This species is principally distinguished by its narrow head and large hind feet. Carapace colouration is light chocolate brown. *Gopherus polyphemus* is externally somewhat similar to *G. (X.) agassizii*, of almost identical colour, but the head is much wider and typically the animal is smaller (approximately 250 mm although some much larger specimens are encountered). *Gopherus (Xerobates) berlandieri* is the smallest of the Gopher tortoises attaining a typical adult SCL of 160 mm SCL although some larger specimens are seen (to about 215 mm). The scutes have a much darker brown ground colour than *G. (X.) agassizii* (often virtually black), but feature prominent yellowish central areolae; these can however, be less obvious in very ancient specimens. The gular projection is very well developed in males, less so in females. *Gopherus flavomarginatus*; this tortoise is the largest terrestrial testudine in North America, and attains the very considerable SCL of 400 mm and weighs in excess of 14 kg. It has two very large black-pointed spurs on the thighs, a brown and yellow carapace with yellowish-horn coloured plastron and the rear marginals are markedly flared and serrate.

Captive environment: All Gopher tortoises are very highly adapted to their native habitat conditions and are by no means easy to maintain successfully - especially outside their natural bioclimatic range. In addition, the various species do differ considerably in terms of temperature and humidity requirements. There are however common threads, one of which is their distinctive habit of residing in burrows - these can be up to 8 meters long in the case of *G. flavomarginatus*, and up to 14 meters long in the case of *G. polyphemus* (although *X. berlandieri* burrows rarely extend for more than 30 - 40 cm). Not only do these provide a means of retreating from unfavourable weather conditions generally, but they provide a microclimate where humidity as well as temperature are relatively stabilised.

In captivity, all Gopher tortoises tend to do badly if overcrowded and if mixed at random with other species. Ideally, they should be provided with an outdoor area of light but excavatable soil, lightly planted with scrub, grass and succulents. An overnight shelter is essential. A small wooden hut is generally satisfactory if provided with a ramp for exit and entry. An even better option is to provide a natural or artificial burrow. Damp environments are categorically not suitable for Gopher tortoises - with the possible exception of *G. (X.) berlandieri* which I have found to positively thrive under more humid conditions and *G. polyphemus* which also prefers a relatively high level of ambient humidity. Cold and damp, however, are definitely to be avoided. Most Gopher tortoises prefer it hot and dry and will readily take advantage of both natural sunlight and artificial basking facilities. The only moisture in desert tortoise accommodation should comprise the drinking pool; this should be 25 - 35 mm deep and the water changed daily. Gopher tortoises hibernate during the winter (usually from November or December through March). The best place for such hibernation is a natural or artificial burrow. The temperatures required for hibernation are as described previously and are similar to those for *T. graeca* and *T. hermanni*.

Diet: In their native habitat Gopher tortoises are virtually 100% herbivorous, with *G. (X.) berlandieri* alone showing some interest in the occasional snail and chance piece of carrion. The bulk of their diet consists of grasses and low growing seasonal herbs, flowers (including lupine and morning glory), succulents and cacti. *Opuntia* pads and fruits are especially favoured but grasses generally comprise more than half of the total dietary intake in the period following Spring when flowers comprise the most favoured food. In captivity it is vitally important that the basic chemical balance and profile of the natural diet is followed as closely as possible, even if exactly the same constituents may not be available. In practice, this translates to a high fibre and low protein dietary regime rich in essential trace elements. Captives reared on high protein diets have a high incidence of liver and renal disease, high rates of bladder stones (uric acid calculi), excessive rates of growth and a likelihood of carapace deformity and metabolic bone disease. Overfeeding is also a major problem in captivity.

Common health problems: Serious upper respiratory tract disease problems afflict this genus. *Mycoplasma* pathogens are believed to be responsible. Treatment with Baytril® has proved useful. Do not mix with other species and quarantine carefully. There is a particularly high rate of disease and mortality when Gopher tortoises are mixed with Mediterranean tortoises, especially *Testudo (g.) ibera* from Turkey. It is possible that this latter species may harbour organisms to which Gopher tortoises have little resistance.

Breeding: In such a diverse group of animals as the Gopher tortoises it is hardly surprising that considerable variation is found between the various forms in respect of their reproductive biology; *G. (X.) agassizii* typically lays clutches of 4 - 8 eggs (sometimes as many as 14) each approximately 39 mm x 44 mm.

Incubation in the wild takes approximately three and a half months. In captivity, they can be successfully incubated artificially at 30 - 31°C in a type I incubator at low to medium humidity which typically results in emergence at 80 - 130 days. The hatchlings typically measure about 48 mm SCL and weigh approximately 28 grams. *G. (X.) agassizii* has been known to hybridise with *G. (X.) berlandeieri* so these species should not be maintained together (Woodbury, 1952). *G. (X.) berlandieri* has a lower average clutch density than *G. (X.) agassizii* typically depositing 3 or 4 eggs, sometimes as few as a single egg, and occasionally as many as 5. The eggs from a single clutch may be also laid in different nests, singly. These eggs are quite different from those of *G. (X.) agassizii* and when freshly laid are somewhat pliable. They rapidly harden to normal consistency, are markedly elongate and measure approximately 48 mm x 35 mm. The hatchlings are smaller than those of *G. (X.) agassizii*, measuring on average 40 mm long and weigh about 21 g. Somewhat surprisingly considering the shape of their egg, they are rounder and less elongate than *G. (X.) agassizii* hatchlings. They can be incubated at the same temperature as *G. (X.) agassizii* eggs but seem to require a much higher level of ambient humidity throughout the incubation process if embryonic dehydration is to be avoided. A Type II high humidity incubator is recommended for this species with a vermiculite substrate partly hydrated with water.

Gopherus polyphemus lays spherical, hard-shelled eggs measuring approximately 40 mm in diameter in clutches ranging from 4 to 7, although as many as 25 can be deposited. The number of eggs varies in accordance with the size of the laying female and also appears to be subject to geographical variation. The incubation period in the wild varies from 80 - 110 days but little data is available on incubation times under artificial conditions.

Gopherus flavomarginatus are unlikely to be encountered in captivity as it is estimated that the total world population is less than 10,000 individuals. However, their eggs, which closely approximate those of *G. (X.) agassizii* in size can be incubated under very similar conditions. It is interesting to note that the conservation captive breeding program for this tortoise in Mexico has made extensive and routine use of oxytocin injections to induce egg laying. It is a significant reflection of our lack knowledge of tortoises that, at present, it is unclear what, if any, ESD thresholds apply to the *Gopherus/Xerobates* complex.

Spotila and Sandora (1986) have suggested that sex determination in *G. (X.) agassizii* may be temperature dependent with a threshold of 30 - 31°C. It is not known if this trait is shared with other members of the genus. This aspect of their reproductive ecology urgently requires more research.

GRAPTEMYS SPP. Agassiz, 1857

Map Turtles

3/5/14

General observations: So-called from the fine pattern of lines on the skin and, in some subspecies, a carapace pattern that resembles contour lines on a map. Map turtles are under intense pressure in the wild from habitat degradation and pollution of waterways. Road-kills are also a significant problem in many areas.

Taxonomy: At the time of writing 12 species and 6 subspecies are generally recognised. The taxon is under intense study, and hence further revisions are likely. Newly described forms include *G. ernsti* and *G. gibbonsi*.

Description: This is a very varied genus with considerable morphological divergence between its constituent species and subspecies. The Sawback turtle, *G. pseudogeographica* is probably the most distinctive member of the group with its small head and characteristic keel. *G. geographica*, the Common Map turtle, features specially adapted wide jaws for crushing the shells of molluscs. Map turtles vary greatly in size, the largest species attaining in excess of 33 cm. Identifying the various species and subspecies that form this complex genus can prove difficult; a good regional field guide is essential. The most comprehensive descriptive text to date is that presented by Ernst, Lovich and Barbour (1994).

Captive environment: The suggested water temperature range for this turtle is between 21 - 28°C, seasonally adjusted if over wintering is required. Some species and subspecies hibernate, when <10°C may be appropriate in winter and may stimulate post-hibernation breeding behaviour. Map turtles primarily inhabit rivers rather than lakes or ponds in the wild, however, most species seem to avoid rapid currents preferring instead slower moving waterways. *G. caglei* (from the Guadalupe river complex) inhabits shallow silt and gravel streams and are enthusiastic baskers. A generally shy and nervous animal, privacy is required in captive enclosures. Stress can lead to reduced immune response and shell injuries sustained in efforts to dive from basking areas when disturbed or surprised. Sandy bottoms to tanks or ponds are advised. These will minimise injuries from bottoming out. Basking areas are essential for all these species, which will take great advantage of any convenient log or rock under a light and heat source.

Diet: Omnivorous. The precise dietary intake appears to vary between species, subspecies and even between males and females. *G. caglei*, for example, feeds extensively upon caddis fly larvae (Killebrew, 1991). Broad jawed varieties tend to exhibit a preference for molluscs and snails. In captivity, a wide variety of foods are accepted. Most species feed by hunting along the bottom among the stems of aquatic plants and reeds. Food is almost always swallowed underwater. Most feeding also occurs in the morning and late afternoon (Ernst, Lovich and Barbour, 1994).

Common health problems: *Herpes* type virus infections have been recorded in turtles of this genus (Jacobson, Gaskin and Wahlquist, 1982). Poor water quality is not well tolerated and can lead to skin and shell problems.

Breeding: Very similar to Red-eared sliders in terms of courtship behaviour. Males of some species stimulate heads and faces of females with their long front claws in a rapid vibrating action. Exact details of this behaviour appear to vary between species as do egg dimensions and clutch densities. Most female Map turtles prefer a well-drained sandy beach or open clearing for egg deposition with clutch densities ranging from 5 to 16. According to Caldwell and Collins (1981) *Graptemys geographica* in Kansas deposit their eggs in a double layer within the nest, an intervening covering of earth separating the two layers. According to Ernst, Lovich and Barbour (1994) most nesting occurs early in the day, before 0800. Up to two separate clutches may be laid each season. ESD has been reported in *G. pseudogeographica* when eggs incubated at 25°C produced all males and those incubated at 30°C or higher produced females. Other species and subspecies may be similarly affected, but details are unclear at the time of writing. ESD is also confirmed in *G. geographica* (Ewart and Nelson, 1991) with identical parameters to *G. pseudogeographica*. Incubation temperatures throughout the *Graptemys* complex may exert very different influences; some species (e.g. *G. kohnii*) appear to demonstrate higher hatch rates at lower, rather than higher temperatures. Egg dimensions even within a single species, (e.g. *G. kohnii*) also vary considerably in size, possibly according to the size of the laying female. Incubation temperatures also influence the time taken to hatch. At a constant 28°C emergence can be anticipated between 55 - 65 days, at 27°C the incubation time may be extended to 75 days. Hatchlings of *G. khonii* measure approximately 35 mm long and weigh 9 g.

HEOSEMYS GRANDIS (Gray, 1860)

Giant Asian pond turtle

General observations: An Asian semi-terrestrial batagurine turtle, known for its large size and religious significance.

Taxonomy: No subspecies are currently recognised.

Description: Carapace to 45 cm, serrated at posterior. Carapace colour dull brown to black. Plastron and marginals are yellow and typically feature distinct pattern of fine radiating brown lines.

Captive environment: Mostly aquatic, but also enjoys basking, resting and walking on land. Require a large and well-filtered aquarium with access to land whenever desired. Small to medium-sized specimens can be adequately filtered by means of a powerhead assisted under-gravel system but large adults will require an additional external canister filter. A suitable land area substrate is pine bark, peat, sand and leaf litter. For basking a medium-wattage incandescent lamp should be provided above the land section. In the wild, this species inhabits freshwater streams, ponds and swamps. A very high humidity environment is therefore recommended. This turtle can tolerate quite low water temperatures (to 12°C) although is most active at 18 - 22°C. Below 12°C the turtle becomes torpid, and rests on the bottom for extended periods. Air temperatures should be maintained above 25°C if activity is to be sustained.

Diet: Omnivorous. Red and yellow coloured fruits and flowers are often taken in preference to other items. Healthy specimens feed readily and aggressively.

Common health problems: None immediately evident.

Breeding: Mating usually occurs immediately after the water temperature rises following a rest period; at this time both males and females may exhibit a tendency to aggression. The eggs measure approximately 65 x 35 mm and if incubated at 28°C in a 100% humidity environment usually hatch in 150 - 170 days. The juveniles measure approximately 43 mm long with a mass of 23 g. Neonates are initially exclusively carnivorous. Following hatching growth is swift, and juveniles are very susceptible to developing metabolic bone disease as a result of dietary deficiencies. A good quality calcium and vitamin D3 supplement should be applied to each meal.

HEOSEMYS SPINOSA (Gray, 1831)

The cog-wheel turtle

General observations: A curious looking batagurine turtle from Asia that well deserves its alternative colloquial name the "Spiny turtle".

Taxonomy: No subspecies have been described.

Description: Unmistakable in appearance, the marginals of this turtle are composed of a series of sharp spines. The carapace is dull brown, but the yellow plastron and ventral aspect of the marginals are finely covered in an attractive pattern of brown-black lines. Maximum size of this species is approximately 22 cm, but most examples are much smaller, typically around 15 cm. Waagen (1984) described plastral kinesis as a sexually dimorphic feature in female *H. spinosa* and suggested that this may occur to permit passage of eggs.

Captive environment: By nature, a quiet and secretive turtle often active at dawn or dusk. This species has also been observed feeding in almost total darkness. Light levels in the terrarium should therefore not be excessive. A peat, sphagnum and leaf litter substrate is preferred for the terrestrial area. A shallow (3 - 10 cm depending upon the dimensions of the specimens) water section employing an under-gravel or small canister filter should also be provided. Terrarium temperatures should normally be maintained in the range 26 - 29°C with a basking lamp to provide additional capacity for thermoregulation. Regular misting with a water spray is also suggested as *H. spinosa* prefers a high humidity environment. Some plants in the terrarium and a generous quantity of damp sphagnum will also help in this respect. Temperatures in the water section should normally be maintained in the region of 23 - 25°C or slightly higher depending upon observation of the turtle's reactions. With a range extending from Burma to Sumatra and Borneo it is likely that the origin of a specimen may have a bearing upon its individual preferences. In parts of its range it occurs in high (3000 m) altitude hill streams. Some specimens appear to prefer cooler environments and do better at water and air temperatures below 23°C. This species typically fasts for prolonged periods, refusing food for weeks at a time. This seems to cause it no harm. It is also inclined to remain practically motionless for days at a time. Again, this seems to constitute normal behaviour for the species.

Diet: Most captives are omnivorous, but with a very strong preference for vegetable foods. Reluctant feeders can often be tempted with red, yellow or purple coloured foods including red cabbage, tomato, strawberries or orange (O'Leary, pers. comm.). Together with whatever additional green plants it can be persuaded into accepting these should constitute at least 90% of its dietary intake. Some animal protein (in the form of earth worms or prepared items) is also recommended. Many specimens remain exclusively herbivorous. A pattern that is believed to be closest to its natural diet.

Common health problems: The digestive tract of this species seems particularly sensitive.

Breeding: Herman (1992) reports what is believed to be the first breeding in captivity of this species. Sexual interest was stimulated by spraying with water which was followed by copulation in the water section of the terrarium. A typical clutch consists of one or two eggs, sometimes nested, but occasionally deposited on the surface. The fertile egg described by Herman (op. cit.) was incubated in a medium of damp sand, ground peat moss and sphagnum for 35 days at 28 - 30°C, followed by a reduction to 26 - 28°C for the remaining 71 days of the incubation period. The neonate measured 55 mm SCL with a mass of 34.1 g and was maintained at 26 - 30°C in a similar environment to that described above.

HOMOPUS SPP. Dumeril and Bibron, 1835

The Padloper tortoises

General observations: This group of South African tortoises is rarely encountered in captivity. They are neither easy to maintain or breed, but with adequate attention to detail success can be achieved. Much of their natural life cycle remains understudied.

Taxonomy: Four species, *H. boulengeri* (Karoo Padloper), *H. femoralis* (Greater Padloper), *H. areolatus* (Parrot-beak tortoise), and *H. signatus* (Speckled Padloper) this later taxon currently divided into two subspecies, *H. s. signatus* and *H. s. cafer*. The subspecific division of *H. signatus* is presently under revision and there appear to be doubts as to whether any real differences actually exist. "*Homopus bergeri*" is apparently junior synonym of *Psammobates tentorius verroxii* and the tortoises referred to this are presently undergoing further revision and will subsequently be renamed (Branch, 1992).

Description: *H. femoralis* is the largest member of the genus at 10 - 13 cm (maximum recorded size 16 cm). Carapace is typically red-brown. Thigh tubercles are present. Beak not hooked. Forelimbs feature large imbricate scales and 4 claws. The plastron of males is not depressed. *H. signatus* is the smallest member of the genus at 6 - 8 cm (maximum 9.5 cm) and at these dimensions is also the smallest living land tortoise in the world. As its common name suggests, the carapace of this species features a light brown carapace with numerous black spots; the spots are extremely fine in *H. s. cafer*, much less so in *H. s. signatus*. The marginals of *H. s. signatus* are serrated but smooth in *H. s. cafer*. Both subspecies possess thigh tubercles. *H. areolatus* typically measures from 7 - 9 cm (maximum 11 cm). The scutes of the carapace, which has an olive ground colour and red-brown markings, are often indented at the centres. Thigh tubercles are absent in this species. The beak is strongly hooked. The fore-limbs feature 4 claws. *H. boulengeri* typically attains 10 - 13 cm (maximum recorded 16 cm). The carapace is overall dark-red-brown, occasionally olive. Thigh tubercles are absent. Males possess an indented plastron. "*H. bergeri*" (the Aus race, from southern Namibia) is the least known of the Padlopers, typically attaining 10 - 15 cm. Carapace coloration is red-brown with pale centres and black borders. The plastron is pale yellow or greenish. Each fore-limb has 5 claws. Thigh tubercles are absent in this species.

Captive environment: It is absolutely imperative that these species are not mixed with others as their resistance to alien pathogens is very poor. Mixing of species and contamination due to inadequate hygiene measures is one reason why captive mortality rates among *Homopus* are usually extremely high. In this, they closely mirror many other very small tortoises including *Testudo kleinmanni* and *Psammobates* species. If maintained in strict isolation, and in the correct environmental conditions, then *Homopus* can survive and breed successfully in captivity. Some adjustments are required to temperature and humidity depending upon the species in question. *H. areolatus* is relatively versatile in its habitat requirements, but typically favours a semi-arid maquis type environment; *H. boulengeri* favours similar habitat with a predilection for grasslands; *H. femoralis* is often found in rocky environments with extreme temperatures in summer and sub-zero conditions in winter (when it hibernates. It also inhabits grasslands; *H. signatus* also favours rocky terrain and grasslands but those with far less severe climatic extremes. In captivity, a stony, sandy substrate with rocks for climbing will be much appreciated. A basking source is also mandatory. For *H. signatus*, daytime temperatures in the vivarium should be maintained at 32°C directly under the basking source. Overnight temperatures can be reduced to 12°C. Overall ambient temperatures (excluding the basking site) can be considerably cooler - *H. signatus* is active and will feed at temperatures in the 15 - 18°C range. A winter rest period can be given for 6 - 10 weeks when the temperature can be reduced to 5°C, following which peak breeding activity often occurs. If a cool period is not provided, females may not be receptive.

Diet: A high dry fibre intake is essential; excessive provision of wet fruits can lead to enhanced gut motility and protozoan proliferation, diarrhoea and consequent acute dehydration. All *Homopus* species show a preference for feeding upon brightly coloured red and yellow flower heads. *Hibiscus* flowers are especially favoured. Succulent plants are also eaten, and although *Homopus* species have been observed drinking from rock pools in the wild, probably contribute a major portion of their fluid intake. In the wild, these tortoises also consume hyena faeces and the occasional snail or beetle.

Common health problems: *Hexamita* infection; pneumonia; viral stomatitis.

Breeding: Until recently, very little serious captive breeding work had been undertaken with these remarkable - and very fragile - tortoises. Egg dimensions vary between *Homopus* species; *H. boulengeri* lays a single egg of approximately 35 mm x 22.5 mm; *H. signatus* also lays a single egg of very similar size; *H. femoralis* lays clutches of 1 - 3 eggs of approximately 30 mm x 25 mm; *H. areolatus* also lays in clutches, of between 2 - 5 eggs (most often 2 - 3, although single egg clutches are also reported) and may lay up to two clutches per season making this the most prolific of the *Homopus* group. Males of this species also undergo a colour change during the breeding season, with the prefrontal scales of the head turning a deep orange-red hue. Male competition and aggression may be intense and violent. Males also bite at the female's head and legs prior to copulation, and occasionally injuries may be inflicted. Eglis (1963) records that a captive female *H. areolatus* dug repeated trial nests over a 10 day period before depositing one egg measuring 33 x 21.5mm followed 2 days later by a second measuring 32.5 x 20.5 mm. The hatchlings of this species typically weigh between 5 - 8 g and have a SCL of between 25 - 35 mm. If incubated at 27°C hatching occurs (on average) after 130 days, although this appears to be very variable. In the wild, incubation periods of up to 320 days have been reported - suggesting that *Homopus* eggs may be diapausal. It is reported from South Africa that *H. signatus* eggs incubated at 28°C hatch in 115 - 135 days and that the neonates of this species measure 33 mm long with a mass of approximately 12 g.

However, Silverman (1993) reported upon a captive pair in New York which laid an egg measuring 30 mm x 20 mm. This was incubated at 83 - 87°F and hatched after 118 days. The neonate in this instance measured 25 mm SCL and weighed 5 g. Initial growth was rapid, attaining 6 grams after 12 days and 7 grams after 17 days. Incubation humidity for *Homopus* species should be moderate to low; a standard type I incubator with water tray has proved consistently successful.

HYDROMEDUSA TECTIFERA Cope, 1870

Argentine snake-necked turtle

General observations: The Argentine snake-necked turtle is an interesting species that is not often encountered in captivity. It is, however, relatively easy to maintain. Externally, *Hydromedusa* spp. closely resemble Australian side-necks of the genus *Chelodina*.

Taxonomy: Together, *Hydromedusa tectifera* and *Hydromedusa maximiliani* (Mikan, 1820) form the South American genus *Hydromedusa*. No subspecies of either species have been described. The range of *H. tectifera* includes south-eastern Brazil, eastern Paraguay, north-eastern Argentina to Uruguay. The range of *H. maximiliani* is much more restricted and appears to consist of only a certain limited region of south-eastern Brazil.

Description: A medium-sized turtle, attaining up to 30 cm SCL, *H. tectifera* has an oval, flattened carapace with an obvious medial keel present on vertebrals 1 to 4. An additional conical projection is present on vertebral 5. Similar projections are found on the pleural scutes. The carapace is dark brown and the plastron is yellow, sometimes with dark blotches. The head is olive-grey with a broad cream stripe bordered in black reaching from the upper jaw along the length of the neck and the chin is yellow with fine dark spots. The limbs are olive-grey on their upper surfaces but yellow-cream on their ventral surfaces. Large transverse scales are present on the forelimbs. The neck is exceptionally long and its lateral aspect bears a series of spiny tubercles.

Captive environment: In nature, *H. tectifera* is found in slow-moving streams, lakes, ponds, marshes and rivers. It is usually found in association with aquatic vegetation and often prefers a soft-bottomed environment. In captivity, it appears intolerant of alkaline water conditions and prefers a slightly acid environment (pH 6.8 or lower). For normal activity water temperatures should be maintained in the region of 23 to 24°C. In the wild, in Uruguay, these temperatures occur during December, January and February. A cooler winter period is also experienced, from June, July to August when temperatures fall to below 17°C. In other parts of this turtle's range even lower temperatures are experienced and there is some evidence that they may hibernate for a brief period buried in the soft mud at the bottom of ponds or lakes. Some keepers have replicated this behaviour in captivity, but most prefer to maintain year-round activity, perhaps with a seasonal period of brief torpidity in winter. Good quality filtration is important and if not provided will result in eye, skin and respiratory infections. Large external canister filters with activated carbon and additional biological media are ideal. Under-gravel filtration can also be employed, but the gravel may require protecting by means of a gravel-tidy. Air temperatures should also be maintained at a few degrees above that of the water. A soft silt or fine, non-abrasive gravel substrate is suggested. Although very largely aquatic, this species does bask and so a smoothly sloped basking site should be provided. Chromalux® lamps are well suited to this purpose.

Diet: Fish and small invertebrates form the staple diet of *H. tectifera*, although in captivity a wide range of other foods are readily accepted including trout-chow, crickets, cat pellets and tinned dog food. Recent studies on the feeding habits of wild *H. maximiliani*, in Brazil, reveal that freshwater shrimp and insect larvae comprised a high proportion of their total dietary intake (Souza and Abe, 1995).

Common health problems: Skin and shell infections; possibly as a result of contaminated live foodstuffs. Water hygiene is especially important if such problems are to be prevented.

Breeding: This species is rarely bred in captivity but occasional successes have been recorded. Mating behaviour closely resembles that of soft-shell turtles, with the male using his mouth to bite and hold onto the fleshy neck of the female during copulation. Eggs measure approximately 36 mm x 28 mm and weigh approximately 11 grams. Incubation can be achieved at temperatures from 25 - 30°C on a vermiculite substrate hydrated 1:1 with water. The hatchlings measure approximately 37 mm long and weigh about 8 grams upon emergence.

INDOTESTUDO ELONGATA (Blyth, 1853)

The Elongated tortoise

General observations: Infrequently encountered in captive collections, yet enjoys a wide natural distribution in Asia.

Taxonomy: No subspecies have been described. Distribution includes Thailand, India, Bangladesh, Nepal, south China, Myanmar, Laos, Vietnam, Malaysia and Kampuchea.

Description: Carapace to approximately 33 cm (males) and 29 cm (females). The body of males is also narrower than that of females (Biswas, et. al. 1978). The carapace is markedly elongate, flattened dorsally. The plastron is deeply notched posteriorly. The gular is broad and flattened. Tail features terminal claw. Carapace colour yellow-greenish, yellow-brown or bright yellow, a single black mark may be visible on the costal and vertebral scutes. A narrow nuchal scute is present. The plastron typically possesses a uniform yellow ground with black blotches. Limbs are light brown to olive. The head is pale yellow except in the breeding season when both sexes undergo a colour change to feature pink hues around the eyes and nostrils.

Captive environment: In the wild, *I. elongata* typically occurs in teak and sal (*Shorea robusta)* forests where the humidity is high, although it is also found in hot dry conditions. It is most active during the early part of the rainy season (when breeding also occurs). In captivity it seems reasonably tolerant and can, for the most part, be treated similarly to *Kinixys belliana* whose dietary preferences it also closely follows. Some keepers report that *I. elongata* is most active at dawn and dusk, when it can be observed hunting for food. This tortoise typically avoids strong sunlight, and does not normally seem interested in basking facilities (although, given its wide distribution, regional preferences may exist). As in the wild, peak activity is often seen following heavy, warm, summer rain. Daytime environmental temperature should be maintained in the 26 - 30°C region during summer. In winter daytime temperatures can be reduced to 24°C. At night, temperatures can be reduced to 19 - 20°C. Annual temperature cycling is important if breeding is to be achieved.

Diet: Keepers report that this tortoise regularly takes snails, slugs and worms in addition to green leafy material, fruit and vegetables. A bathing pool is essential, as *Indotestudo elongata* is known to drink copiously and likes to sit, half-submerged, for several hours at a time. In the wild, fallen fruits are believed to comprise a high proportion of its diet. In captivity, the Minnesota Zoo found rehydrated rabbit pellets were taken readily and produced good results (Spencer, 1988). Many keepers provide a diet rich in prepared meats such as dog food for *I. elongata*, but this is probably inappropriate. Only a small amount of low fat animal protein (such as rehydrated cat pellets with added vitamins and calcium) is provided on an irregular basis to the Elongate tortoises in the Tortoise Trust collection. This appears to be entirely adequate and is conducive to long-term good health.

Common health problems: None immediately evident.

Breeding: Published breeding records in captivity are comparatively rare. However, Dunn (1976) describes a female that laid 3 eggs measuring approximately 50 mm long in April. A second clutch of 4 was then laid on 28th June. These were incubated at 28°C in a still-air incubator. The first clutch proved infertile, but the second clutch resulted in 3 healthy hatchlings and one dead neonate. Spencer (op. cit.) reported that hatchlings weighed 25 - 27 g after an average 116 day incubation period "in the low 80's °F". After 12 months, growth to between 114 - 180 g had been achieved for a group of 4 neonates. Despite a lack of detailed published data, an increasing number of private keepers are succeeding in the captive breeding of *I. elongata*. Provided that well matched sexually mature pairs of are maintained, it is not especially difficult to breed this species. Mating behaviour involves the male chasing the female, with attendant ramming of her carapace. Typical clutch sizes range from 5 - 9 eggs and up to 3 clutches are deposited each year, making this a potentially highly productive species. The most successful incubation temperature has proved to be in the 28.5 - 30°C range on a moist vermiculite and sphagnum substrate. Unfortunately ESD thresholds, if they apply, are unknown. At least one private keeper has succeeded in multiple second-generation captive breeding of *I. elongata* (McCormick, 1992) - a commendable achievement with any species, and especially so in the case of a species as infrequently bred as this. Juveniles can be successfully maintained in a covered vivarium where the ambient humidity is 90%+. A peat and sphagnum moss substrate has proved effective. The plastic seed propagators referred to earlier (as used for box turtles) are ideal for this purpose and can easily be base heated which contributes to maintaining environmental humidity. Captive bred stock becomes sexually mature at 7 or 8 years of age, or when a carapace length of 19 cm is attained, whichever is the sooner.

INDOTESTUDO FORSTENII (Schlegel and Muller, 1844)
Travancore tortoise

General observations: A little known species from India and Indonesia that closely resembles, and may be mistaken for, *I. elongata.*

Taxonomy: Previously known as "*Testudo travancorica*" or "*Geochelone travancorica*".

Description: The carapace, which is typically dull yellow-olive, can attain 33 cm. Males tend to be larger than females. It is distinguished from *I. elongata* by the lack of a nuchal scute and by a shorter interpectoral suture. As with *I. elongata* this species exhibits colour changes associated with breeding, the temporal region and nares taking on a bright pink hue, especially so in males.

Captive environment: Essentially as for *Indotestudo elongata.* The Travancore tortoise's natural habitat includes moist evergreen forests up to an altitude of 450 m. According to Das (1991) a rocky biotype is preferred, with many tortoises inhabiting rocky clefts along rivers or streams and under boulders within forests. Unlike *I. elongata*, however, basking behaviour is common in this species. The substrate in captive enclosures should approximate that of the wild, e.g. a mixed leaf litter, bark and loamy mulch in one section and a drier, gravel substrate in a second area. Background heating should be the main source of warmth, with only low intensity basking sources. Bright lights are usually not well tolerated, the tortoise seeking escape by burrowing into its substrate. Some plants for cover should be provided if at all possible. Terrarium temperatures should be maintained above 26°C during the day although a reduction to 18°C over night is permissible.

Diet: This tortoise appears to be largely herbivorous, although it is also known to consume a small number of insects and amphibians. The natural diet of this tortoise includes bamboo shoots, grass, fungi and fallen fruits which are said to be its favourite. In captivity it will accept a wide range of green leafed vegetation and fruit. A limited amount of low fat animal protein should also be provided. Most feeding occurs after dusk or in the early morning.
Common health problems: None immediately evident.

Breeding: This species is rarely bred in captivity, but generally behaviour and requirements are similar to *I. elongata.* The species vocalises when foraging in rain, and has also been heard to make similar sounds during mating. Clutch density even for fully grown females is surprisingly low, with 3 eggs each measuring 45 - 50 mm x 38 - 41 mm and weighing 25 g being laid on average. Little data on incubation conditions for this species is available, but one report (Sane and Sane, 1989) mentions an incubation period of 146 - 149 days at an unspecified temperature. Hatchlings measure approximately 55 mm SCL.

KACHUGA TECTA (Gray, 1831)
The Indian Roofed terrapin

General observations: The most frequently encountered member of the Batagurine genus *Kachuga* that includes 7 species from the Indian subcontinent. This species is currently listed on CITES Appendix 1 and is also protected under the Indian Wildlife Protection Act. Captive maintenance is similar for all species, although there are differences in water depth preferences and diet, some being considerably more carnivorous than others.

Taxonomy: No subspecies of *K. tecta* are currently recognised.

Description: The carapace is elongate, high domed and bears a single medial keel. This keel features several spikes or projections, especially in the region of the 3rd vertebral scute. *K. tecta* can attain up to 23 cm SCL but most specimens are much smaller. The carapace is brown in colour but the first three vertebral scutes may be bordered in orange and the marginals may be bordered in yellow. The plastron is yellowish with 2 to 4 black markings on each scute. The head is blackish dorsally, but with red or orange postorbital blotches. The neck bears a clearly defined series of thin yellow stripes. Agarwal, Wadhwan and Lavania (1986) report sexual dichromatism in *K. tecta*; white bands are present on the tails of males whereas in females these bands are yellow. Females also possess pink irises whilst those of males are red. Males are also smaller than females, 1:2 by body size and 1:9 by weight (Vyas and Patel, 1993), with thicker tails and darker coloured carapaces.

Captive environment: *Kachuga tecta* occurs mainly in slow-moving water and is an inhabitant of rivers, ponds and static water bodies such as drainage ditches with plentiful aquatic vegetation. It is often seen basking on riverbanks and partly submerged logs. In captivity, it is relatively undemanding and does well in large and well-filtered aquaria that must be provided with a land section and with a basking lamp. Under-gravel filtration is well suited to this species. A system as used by the author for accommodating young *Cyclemys dentata*, but with deeper water, is probably ideal. A captive-breeding project in India accommodated 3 males and 5 females in a 4 x 4.5 m enclosure with a 50 cm peripheral wall and central 1.5 x 1.5 m pond of 50 cm depth. The soil in the enclosure was mixed with 50% sand which is preferred by this species for nesting purposes (Vyas and Patel, 1993). *Kachuga tecta* is reasonably tolerant of water temperature fluctuations, but for maximum activity a temperature of approximately 25°C is suggested. Water pH does not appear to be critical but is best maintained on the slightly acid side of neutral. Air temperatures should be maintained at parity or slightly above the water temperature. A high level of ambient humidity is also recommended. This appears to be especially important for hatchlings and juveniles. Most *Kachuga* species are non-aggressive in captivity and rarely bite.

Diet: Das (1991) and Tikader and Sharma (1985) indicate that in nature this species is almost exclusively herbivorous, feeding upon a wide range of plant matter including water hyacinth and corriander leaves (Vyas and Patel, 1993). However, Hossain and Sarker (1995) report that in Bangladesh *K. tecta* also consume crabs, snails, dead animals and even human waste. In

Diamondback terrapin, *Malaclemys terrapin,* a brackish water species from North America. Its jaws are especially adapted to feeding upon molluscs.

Home's hinge-back tortoise, *Kinixys homeana,* a tropical species from Africa which requires an omnivorous diet and a high humidity environment in captivity.

Juvenile *Kinixys homeana*. The sharp serrated marginals are a deterrent to potential predators and its overall shape and colour blends in perfectly with a forest leaf substrate. The hinge is not yet developed.

Bell's hinge-back tortoise, *Kinixys belliana*

captivity, most specimens appear to be largely herbivorous but will accept some animal matter including prepared items such as trout-chow and rehydrated cat and koi pellets. Discussing *K. tentoria* Das (1991) suggests that males and juveniles are more carnivorous than females which remain largely herbivorous. It is not presently known if this pattern is replicated in *K. tecta*.

Common health problems: None immediately evident.

Breeding: None of the species comprising *Kachuga* are frequently bred in captivity, although the potential for doing so clearly exists. *K. tecta* lays clutches of between 7 to 10 eggs measuring 37 x 21 mm (Moll, 1987). Eggs from the closely related *Kachuga tentoria* (the Indian Tent terrapin) have been successfully incubated at a range of temperatures from 24 - 33°C with a mean incubation time of 95 days (Moll, op. cit.). Eggs from the subspecies *K. tentoria flaviventer* were incubated by Vijaya (1982) at 27.3 to 28.5°C and took 125 to 144 days to hatch. Incubation can be achieved on a mixed peat and vermiculite substrate hydrated 1:1 with water. Vyas and Patel (1993) note that *K. tecta* excavates nests of up to 20 cm depth, surprisingly deep for its body size. Eggs incubated in the ground in India which were laid in February and March hatched between 70 and 78 days later. Throughout the incubation period absolute maximum and minimum external air temperatures ranged from 39°C to 22°C whilst nest temperatures varied from 22°C to 33°C. The mean variation in nest temperatures, however, was only 3 to 4°C. The hatchlings measure approximately 3.5 cm SCL and weigh approximately 9 g. Hatchling care is straightforward. As stated above, however, these may prove to be considerably more carnivorous than adults. Chopped earthworm is usually accepted enthusiastically.

KINIXYS SPP. Bell 1827

African Hinge-back tortoises

General observations: Members of the genus *Kinixys* are distinguished by their uniquely hinged carapace that allows the rear of the shell to close giving additional protection to the tail and legs. This unique character sets them apart from all other terrestrial tortoises. This hinge is located between the 7th and 8th marginals and 4th and 5th costals.

Taxonomy: The status of *Kinixys* species is, at the present writing, still under extensive revision. Until recently, only three species were recognised by most authorities; *Kinixys belliana, K. homeana* and *K. erosa*. The latter pair are readily distinguishable from the former. *Kinixys belliana* was assumed to have a wide distribution, from Senegal and northern Cameroon, via southern Africa to Madagascar. As is often the case where wide distributions are assumed, however, this appears not to be the case. This apparently extensive distribution is misleading and what passed for "identical" populations of *Kinixys belliana* in much of its range in fact appears to be formed of populations comprising not only of several different subspecies, but no less than 3 additional full species. In many respects this a situation that finds a parallel in North Africa with regard to *Testudo graeca*. The current checklist for *Kinixys* (based upon the pioneering work of Donald G. Broadley with this genus) therefore includes *Kinixys homeana, K. erosa, K. belliana belliana, K. belliana nogueyi, K. belliana* *zombensis, K. spekii, K. lobatsiana* and *K. natalensis*. Some authorities also recognise *K. b. mertensi* from northern Zaire and Uganda. It is quite likely that as studies progress additional forms will be identified. From the captive breeding point of view it is readily admitted that such a profusion of species creates some difficulties - not the least of which is obtaining a satisfactory identification of specimens. Fortunately, those species most likely to be encountered under captive conditions (*K. homeana, K. erosa* and *K. belliana belliana)* are relatively easy to identify and in the case of unusual specimens, study of specialist works on South African testudines should provide the answer.

Description: The maximum dimensions recorded for male *K belliana belliana* are SCL (straight carapace length) 206 mm and for female specimens 217 mm. The carapace is a dull yellow-buff colour with darker brown or reddish-brown central scute markings. The upper posterior section of the carapace is gently rounded. *Kinixys homeana* and *K. erosa* are very different from *K. belliana* in overall appearance, being an overall reddish-brown colour with lighter rather than darker centres to the scutes. In both cases these tortoises are much more sharply angular at the rear portion of the carapace than *K. belliana*. This characteristic is much more marked in *K. homeana* than in *K. erosa* and may be used to separate the two. In *K. homeana* there is typically a vertical descent from the 5th vertebral scute to the supracaudal. *Kinixys erosa* is the largest of the hinge-backs, with males often exceeding 315 mm and females 250 mm. *K. homeana* is a smaller species, with males rarely in excess of 208 mm and females 220 mm. *Kinixys natalensis* is the smallest of the presently known *Kinixys* complex, to 15.5 cm, and more closely resembles K. *belliana* than *K. erosa* or *K. homeana*.

Captive environment: It is not easy to generalise the requirements of *Kinixys* specimens, as they inhabit a surprisingly wide range of disparate biotypes from coastal plains and savannah to the edges of forests and swamps. Without knowing the origin of specimens it can therefore be extremely difficult to provide the sort of environment to which the animal is accustomed. Some experimentation is usually required, the environment being adjusted in accordance with the tortoises' responses. As a starting point, a relatively high humidity should be provided with a daytime temperature in the order of 24 - 28°C. For *K. natalensis* and *K. belliana* a drier habitat is usually preferred as these are principally grassland and savannah habitat tortoises. Water should be available at all times, as *Kinixys* species (especially *K. erosa* and *K. homeana*) like to soak and even swim on occasions. Those from forest habitats (e.g. *K. erosa* and *K. homeana*) prefer more shade than those from open or savannah habitats, but all tend to be secretive and appreciate a secure retreat area Most *Kinixys* tortoises tend to be more active during wet and rainy weather, and in southern Africa *K. belliana* is known to aestivate during very dry periods. These tortoises frequently also show a tendency to feed and become active at dawn and dusk. It will be noted that all have comparatively large eyes compared to most tortoises from bright habitats with daytime feeding patterns. In good weather *Kinixys* species can be maintained outside successfully in both Europe and the Unites States An outdoor pen is generally satisfactory provided it is well planted, kept moist, and has plenty of shade. To maintain humidity a plastic sheet covering the enclosure is highly effective, and this is particularly recommended for *K. erosa* and *K. homeana*. A heated indoor retreat may, however, be required on all but the warmest of summer nights. In cool weather these tortoises are best maintained under tropical greenhouse conditions. In South Africa, *K. natalensis* and *K. belliana* hibernate during the winter months. In captivity it is probably simplest (and safest) to over winter by providing an environment geared to normal activity. However, there is some evidence that this may inhibit breeding. If this is a priority, then a conditioning period of approximately 2 months from December at 12 - 14°C is suggested. This should be undertaken in their normal terrarium, allowing them to emerge on warm days if desired or to take a soak occasionally. During this cooler, dry period reduce misting or spraying of the terrarium. After 8 weeks increase temperature to normal range, provide plenty of extra soaks, and begin misting terrarium regularly. Breeding activity should begin within 3 - 6 weeks.

Diet: *Kinixys* species are typically omnivorous with a marked preference for mushrooms, slugs, snails, mixed fruit (especially banana) and earthworms. A good variety of green plant leaf material should also be provided. In a suitable outdoor enclosure the tortoises will find a high percentage of their food for themselves, spending a considerable time engaged in hunting down snails, worms and fresh shoots of weed.

Common health problems: Beware of *Hexamita* infection in these species, especially in trade animals. Many specimens also carry a large intestinal worm burden so routine worming is recommended. *K. erosa* and *K. homeana* are prone to eye problems if maintained at incorrect humidity and temperature. It is advisable not to mix different *Kinixys* species, as there is not only a danger of hybridisation but also because there are behavioural incompatibilities.

Breeding: Male *Kinixys* can be very aggressive and it may not be possible to maintain more than one per enclosure. *K. erosa* appear to be the most aggressive of all, and two males will sometimes inflict serious injuries upon each other. Mating can likewise prove a vigorous affair. Female *K. belliana* may lay more than one clutch during the summer, often at intervals of about 5 - 8 weeks. A clutch typically comprises between 4 - 8 eggs, occasionally as many as 10 in the case of large individuals. The eggs are very elongate and usually measure approximately 38 mm x 48 mm and range from 23 g to 32 g in weight. There are inexplicable size variations in the literature pertaining to the eggs of *Kinixys belliana*. It seems probable that the various populations (and subspecies) in all likelihood produce eggs that are significantly different from each other in size and form. The hatchlings of *K. belliana* typically measure some 38 - 47 mm SCL and weigh approximately 17 - 25 g at emergence - again there are significant differences between the different populations. The carapace hinge is not evident in hatchlings and juveniles and in the case of *K. erosa* and *K. homeana* the hatchlings have powerfully serrated marginals giving them a distinctly spiky appearance. Artificial incubation is most successfully carried out at approximately 30.5°C at a medium-high humidity (recommended 75 - 80%) in either a type I or II incubator. At 30 - 31°C the incubation period is typically 90 - 110 days. In the wild the incubation period is variable according to the time of oviposition; it can take anything up to a year. At lower incubation temperatures the eggs may remain viable, but the incidence of dead-in-shell hatchlings increases and incubation times become very extended. In the *South African Tortoise Book* Boycott and Bourquin give an example of one egg that took 10 months to hatch when incubated at 25 °C and describe another egg which took 12 months.

KINOSTERNON SPP. (Spix, 1824)

Mud and Musk turtles

General observations: Widely distributed genus of New World Mud and Musk turtles.

Taxonomy: Under continual revision. At the time of writing, over 20 species and 25 subspecies are recognised. The intensity of research on this taxa suggests that further species and subspecies are likely to be described. *Kinosternon* is now sometimes considered to include many species previously referred to *Sternotherus*. This arrangement does, however, pose a number of serious taxonomic questions and at present is still very much in dispute. Definitive answers are as yet lacking. Regardless of taxonomic designation and nomenclature, captive care and breeding of *Kinosternon/Sternotherus* species are very similar and for this reason they are treated as one here.

Description: The genus *Kinosternon* is distinguished by a doubly hinged plastron and an absence of an entoplastron. *Male K. (S.) odoratus* can be distinguished from females by the presence of a thicker tail and two rough patches of skin on the hind legs which are used to provide additional grip during mating. This same species is easily distinguished from others of the genus by the presence of two light stripes on the side of its head and barbles on the throat as well as on the chin.

Captive environment: Suggested water temperature range: 18 - 24°C seasonally varied, with 22°C average. Many inhabit brackish waters (especially *K. subrubrum* and *K. bauri*). For brackish water species, a salinity maintained at 25% that of sea water is suggested. In the wild, Mud and Musk turtles are found in a variety of habitats including rivers, lakes, oxbows, tidal marshes, swamps and ditches although preferences vary greatly according to species. Some species prefer quiet, still waters whilst others occur in fast flowing streams. Mahmoud (1969) studied the habits of *K. (S.) odoratus* in Oklahoma and discovered that this species occurred most frequently at sites which possessed a gravel or sandy bottom and where the water depth ranged between one and five feet. A current of one to four feet per second also seemed to be favoured. Reference to the technical literature regarding the particular requirements of the species in question is essential if an appropriate habitat is to be provided. Most species prefer heavily vegetated water and certainly captive specimens maintained by the author spend a considerable amount of time entirely hidden from view beneath the plants in their tank. Some species, e.g. *K. (Sternotherus) odoratus* are predominantly nocturnal with minimal activity being observed during daylight hours. Other species, e.g. *K. (S.) minor* and *K. flavescens* are predominantly diurnal in behaviour. Some mud and musk turtles prefer to spend at least some time on land, so an adequate habitat area for this activity should be provided. Other species rarely leave the water, e.g. *K. (S.) odoratus.* The majority of Mud and Musk turtles are bottom scavengers and this is where most activity will be observed. As these are all relatively small turtles, under-gravel filtration is usually more than adequate. I have maintained them without difficulty in a 1 m x 600 mm tank provided with a 50 mm deep gravel substrate filter bed and a small 200 litre per hour powerhead.

Diet: Adults are typically omnivorous, feeding upon molluscs (which form a high percentage of the diet), vascular aquatic plants, filamentous algae (*Chlorophyta*), insects and their larvae, crayfish and small fish. Mahmoud (1968) determined that *K. (S.) odoratus* did not eat live tadpoles and consistently ignored young garter snakes that were offered as potential prey. Juveniles and specimens below 5 cm carapace length tend to feed mainly upon aquatic insects, larvae and carrion. Above 5 cm and molluscs are taken with increasing frequency. In captivity, earthworms are taken with relish, as are crickets. These can be dusted as necessary with a multi vitamin and mineral supplement. Pewtress (1990) notes that preferred prey items in captivity of *K. (S.) odoratus* are aquatic snails, land snails being rarely eaten despite their ready availability Some specimens will also take rehydrated dried cat food or tinned dog food. Low fat varieties are recommended.

Common health problems: None immediately evident.

Breeding: Suggested incubation humidity for all *Kinosternon* species eggs is between 90 - 95% and the temperature should be maintained between 25 - 30°C. In the case of *K. (Sternotherus) odoratus*, temperatures of 25°C typically result in a majority of males, temperatures of 28°C or higher normally produces all females whilst temperatures between 25 - 27.5°C tend to produce mixed clutches. Damp vermiculite and sphagnum moss are suggested as a suitable incubation medium. A constant temperature of 28°C will frequently produce a mixed clutch and at this temperature hatching can be expected between 90 to 130 days. Lower temperatures can result in extended incubation periods, exceptionally to over 300 days (320 days has been reported at 25°C). The hatchlings should be placed in a shallow aquarium at the same temperature range as adults. The eggs of *Kinosternon minor* typically measure 27 mm x 15 mm and weigh approximately 4 - 5 g. An average clutch comprises 2 - 4 eggs and females may lay 2 - 4 clutches per season. Incubated at 27 - 28°C in a high humidity environment hatching can be expected in 110 - 120 days. It appears that in the wild, emergence may be triggered by rain. In captivity damping the incubation media can produce the same result. A useful indicator of fertility in *Kinosternon* eggs is the appearance of a central white band. The neonates measure 24 mm long and weigh between 2 - 3 grams. There are slight differences in egg dimensions between *Kinosternon* species. For example, the eggs of *K. odoratus* are slightly shorter at 25 mm, but wider at 16 - 17 mm. The hatchlings of this species are, however, of almost identical size to *K. minor.* For all practical purposes, incubation and rearing is also identical.

MALACLEMYS TERRAPIN (Schoepff, 1793)
The diamondback terrapin

General observations: Once heavily exploited for human food, populations of diamondback terrapin are now much depleted, although some recovery is evident.

Taxonomy: Seven subspecies are currently recognised; *M. t. terrapin* (the northern diamondback), the median keel of which does not feature knobs and the carapace of which is brown to black with distinct concentric rings; *M. t. centra* (the Carolina diamondback), with a similar keel, parallel carapace sides and reverted posterior marginals; *M. t. rhizophorarum* (the mangrove diamondback), which features a prominent keel, grey skin and plastral scutes outlined in dark pigment; *M. t. tequesta* (the Florida east coast diamondback), which has a smooth and dark carapace with backward facing knobs along the median keel; *M. t. macrospilota* (the ornate diamondback), the most distinct feature of which are the orange-yellow centres of its carapace scutes; *M. t. pileata* (the Mississippi diamondback), which features a median keel with terminal tuberculate knobs, and reverted marginals bordered in orange or yellow. The plastron is yellow and the head, neck and limbs are pigmented with black dorsally; *M. t. littoralis* (the Texas diamondback), which features a pale or even white plastron, scutes without light centres, a median keel that includes terminal knobs and heavily spotted green-grey limbs. The head is pale dorsally.

Description: Carapace to 23.8 SCL, with distinct light coloured skin on the neck and limbs that features a fine array of dark spots or flecks. The jaws are pale and the eyes black. The carapace is grey, brown or black and in some subspecies features distinct patterns of concentric rings.

Captive environment: *M. terrapin* is a tidal estuary dweller, and is found among reed beds and salt marshes. It has a high tolerance to saline conditions and in captivity should be maintained in brackish water at 1.017 - 1.012 and pH in the range 7.5 - 8.25 (which is typical of the natural habitat). The use of commercial marine salt and pH buffer is recommended to attain these conditions. These should normally be constituted so that the final mix is in the region of 25 - 30% sea water or until the readings above are obtained. Ordinary salt can be used, but marine salts intended for aquatic use are carefully formulated using natural sea-salts and trace elements, without the unnatural additives sometimes found in domestic salt. Water temperatures should be maintained between 24 - 28°C for enthusiastic feeding. Excellent quality filtration is essential for this species; in poor water conditions diamondbacks suffer readily from skin and shell infections. Under gravel biological filtration plus a large external canister filter containing activated charcoal for chemical filtration is recommended. This should be changed regularly to ensure its effectiveness is maintained. It should be noted that filters containing zeolite cannot be used with brackish water species. A basking lamp and land section must also be provided.

Diet: In the wild, *M. terrapin* feeds upon crabs, shellfish, snails (*Littorina* species) and fish. Aquatic plant material is also consumed. In captivity, snails are very popular, although most diamondbacks will feed readily upon koi pellets, Purina® trout-chow and earthworms.

Common health problems: Mycoses and ulcerative skin and shell diseases of bacterial origin are the most frequent conditions affecting this species. They are usually associated with incorrect water conditions.

Breeding: Clutch density ranges from 4 - 18 leathery, pinkish eggs of 26 - 42 mm long and 16 - 27 mm wide. There is significant geographical variation in egg dimensions and clutch density is greatly influenced by the female's size. Incubation in a high (90% +) humidity environment is necessary, and a combination of vermiculite and sphagnum substrate has proved consistently satisfactory. This species employs temperature-dependant sex determination with low temperatures (24 - 29°C) resulting in males, whilst temperatures >30°C result in females. Lower temperatures also result in extended incubation periods; eggs incubated at temperatures between 24.5 - 26°C took 82 days to hatch, compared to 54 days for those incu-

Mud and musk turtles, such as this *Kinosternon baurii*, the Striped mud turtle, are almost wholly aquatic, emerging onto land only infrequently. They are relatively easy to maintain and breed in captivity.

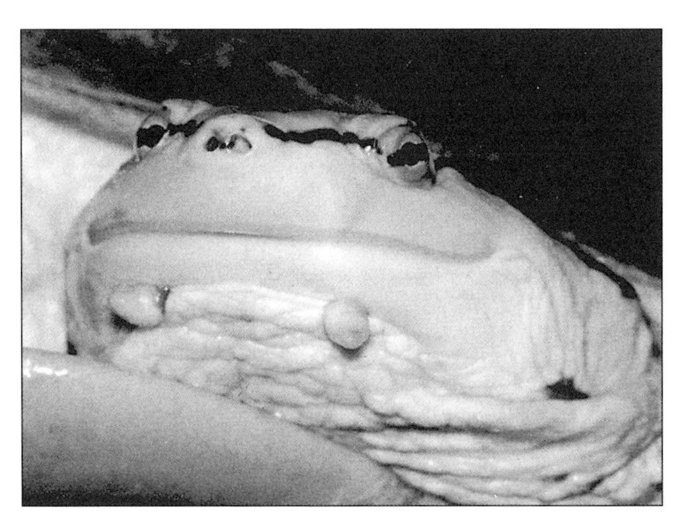

Melanochelys triguja, the Indian black turtle, another species with jaws well adapted to feeding upon snails.

Platysternon megacephalum, the Chinese Big-headed turtle.

Platysternon megacephalum, plastron. Note exceptional tail length of this male specimen.

bated at 28.5 - 29.5°C (Dimond, 1987). Hatchlings typically measure 30 - 40 mm long and weigh between 5 - 10 g. Sexual maturity typically occurs at 9 cm for males (usually in the third or fourth year) whilst females mature later at >12 cm (> sixth year).

MALACOCHERSUS TORNIERI (Siebenrock, 1903)

The Pancake tortoise

General observations: *Malacochersus tornieri*, the Pancake or Soft-shelled tortoise, is in many ways, the most unusual tortoise in the world. It is certainly one which demonstrates a remarkable degree of adaptation. Not only is it almost completely flat, but throughout life it remains soft and surprisingly flexible - a capability it employs to useful effect in defence by wedging itself tightly into rocky fissures where it does not actually inflate but pushes itself against the ceiling (Ireland and Gans, 1972; Bruekers, pers. comm.). It is, in addition, rated as possibly the world's fastest tortoise, and surprised specimens will usually run for cover rather than seek withdrawal into their shells for protection. Its distribution is limited to Kenya and Tanzania where it occurs in thorn covered rocky outcrops to an altitude in excess of 1600m.

Taxonomy: This tortoise's taxonomy and nomenclature are not currently in dispute. There are no recognised subspecies.

Description: Both males and females are flat and entirely lack any evidence of the usual carapace dome. Females are only marginally deeper in the body than males. The normally encountered maximum size of males is approximately 167 mm (height 36 mm) whist that of females is 177 mm (height 45 mm). A male and female in our collection measure 160 mm long by 34 mm high and 170 mm long by 43 mm high respectively. The male weighs 360 g and the female 550 g. The ground colour of the carapace is typically a golden brown or horn colour with a distinct pattern of radiating black-brown marks. Females tend to have more of a rayed pattern than males which are characteristically more mottled in appearance.

Captive environment: Pancake tortoises prefer a dry, rocky environment in captivity as they do in the wild. If a large, artificial "mountain" can be provided with plenty of retreats and cracks then so much the better. These tortoises will spend hours scrambling over even the most precipitous terrain. Peak activity occurs in the morning and early evening, much of the day being spent in retreat under a convenient rocky ledge. They are inclined to be gregarious in habit, with several tortoises stacking themselves on top of the other in a particularly favoured retreat. Two males placed together will, however, fight viciously during the breeding season, biting and snapping at each others heads and attempting to turn each other over. Their agility is such, however, that they can right themselves with little difficulty. Daytime temperatures should be in the order of 25 - 29 °C, although as is frequently the case with tortoises that inhabit high, dry places *Malacochersus tornieri* can withstand considerably lower temperatures overnight. In captivity a minimum of 13 °C is recommended. Damp is not much appreciated and should be avoided. This tortoise rarely drinks water, seemingly obtaining almost all of its fluid requirement from its food.

Diet: As for *G. pardalis* with a preference for grass and succulents. In captivity cabbage, lettuce, tomatoes and cucumber are taken readily. They seem little interested in most fruits, although melon is often an exception to this rule. The diet should be supplemented as required with multi-vitamins and calcium - especially for egg laying females and juveniles.

Common health problems: Viral stomatitis (numerous cases recorded); *Hexamita parva.*

Breeding: *M. tornieri* mate in a state of high excitement, the male vigorously snapping and biting at the female's head and legs as he quickly and repeatedly circles her. Eggs are laid singly, and often at intervals of 6 - 8 weeks. A female in our own collection regularly produces such eggs which on average measure 47 mm long by 31 mm wide and weigh 35 g. At 30 °C incubated in a Type I container the incubation period is typically 140 days, but this does appear to be quite variable sometimes taking much longer. Incubation humidity does not appear to be particularly critical, with success recorded from 50 - 90%. In the wild, eggs are laid in July or August, and hatching usually occurs in December. In captivity, females may choose to nest either during the daytime or early evening digging a fairly normal nest approximately 100 mm in depth, or alternatively simply secreting the egg in a convenient nook or cranny among the rocks. Hatchlings upon emergence are strangely not particularly odd looking and are somewhat domed. Their profile is not dissimilar to that of *T. hermanni*, for example. The hatchlings have a bright yellow ground colour and plastron with deep brown-black spots on the vertebral and costal scutes. Typically, newly emerged hatchlings measure about 40 mm in length and weigh about 16 - 18 g. Darlington and Davis (1990) point out that populations of *M. tornieri* are discontinuous and that genetic disparity may account for the low overall rates of captive reproduction attained. The present author would tend to agree with this analysis and notes that whilst certain pairs are consistently successful many captive breeding attempts fail without obvious cause. In such instances, realignment of existing or introduction of new breeding stock may improve the situation.

MELANOCHELYS TRIJUGA (Schweigger, 1812)

Indian Black turtle or Indian Snail-eating turtle

General observations: A large (to 38 cm) batagurine turtle from India, Bangladesh, Sri Lanka and some Indian Ocean islands. Infrequently bred in captivity.

Taxonomy: Six subspecies are currently recognised. A useful table of comparative characters to differentiate the races is given in Ernst and Barbour (1989) and considerably more detail is provided by Tikader and Sharma (1985). The most frequently encountered race in captivity is *M. t. thermalis.*

Description: The carapace is black, the plastron pale. Head and skin colour typically grey. The carapace is elongate and tricarinate. The feet are strongly webbed.

Captive environment: In the wild, this turtle is mainly found in freshwater streams and ponds. It reportedly has a low tolerance to contaminated water. *M. t. indopeninsularis* is the most terrestrial race, preferring moist habitats near to pools and streams. Typically a shy creature, it rarely becomes accustomed to handling. Some specimens may be aggressive. Terraria for *Melanochelys* species require a large water section with a land section formed of peat and sand. Water temperature to a maximum of 26°C. A winter rest or dormancy period can be given, when water temperatures may be reduced to 15°C. Good filtration is important and frequent water changes should be made. A combination of undergravel and external box or large canister filters is usually satisfactory.

Diet: Fish, snails, and assorted meats are taken readily in captivity. Some green-leafed plants and pond weeds are also taken. The diet is essentially omnivorous with a bias towards meats.

Common health problems: None immediately evident.

Breeding: Males tend to be aggressive, and females should be examined for injuries frequently. Two males should not be kept together in the same accommodation. Sexual maturity occurs in most races as the carapace attains a length of 15 cm. Captive bred specimens can attain this in approximately 5 years. A seasonal temperature reduction, as described above, can greatly encourage subsequent mating. For breeding pairs, the terrarium land section needs to be at least 20 cm deep, as nests are excavated to 15 cm. A *M. t. thermalis* in captivity in Britain laid a series of eggs measuring from 58 x 27 mm to 49 x 27 mm (Inskeep, pers.comm.) Incubated at 25 - 26°C in a 100% humidity environment, hatching can be expected in about 70 days. The juveniles measure approximately 40 mm in length and for the first year of life are predominantly carnivorous.

Above: A large (60 cm) *Manouria emys phayrei* male.

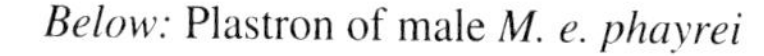

Below: Plastron of male *M. e. phayrei*

MANOURIA EMYS (Schlegel and Muller, 1844)

The Burmese Brown tortoise

General observations: The largest Asiatic land tortoise. The genus *Manouria* is recognised as the most ancient of extant terrestrial genera.

Taxonomy: Described as *Testudo emys* by Schelgel and Muller in 1844 the taxonomy of this tortoise since has undergone a number of revisions and includes several synonyms. Most authorities now recognise two races; *Manouria emys emys* (Schelgel and Muller 1844) and *Manouria emys phayrei* (Blyth 1853), this later is perhaps better known under the synonym *Geochelone nutapundi* (Wirot 1979). Of the two currently recognised subspecies *M. e. phayrei* is by far the larger, with recorded carapace lengths to 60 cm and weights to 37 kg. In contrast, *M. e. emys* rarely exceeds 40 cm (exceptionally to 50 cm) and weighs much less, typically below 20 kg.

Description: The carapace colour ranges from deep brown to black. *M. e. emys* tends to be higher domed than *M. e. phayrei* which has a broader, flatter carapace. Several very large tubercles occur on each thigh.

Captive environment: This tortoise is found in tropical, humid evergreen forests and favours sites close to running water. Captive specimens should be given constant access to bathing facilities as they often soak themselves in shallow water for prolonged periods. Despite the inference from the habitat type that this is a tortoise that requires high temperature maintenance, the opposite is true. Many keepers report both *M. e. phayrei* and *M. e. emys* are most active at low temperatures; enthusiastic feeding as low as 10°C has been observed. Peak activity seems to occur between 15°C to 20°C. This tortoise greatly enjoys rain, so outdoor maintenance should be possible in many localities.

Diet: Primarily herbivorous and will accept most green vegetables and fruits. Some small quantity of animal protein should also be provided on a regular basis.

Common health problems: Pneumonia; stomatitis; flagellate infections.

Breeding: A comprehensive description of pre-nuptial behaviour in *Me. e. phayrei* is provided by McKeown, Meir and Juvick (1990) and anyone seriously interested in breeding this tortoise should consult their paper that also discusses details of vocalisation in this race. *M. e. phayrei* also engages in a unique nest building process using leaf litter and actively guards her nest - behaviour extremely rare in testudines. Clutch densities in *M. e. phayrei* are typically very high with as many as 51 eggs per clutch (35 - 45 is average), the highest number of any known land tortoise. The eggs measure approximately 54 mm in diameter and usually weigh between 45 - 65 g. Incubation at 28.5 - 30°C in a high (90%+) humidity environment will result in hatching in approximately 60 - 75 days. There is some evidence that higher incubation temperatures may render the eggs non-viable. Moist vermiculite has proved to be a consistently successful incubation medium.

MANOURIA IMPRESSA (Gunther, 1882)

The Impressed tortoise

General observations: Undoubtedly the most difficult of all Asian tortoises to maintain successfully. Should not be considered as suitable for routine collecting or breeding programs. Very few specimens survive for more than a few months in captivity. This tortoise requires in-depth study which is best accomplished within its natural bioclimatic range. Long-term captive maintenance is rare even within Thailand, however.

Taxonomy: No subspecies have been described. The tortoise is found in Eastern Burma, Thailand (where most trade animals originated prior to an export ban now in place) to Malaysia and Vietnam where they are heavily exploited for food and medicinal purposes. For a full review of the problems and literature related to *M. impressa*, the reader is advised to consult Espenshade and Buskirk (1994) who present a very comprehensive analysis of the situation.

Description: Carapace to approximately 30 cm, markedly flattened with anterior and posterior marginals strongly serrated. The carapace is coloured red-brown with black and sometimes orange-yellow borders to the scutes that are often noticeably indented. The plastron is also reddish-brown. The limbs are brown, and the head is yellow.

Captive environment: As virtually all attempts to keep these animals alive in captivity fail, it is not a simple matter to make useful suggestions. However, it would seem that "Impressa Disease" could be related to mixing with other species following capture. This was certainly a possibility considered by McMorris and Burns (1975) in their speculations on the topic. Unfortunately, even prompt prophylactic treatment with antibiotics and metronidazole has failed to improve the prognosis. The Tortoise Trust maintained a pair, referred from a dealer who was growing desperate at their decline, for 9 months - but only by tube-feeding. The pair never once fed for themselves, despite many attempts with different foodstuffs and at different environmental temperatures and humidities. Ultimately, both expired with apparent symptoms of renal failure. The natural habitat includes broad-leaved evergreen forest with a deep leaf-litter substrate. This habitat is described as "fairly dry" (Nabhitabhata, 1991). Should the reader encounter *M. impressa*, it is advised that urine samples should be taken and tested for *Hexamita parva* and for renal function. Specimens must be strictly isolated and stress avoided as far as possible.

Diet: The natural diet of this species is insufficiently known but is believed to include grasses, bamboo sprouts and fallen fruit. In captivity, most animals refuse to feed at all, and die of starvation. Weissinger (1987) reported that a specimen eventually accepted banana and thereafter ate 3 a week. Peter van Dijk (quoted in Espenshade and Buskirk, op. cit.) has suggested feeding hard fruits such as berries and figs rather than soft fruits and further suggests placing bamboo shoots in an upright position (as though growing) instead of presenting them lying on the ground. McMorris and Burns (1975) provide an interesting account of the problems associated with this species.

Common health problems: See above.

Breeding: A captive breeding project in China is the only known program involving this species which has met with any degree of success (Huang, Q. 1991). Post-mortem, several females have been found to be carrying between 17 - 22 eggs (including one of a pair that the author attempted to maintain).

MAUREMYS SPP. Gray, 1869

Mediterranean and Asiatic pond terrapins

General observations: Widely distributed group of bataurine turtles from the Mediterranean, Asia and Japanese islands.

Taxonomy: The genus *Mauremys* includes four species, of which the best known are the Mediterranean terrapins *Mauremys caspica* (Caspian terrapin) and *Mauremys leprosa* (Spanish terrapin). No subspecies are currently recognised for *M. leprosa* (although recently two have been proposed) but *M. caspica* is generally recognised as comprising two subspecies, *M. c. caspica* and *M. c. rivulata*. The races are differentiated by their plastral formulae (>fem >abd > pect > gull >hum >an = male and abd > fem > pect >gul >hum >an = female in M. c. caspica whereas in *M. c. rivulata* both sexes share the same formula: abd >fem > pect > gul >an >hum). The plastron of *M. c. rivulata* is also black, compared to the paler, blotched, plastron of *M. c. caspica*. The two other members of the genus are less frequently encountered; *Mauremys nigricans* (the Asian yellow pond terrapin) and *Mauremys japonica* (the Japanese turtle). In some accounts, reference may also be found to *"Mauremys mutica"*(Vietnamese leaf turtle). This is now recognised as consisting of a species contained within the monotypic genus *Annamemys*, *Annamemys annamemys* (Siebenrock, 1903), and *"Mauremys mutica"* is regarded as a synonym. The name *"Mauremys mutica"* has also been applied, as a synonym, to the tricarinate form of *M. nigricans*, a species that exhibits considerable geographic variation. The genus *Mauremys* is presently in a confused state and several revisions likely to result in changes of nomenclature and known distribution are in progress (Fritz and Freytag, 1993).

Description: Terrapins of the genus *Mauremys* are small to medium sized. Typical maximum dimensions are; *M. leprosa* 18 cm, *M. caspica* 23.5 cm, *M. nigricans* 19.5 cm and *M. japonica* 18.2 cm, but most examples of all species are considerably smaller (150 - 170 cm). None of the *Mauremys* group are brilliantly marked; most are of a uniform dull appearance apart from some head and neck striping. The most colourful member is *M. nigricans* which features a broad yellow post orbital stripe, a yellow-orange plastron, and yellow chin. The carapace is typically dull brown. The other Asian species, *M. japonica,* features a brown to black plastron, with light brown skin on the head and neck which under close examination reveal a pattern of darker brown spots. The neck also features a series of understated brown-yellow lines. The carapace is distinctive among *Mauremys*, however, as it displays not only clear growth annuli but also a pattern of radiating striae. The carapace and skin of *M. caspica* are typically olive-green or olive-grey. The neck and limbs feature a fine pattern of yellowish stripes, and a stripe of the same colour runs from the nares to the eye. The plastron is usually of a plain yellow-green hue. The North African and Spanish *M. leprosa* are similar in colour, but feature a yellowish post-orbital spot. The plastron is yellow, and usually displays a darker central blotch which may be medially divided. This species is especially prone to develop shell infections from fungal, bacterial and algae growths. This trait was a factor in it receiving its name *Mauremys leprosa*, or the "leprous terrapin".

Captive environment: All *Mauremys* species are relatively tolerant of water conditions, especially *M. leprosa* and *M. caspica.* I have found *M. caspica* in fast flowing cool mountain streams, lakes, ponds, drainage ditches and brackish lagoons in Turkey and Greece. In northerly areas, this species hibernates in winter. It also aestivates in summer in parts of its range. In Morocco, Spain and Tunisia I have often found *M. leprosa* inhabiting ditches, temporary reservoirs, shallow brackish lakes, ponds and fast flowing mountain streams. Both *M. caspica* and *M. leprosa* appear to be able to tolerate even very filthy and contaminated water. I once found a healthy colony of *M. leprosa* in Morocco thriving in a drainage outfall from a rubbish tip. Another population was thriving in extremely brackish reed-beds. In captivity, all *Mauremys* species will do best if maintained in clean water at a temperature of 16 - 25°C with a neutral pH. *Mauremys* species are fond of basking and also require constant access to a good sized land area.

Diet: Omnivorous, with a preference for animal matter. The natural diet includes fish, earthworms, molluscs, insects and their larvae, frogs, tadpoles and aquatic plants, especially filamentous algae (Sidis and Gasith, 1985). In captivity most will readily accept trout chow, koi pellets, tinned pet foods and similar items. Juveniles are more herbivorous than adults.

Common health problems: None immediately evident.

Breeding: Mating usually occurs underwater, but occasionally may take place on land. Females can sustain serious bites to the face and neck at this time, so should be placed under careful observation. Males can sometimes be mutually aggressive, but I have maintained two male *M. caspica* together for several years with no evident problems (these specimens also share a pond with *Cuora amboinensis*). *M. caspica* lays clutches of 4 - 6 eggs measuring 25 x 38 mm. *M. leprosa* lays slightly larger clutches, of between 5 - 10 eggs measuring 36 x 22 mm. *M. japonica* lays 5 - 8 eggs measuring 28 x 25 mm and *M. nigricans* lays clutches of 5 - 9 eggs measuring 38 x 21 mm. All will incubate successfully in a medium-high humidity environment (75 - 90%) at 27 - 30°C. The natural incubation period for most species is approximately 65 - 75 days. Incubated at a constant temperature of 28°C the eggs of *M. nigricans* can be expected to hatch in about 70 days. The method of sex determination in *Mauremys* is presently unknown.

PELOMEDUSA SUBRUFA (Lacepede, 1788)
African helmeted terrapin

General observations: A side-necked turtle from Africa and Madagascar.

Taxonomy: *Pelomedusa* is a monotypic genus distinguished from the outwardly similar pelomedusid genus *Pelusios* (with the exception of *Pelusion broadleyi*) by the absence of a hinged anterior plastral lobe in the former. Three subspecies have been described; *P. s. subrufa* from the Sudan, Somalia, Madagascar and Ghana, *P. s. olivacea* which also occurs in Nigeria and the Cameroons and *P. s. nigra* which is only found in South Africa. Intergradation is reportedly widespread.

Description: The carapace of this medium sized turtle (to 330 mm, but more usually 150 - 175 mm) is brown to grey. No nuchal scute is present. The head is also brown-grey dorsally, with a pale throat and two distinct chin barbles. The plastron is typically yellow or cream with dark markings sometimes present along the scute seams. Sexual dimorphic features include slightly concave plastra and longer and thicker tails in males, with the vent located near the tip. The carapaces of females are usually broader than those of males of comparable size. These characters may differ between races; of *P. s. nigra* Boycott and Bourquin (1988) state that no plastral depression is present in males.

Captive environment: The natural habitat of *P. subrufa* includes seasonal ponds, lakes and watering holes. In summer, these are subject to drying up and at such times *P. subrufa* aestivates under the mud; it may also cross land for long distances in search of any remaining water. In parts of its range it also hibernates during cold weather. *Pelomedusa subrufa* are undemanding in captivity and are often housed in large glass aquaria. Water temperature should be maintained between 20 - 26°C and a combined light-heat lamp should also be provided as this species spends long periods basking. In hot weather, *P. subrufa* also does well in shallow outdoor ponds. Water pH is not critical, but excessively alkaline conditions should be avoided. As they are messy feeders, good filtration is advised. A combination of an undergravel and internal foam-filled canister filter works well for this species.

Diet: *P. subrufa* is largely carnivorous and is known for its tendency to hunt in packs, several terrapins may engage in a group attack upon a wading bird, dragging it underwater to devour it. In captivity swallowing invariably takes place in the water although food will be seized both in and out of water. A wide range of foods are readily accepted; rehydrated cat pellets, Purina Trout-chow®, tinned low-fat dog food and a quantity of fruit. Some pond weeds are also consumed.

Common health problems: None immediately evident.

Breeding: Although not often bred in captivity, this species reproduces readily. *P. subrufa* is, however, an aggressive turtle and this can cause problems. Females frequently sustain injuries as a result. To encourage breeding, males should be maintained separately and females introduced intermittently. The clutch size varies with the size of the female, but 12 - 15 eggs is typical. Eggs measure approximately 32 x 22 mm, although much larger examples have been recorded. This species can be difficult to induce to nest in captivity (Harding, 1981) and recourse to oxytocin may be required. A large, sloping sand tray of at least 200 mm depth placed beneath a basking lamp has proved successful, however. The eggs of this species can be incubated on a 1:1 water-vermiculite substrate at 28 - 31°C, but details of sex determination thresholds, if applicable, remain unknown. The hatchlings measure approximately 27 mm SCL, weigh 6 - 7 g and require a shallow water environment at 25 - 27°C with floating plants for basking. Hatchlings rarely leave the water entirely.

PELUSIOS SPP. Wagler, 1830

African side-necked terrapins

General observations: Widely distributed genus of side-necked turtles from tropical Africa. Often known as African Mud turtles or African Hinged terrapins.

Taxonomy: The taxonomy of this genus is currently subject to dispute; there is no general agreement on the precise number or diagnosis of many species. Fourteen species are generally recognised. The most commonly encountered species include *Pelusios subniger* from Eastern Africa, *Pelusios castanoides* (the Yellow-bellied Mud turtle) from Malawi, South Africa and Madagascar, and *Pelusios gabonensis* (the African Forest turtle) from West Africa

Description: The plastron is hinged between abdominal and pectoral scutes in all *Pelusios* species and in this way, they can readily be distinguished from other genera. The hind-feet are webbed and feature 5 claws. The carapace lacks a nuchal scute.

Captive environment: Almost all *Pelusios* species occur naturally in swamps, marshes and slow moving rivers with soft bottoms. Many of these habitats are ephemeral and dry out completely during the long, hot summer. During this period, the turtles aestivate beneath the dried mud. In captivity, the water temperature should be maintained at about 26°C, and the pH at 6.5 to avoid shell and skin problems. *Pelusios* species are often secretive by nature but in a secure environment will develop into enthusiastic baskers. A log or gravel haul out area in a sunny position or beneath a basking lamp is therefore essential.

Diet: In the wild, *Pelusios* species feed mainly upon insect larvae, crustacea, molluscs and other small prey animals. Whilst *P. subniger* is believed to be somewhat omnivorous, other members of the genus appear to be exclusively carnivorous, at least as adults. In captivity most specimens seem to prefer to feed from the bottom of the tank and will readily accept feeder fish, trout chow and similar food items.

Common health problems: Skin and shell problems if pH is out of range; pneumonia if air or water temperatures too low.

Breeding: Egg dimensions and clutch density vary according to species, but typically measure 35 mm x 22 mm. *P. castanoides* may lay as many as 25 eggs in a clutch, but 5 - 9 is more typical of *P. subniger*. The eggs should be incubated in a high (95%+) humidity environment on a vermiculite and sphagnum substrate. An incubation temperature of 29 - 30°C will usually result in hatchlings in about 60 - 70 days. *P. castaneus* utilises ESD, with two transition zones. Data on other members of the genus is presently unavailable.

PHRYNOPS SPP. Wagler, 1830

South American side-necked turtles

General observations: A widely distributed genus, with 11 species and numerous subspecies. Some species prefer blackwater environments, others are more frequently found in whitewater streams.

Taxonomy: Under revision, and insufficiently understood. In captive collections *P. geoffroanus* (2 subspecies), *P. gibbus*, *P. hillarii* and *P. rufipes* are the most frequently encountered representatives.

Description: The most striking member of the genus is possibly *P. rufipes*, the Red Amazon side-necked turtle that features a bright head and limbs (26 cm carapace). *P. hillarii* which, with a maximum recorded carapace length of 40 cm, makes it the largest member of the genus, can be differentiated from the similar, but slightly smaller (to 35 cm) *P. geoffroanus* as follows; presence of a large number of irregular black spots covering the plastron, bridge and ventral aspect of marginals. There are two chin barbles, black at the base. In *P. g. geoffroanus* the plastron pattern is best described as a series of red and black wave-like lines. In *P. Hillarii* the underside of the neck is white or cream coloured; in *P. g. geoffroanus* it is heavily patterned. Finally, *P. gibbus* (23 cm) has a smooth, keeled carapace, typically brown-grey in colour, the plastron is chestnut brown to yellow with typical yellow margins to each shield. The feet are heavily webbed, skin grey-black, and the head features two chin yellow chin barbles.

Captive environment: Water temperatures for all species of *Phrynops* in captivity are normally maintained at between 20 - 25°C with air temperatures typically from 24 - 30°C. These turtles are highly aquatic, so a large aquarium is essential. Behaviour and water pH preferences do, however, differ considerably between the various species and geographical races. Some *Phrynops* inhabit predominantly whitewater streams, e.g. *P. williamsi*, some are found in both whitewater and blackwater habitats, e.g. *P. rufipes* but the majority, including *P. gibbus, P. hillarii, P. geoffroanus, P.dahli, P. nasutus, P. vanderhaegei, P. tuberculatus, P. zuliae* and the rare *P. hogei* are more typically inhabitants of blackwater rivers, swamps, marshes or forest ponds rich in vegetation and decayed organic matter. For these turtles in captivity, it is important to maintain water pH in the correct range (<6.25) if skin and shell infections are to be avoided (*P. rufipes* is particularly sensitive to such problems - the addition of dilute acriflavine and Stress Coat to the water greatly reduces the incidence and assists healing where it has occurred). A simple and practical solution to water property problems for many Amazon species is to employ a commercial blackwater essence as supplied by tropical fish medication specialists. In terms of individual behaviour, some *Phrynops* are enthusiastic baskers (e.g. *P. geoffroanus*) but others (e.g. *P. gibbus* and *P. rufipes*) tend towards nocturnal behaviour and only rarely take advantage of basking facilities. For all *Phrynops* species, a land area with a

Species such as this *Phyrnops gibbus,* the Gibba side-necked turtle, are usually only encountered in institutional collections.

Plastron of *Psammobates oculifera,* the South African serrated star tortoise. An extremely delicate species which is demanding in captivity and under serious pressure in the wild.

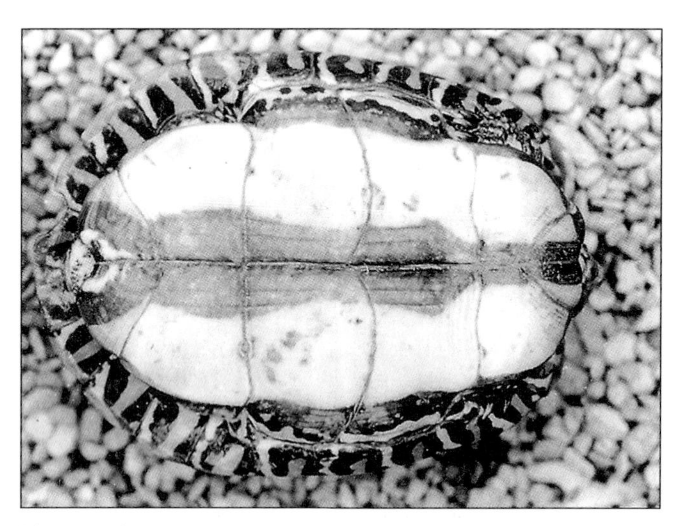

Plastron, *Rhinoclemmys pulcherrima*

Male (left) and female (right) *Rhinoclemmys pulcherrima*, tropical and semi-tropical wood turtles.

peaty, sandy substrate should be provided and a semi-submerged log should be positioned directly under a basking lamp. For general lighting, Vita-lite® has proved entirely effective.

Diet: Essentially wide ranging omnivores. Fish, molluscs, plant matter, earthworms and prepared meats are all accepted. Some *Phrynops* appear more carnivorous than others; *P. nasutus* in particular feeds predominantly upon chopped fish and meat. Fruits are accepted readily by most specimens, although green vegetables are usually refused.

Common health problems: pH sensitivity - see above.

Breeding: Males indulge in biting the female's neck, therefore be alert for injuries. Other signs of imminent copulation include head swaying behaviour on the part of the male (Harding and Ewart, 1989). The eggs of *P. gibbus* measure approximately 40 x 26 mm with a mass of between 15 - 19 g. Clutch density typically varies between 4 - 7. The most successful incubation media for this species has proved to be vermiculite hydrated 1:1 with water. Excessive incubation humidity is believed to cause cracking of the eggs. At an incubation temperature of 25°C hatching can take 192 days (Harding and Ewart, op. cit.), although successful incubation has been achieved at a range of temperatures from 24.5 - 31°C. A similarly wide range of incubation periods have been recorded, from 140 to 248 days with an average of 178.5 days (Goode, 1988). *P. gibbus* neonates measure approximately 46 mm SCL and weigh 14 g. Breeding for other *Phrynops* species is similar. Several keepers report good results at 28°C.

PLATEMYS Wagler, 1830

South American chelid side-necked turtles

General observations: Morphologically, *Platemys* species bear a close resemblance to Australasian short-necked turtles.

Taxonomy: Four species are presently recognised; *P. platycephala* (the Twist-necked turtle), which attains 18 cm and comprises 2 subspecies *P. p. platycephala* and *P.p. melanota*; intergrades are also said to be common; *P. macrocephala* which at 23.5 cm is the largest member of the genus; *P. spixii* (the Spiny necked turtle) which attains 17 cm and *P. radiolata* that attains 20 cm and features radiating striations upon its carapace. The former *P. pallidipectoris* (the Chaco side-neck) is now recognised under a different genus, *Acanthochelys*.

Description: The carapace is flattened, typically oval and features a deep medial groove usually bordered by two parallel ridges. The toes are webbed and each forefoot has 5 claws. Colouration varies between species and subspecies. The most commonly encountered example, *P. p. platycephala*, features a striking yellow-brown carapace with dark brown-black pigment on the central costals and a brightly marked orange-yellow head, with wide black stripes along the neck.

Captive environment: *P. platycephala* is usually found in very shallow water of only a few cm in depth. Typical habitats include swamps, marshes and slow moving streams in tropical rain forests, especially in flooded forest regions. Water temperature should be maintained at 24 - 27°C and ambient air humidity should also be high. *Platemys* species are all very sensitive to cold, and care should be taken to ensure air temperature does not fall below that of the water. The water pH should be maintained in the region of 6.5 - 6.9 for most *Platemys* spp, although some experimentation may be required according to the geographic origin of the specimens in question. *Platemys* species are generally poor swimmers, and often display apparent weakness; this is normal, and does not necessarily indicate a sick turtle. Floating plant platforms are often utilised, especially by juveniles. Buskirk (1991) provides valuable insights into the natural habitats of *Platemys spixii* in Uruguay. The greatest depth of water recorded where *P. spixii* was present was 30 cm.

Diet: According to Lehmann (1988), referring to *P. spixii,* juveniles are more herbivorous than adults - a reversal of the usual trend. In the wild, the diet of most *Platemys* species relies heavily upon molluscs, larval amphibians, and small fish. In captivity adults are almost exclusively carnivorous and will accept most meats and small prey animals.

Common health problems: None immediately evident.

Breeding: *Platemys* species are rarely bred in captivity, and little is known about their reproductive habits, however, incubation on damp vermiculite and sphagnum at a temperature of 29 - 30°C has proved successful and yielded hatchling *P. spixii*, which measured 31 mm SCL and weighed 5 g in approximately 180 days (Lehmann, op. cit.). There are indications that *Platemys* species may require a slightly acidic incubation medium to aid egg-shell degradation. The addition of peat to the vermiculite substrate may assist this process. Harding (1983) noted head swinging behaviour prior to copulation. *P. platycephala* typically lay a single large egg measuring approximately 55 mm x 28 mm. The sex determination methods employed by *Platemys* species are currently unknown.

PLATYSTERNON MEGACEPHALUM Gray, 1831

Big-headed turtle

General observations: The Big-headed turtle is an interesting species widely distributed in Asia. Most races have rarely been bred in captivity and the species deserves more attention with regard to captive propagation.

Taxonomy: *Platysternon* is a monotypic genus. Five subspecies have been described. *Platysternon megacephalum megacephalum* from southern China that has an unpatterned yellow plastron, yellow mottled jaws and narrow radiating lines on the top of the head; *P. m. peguense* from west Vietnam to Burma that has a pronounced keel, unpatterned jaws and a black bordered post orbital stripe; (the questionable) *P. m. tristernalis* from Yunnan, China which has three additional scales at the juncture of the gular and humeral scutes and (also doubtful) *P. m. vogeli* from north west Thailand and finally, *P. m. shiui* from north Vietnam that features a series of pink, orange or yellow spots upon its head, carapace and limbs.

Description: The most distinctive feature, from which this turtle derives both its scientific and common names, is the spectacularly proportioned head. This is typically half as wide as the carapace and is not retractable. The jaws are powerful and hooked. The carapace features a median keel and is indented anteriorly. See above for differences in marking between subspecies.

Captive environment: Suggested water temperature range 14 - 20°C. In the wild, the Big-headed turtle inhabits cool mountain streams. Basks rarely. A gravel substrate is appreciated. It is essential that enclosures are secure, as this turtle is an agile climber. It is most active in late evening or early morning when it forages the bottom for food.

Diet: Predominantly, in some instances exclusively, carnivorous. Takes worms, molluscs, fish, carrion, and in captivity, can often be persuaded to accept rehydrated trout pellets and tinned meats.

Common health problems: None immediately evident.

Breeding: There are probable differences in dimensions between the eggs of subspecies, but these have not been described in detail. Typically, eggs measure 37 x 22 mm. Incubation at 25 - 28°C in at 90% relative humidity is suggested. The juveniles are brightly coloured and feature a more prominent vertebral keel than the adults. They are also highly aggressive.

PODOCNEMIS UNIFILIS Troschel, 1848

Yellow-spotted Amazon River turtle

General observations: A large (to 68 cm) side-necked turtle once frequently encountered in the exotic turtle trade as juveniles. Wide distribution in South America, from Caribbean to Ecuador, Peru, Venezuela and Brazil where it finds itself a popular food item.

Taxonomy: No subspecies are currently recognised.

Description: The most striking feature (of males) is bright yellow blotching of head. Carapace is oval, slightly domed, keeled on 2nd and 3rd vertebral scutes, and of an overall brown colour. The plastron is grey. There is typically a single barb on the lower jaw. Scales of hind-feet are curved and the feet are also strongly webbed. Females are considerably larger than males, have short stubby tails and lack the bright yellow head-spotting of males. The eyes of females are black, those of males and juveniles are greenish.

Captive environment: Predominantly aquatic, rarely leaves the water for purposes other than egg deposition or basking. In the wild, inhabits flood plain pools, swamps and oxbows. In captivity, a land area or convenient log should be provided for basking which is greatly enjoyed. Provision of a Chromalux® spotlight is recommended. Water temperature range in captivity 26 - 30°C, and many specimens seem to prefer blackwater (a tannin-rich acidic environment) although in the wild it inhabits both blackwater and whitewater rivers. The relative humidity of the terrarium should be maintained at around 85% or higher.

Diet: Omnivorous with a preference for vegetation including green leafed material and fruits. Most foods taken with enthusiasm in captivity. In the wild, Medem (1964) analysed stomach contents and discovered that water hyacinth was the most popular food of this species. Belkin and Gans (1968) observed *P. unifilis* feeding on fine floating food by skimming the water surface. In captivity, reluctant feeders can sometimes be tempted by floating flaked foods on the water.

Common health problems: None immediately evident.

Breeding: A prolific egg-layer. Sexual maturity typically occurs in 8 - 12 years or when the animals measure approximately 28 cm in length. Typical clutch density varies considerably, from 10 - 35 (typically 24) eggs, with larger females depositing more eggs than smaller specimens. The eggs measure about 40 x 26 mm and can be successfully incubated at 28°C when the incubation period is usually between 60 - 80 days, but it is probable that this will result in purely male neonates. No specific data on ESD in *P. unifilis* is available but Alho et. al. (1984) noted that this certainly occurs in *Podocnemis expansa* when eggs incubated in the range 30 - 38.5°C (mean 33.4°C) produced female hatchlings at a ratio of 30 to each male whilst eggs incubated in the range 31 - 36°C (mean 33.6°C) resulted in a ratio of 1.7 males for each female. The eggs of *P. unifilis* require incubation in high humidity environment, at least 90% and preferably closer to 100% relative humidity. A damp vermiculite and sphagnum substrate has proved ideal. The hatchlings possess a carapace length of 37 - 42 mm and weigh about 10 g. Hatchlings should be housed in an aquarium with a gentle slope for access and egress. Typically, they feed initially on bright red fruits or green leaf material, minced fish, or food particles floating on the surface. For the well-being of hatchlings it is vital that the aquarium is draft free and humid.

PSAMMOBATES SPP. Fitzinger, 1835

South African tent tortoises

General observations: A genus of small highly decorative tortoises endemic to southern Africa. *Psammobates geometricus* is highly restricted geographically and is equally highly endangered.

Taxonomy: Three species, *P. geometricus, P. oculifer* and *P. tentorius* which itself comprises 3 currently recognised subspecies *P. t. tentorius*, *P. t. verroxii* and *P. t. trimeni*. These latter races are reported to intergrade.

Description: All species have somewhat similarly marked carapaces, with radiated yellow lines upon a black background (similar to *G. elegans*). *P. geometricus* is the largest member of the genus at 145 mm SCL; *P. oculifer* has highly serrated marginals and typically attains a maximum length of 130 mm; *P. t. tentorius* is smaller at a recorded maximum of 125 mm SCL and with narrower yellow rays than the above species; *P. t. verroxii* is slightly larger at 140 mm SCL with a very variable pattern of raying; *P. t. trimeni* is similarly patterned to the above but features a red-orange hue to the rays at the base of each scute and attains 145 mm

SCL. *P. t. trimeni* is quite possibly the most dramatically patterned and coloured tortoise in the world. Sexual dimorphism is pronounced in *P. geometricus*, with females at an average SCL of 123.4 mm and males at an average of 105.2 mm (Baard, 1995).

Captive environment: Very susceptible to disease if contact allowed with other non-sympatric species. All *Psammobates* species are delicate and prone to respiratory disease if maintained at sub-optimum temperatures or exposed to damp. It should be stressed that long-term maintenance of all *Psammobates* species outside their natural bioclimatic range has rarely been attained. The same comment applies to captive breeding. These tortoises are legally protected and should not normally be available to non-institutional keepers. For captive animals (often obtained as a result of customs seizures), a system such as that used for *T. kleinmanni* has proved satisfactory. A dry sandy substrate, with rocks for climbing and potted plants for cover provides the basic landscape; basking facilities can be provided by means of a Chromalux® spotlamp and additional light (and UV-B) by means of two 40W Vita-lite tubes. The entire terrarium should be maintained in a warm (not hot) room at approximately 20°C. Good ventilation is essential.

Diet: Full natural dietary details are presently unknown. It is known, however, that *Psammobates* species are coprophagous to varying degrees. There is debate about the necessity for this in captivity. In general, a diet as provided for *T. graeca* and *T. kleinmanni* is essentially well suited to these tortoises and should form the basis for further experimentation.

Common health problems: *Hexamita* infection; stomatitis; pneumonia. Maintain in strict isolation. If mixed with other species, consequences are generally fatal.

Breeding: Unknown in captivity outside South Africa. There, *P. geometricus* lays clutches of 2 - 4 eggs (not 12 - 15 as cited in Loveridge and Williams, 1957 and Ernst and Barbour, 1989) averaging 30 x 26 mm. The natural incubation period is 150 - 210 days and the hatchlings measure around 30 mm SCL and weigh 6 - 8 g. *P. oculifer* typically lays single eggs measuring 40 mm x 30 mm. Details of incubation and hatchling dimensions are unknown. *P. tentorius tentorius* lay clutches of 1 to 3 eggs measuring 27 - 35 mm x 21 - 28 mm (Boycott and Bourquin, 1988) which hatch after a natural incubation period of 220 days. The hatchlings measure 25 - 30 mm SCL. The breeding details of *P. t. verroxii* and *P.t. trimeni* are also presently uncertain.

PYXIDEA MOUHOTTI (Gray, 1862)

The Vietnamese or keeled box turtle

General observations: Secretive by nature and well camouflaged, the wild behaviour and status of this species are poorly understood.

Taxonomy: Occurs in Myanmar, India, Thailand, Vietnam, Cambodia, Laos and some localities in China. Formerly referred to *Cyclemys*. No subspecies have been described.

Description: The carapace, which typically measures 13 - 15 cm (18 cm max.) is brown, tricarinate and flat-topped. The hind margin is strongly serrated; in some specimens the anterior margin is also serrated. The plastron is pale yellow or brown and typically features brown blotches on each scute. The head is large, coloured brown or yellow with darker vermiculations, features a hooked upper jaw and yellow markings in the temporal region. There are tubercles present on the thighs and base of the tail. The toes are somewhat webbed. The skin of the limbs is dark grey to black and the fore limbs feature large imbricate scales. Sexual dichromatism is present in this species. Males possess brown heads with red lateral lines from the angle of the jaw whilst females demonstrate a yellowish coloured head with a yellow reticulated pattern (Das, 1991).The irises of males also tend to be reddish, whilst those of females are yellowish, although this character is not absolutely diagnostic. The tails of males are also longer than females and also feature a somewhat concave plastron.

Captive environment: This predominantly, but not exclusively, terrestrial turtle inhabits leaf litter substrates in moist tropical forest where it most frequently occurs in close proximity to water. If allowed to become too dry, all activity will cease and the species enters an aestivation-like behaviour pattern. In captivity, a mixed bark, moss and leaf litter mulch is recommended as a substrate. Captive specimens have responded well to gentle ambient heating or base heating from a heat pad located beneath 5 cm of substrate. A low wattage basking source should be provided, although few take regular advantage of this. Vivarium temperatures should be maintained between 22 - 27°C. Regular misting with a water spray is also recommended and the ambient humidity of its enclosure should be high; Sachsse (1973) found that 75 - 95% relative humidity was satisfactory in practice. A shallow water pool should always be provided, as this turtle often soaks for prolonged periods. Wirot, (1979) states that it does not ever enter water, but Tikader and Sharma (1985) report that the species is "at ease in water as well as on land". Most activity occurs at dawn or dusk which is also the preferred time for feeding.

Diet: Omnivorous with a preference for vegetation and fallen fruits. In captivity, it does well on the same diet as provided for American box turtles, or other Asiatic species such as *Geoemyda spengleri*.

Common health problems: None immediately evident.

Breeding: Rarely bred in captivity. Egg dimensions are surprisingly large and typically measure between 40 - 50 mm in length and 25 - 27 mm wide. Incubation humidity should be very high, between 95 - 100% is suggested with a damp vermiculite and sphagnum substrate. This combination has proved successful on several occasions. Buskirk (1993 and pers. comm.) reported the incubation of a 5 egg clutch, laid on 4th September, at a temperature of 27°C. Viability was indicated by banding of the eggs, and hatching occurred between 1st and 13th December. The hatchlings measured 40 mm SCL and weighed 12 g. They fed initially upon chopped earthworms and snails.

RHINOCLEMMYS SPP. Fitzinger, 1835

South American wood turtles

General observations: Semi-aquatic, aquatic and terrestrial Batagurine turtles from South and Central America. Infrequently bred in captivity until very recently. Many species feature attractive skin and carapace colouring making them sought after by terrarium enthusiasts. Of species typically encountered, *R. punctularia* (Spotted-legged turtle) is the most common with the brightly marked *R. pulcherrima* (Painted wood turtle) being in particular demand by collectors.

Taxonomy: Currently under extensive revision. Ten species and 9 subspecies are generally recognised at the time of writing. This genus exhibits considerable regional variation and it is likely that further taxa will be described. *Rhinoclemmys* species occur from Mexico and Panama to Ecuador and Brazil.

Description: Variable in terms of marking, even within individual species. Key features include a medially keeled carapace, typically somewhat elongate in form. In some respects they resemble box tortoises, but lack the hinged plastron. The head, neck and carapace coloration of *R. pulcherrima* is particularly striking, but other *Rhinoclemmys* species are relatively dull in appearance. The hind feet of most species are webbed, slightly in some species, profoundly so in others. The largest member of the genus is *R. funerea* at 32.5 cm, with other races typically not exceeding 23 cm. In respect of *R. pulcherrima incisa*, Hidalgo (1982), described sexual dimorphic characters as comprising females larger than males with a concave plastron and longer tail in males with the vent situated beyond the carapacial edge. Male *R. pulcherrima* in the author's collection do not demonstrate noticeably depressed plastra, but they are definitely smaller than females and their tails are considerably longer.

Captive environment: *Rhinoclemmys* habitat preferences vary considerably, but in captivity most will thrive in a terrarium with a bark, peat and leaf litter substrate and constant access to a bathing pool. See below for a summary of requirements. Some species and subspecies will avail themselves of the water more than others, but in such an environment self-selection of micro-habitat is perfectly possible. *R. funerea* is particularly aquatic and requires a substantial well filtered pool heated to 26°C and slightly acidic water in the pH 6.5 - 6.8 range (this

***Rhinoclemmys* habitat preferences**

Species	Habitat
R. annulata	Primarily terrestrial, rainforest type
R. areolata	Semi-terrestrial, savannah and marsh habitats
R. funerea	Largely aquatic, marsh and tropical river habitats
R. melanosterna	Primarily aquatic, varied habitats from swamps to rivers including brackish waters
R. nasuta	Primarily aquatic, inhabits fast flowing rivers
R. pulcherrima	Primarily terrestrial. Prefers humid habitats.
R. punctularia	Primarily aquatic, varied habitats from swamps to rivers
R. rubida	Primarily terrestrial. Prefers humid habitats

species also copulates in the water). Bright lights are usually avoided by *Rhinoclemmys* species, which typically prefer a shady environment with plenty of plant cover. Although some species are known to bask (especially *R. melanosterna*, *R. funerea* and *R. punctularia*) others are more crepuscular in habit and will rarely be seen during daylight hours. R. funerea, which the author maintains in Britain, bask daily under a 150 watt reflector lamp whilst perched on a partly submerged log. Most of their day is spent in the water, but at night they forage on land for food. Good filtration is necessary for *R. funerea* as they generate a large amount of waste. A low intensity basking source should be provided in the terrarium for all species however, in the event that the turtles desire to take advantage of it. A small 60W spot-lamp has proved more than adequate provided the background temperature is high enough. Under floor or similar gentle radiators should be employed for ambient heating and a constant temperature of 28°C provides a useful starting point for further development. High intensity heat sources are definitely not recommended for the terrestrial species. Some experimentation may be required with regard to humidity, but most *Rhinoclemmys* species will appreciate a twice-daily misting from a plant sprayer or automatic greenhouse misting system.

Diet: The diet of these turtles usually comprises a combination of fruits, green-leafed plants, earthworms, snails and small beetles. They have also been observed taking live crickets. Typically, all *Rhinoclemmys* species are naturally much more herbivorous than they are carnivorous. In captivity, most will also enthusiastically accept tinned dog food, but the wisdom of providing this and its long term effects on these turtles remains unclear. It is suggested that plant matter comprise at least 90% of the diet, with low fat dog food and other animal-derived proteins forming the remainder. Both *R. pulcherrima* and *R. funerea* maintained by the author fed initially upon banana before progressing onto a wide range of green leafed vegetables and other fruits. Even the more aquatic species tend to feed on land, rather than in the water. Feeding almost invariably occurs at night. One dealer who held a large stock of *Rhinoclemmys* reported that they all fed avidly on chopped raw fish.

Common health problems: Pneumonia. Renal problems and articular gout in species maintained on high protein diets. Aquatic species prefer soft, slightly acidic (pH<6.8) water if skin problems are to be avoided.

Breeding: Males circle females, often biting at the head and neck. This is preceded by the male trailing the female, sniffing at the cloaca. Hidalgo (op. cit.) provides a very full description of this behaviour. Copulation may take place either in or out of water but typically occurs during the rainy season, often during periods of heavy precipitation. In captivity, mating can sometimes also be stimulated by changing the substrate in terraria. Females frequently prefer to nest under plant cover and excavate a pit up to 10 cm deep (*R. pulcherrima*). *R. punctularia*, however, usually nests in a shallow scrape or in a convenient crevice on the surface, allowing the eggs to be covered by fallen leaves. Similar behaviour has also been reported in *R. funerea* and *Rhinoclemmys angulata*. Egg sizes vary greatly among *Rhinoclemmys* species but all are unusually large for the size of the turtle (up to 70 x 37 mm in the case of *R. annulata*). ESD thresholds, if they apply, are unknown for this widely distributed genus. Incubation at between 28 - 30°C has proved successful, however, in a high (90%) humidity environment on mixed vermiculite and sphagnum substrate. Diapausal development is common in *Rhinoclemmys*. The egg may remain inactive for a considerable period before tissue formation proper begins - this may take as long as 6 months. A useful indicator of viability in

Rhinoclemmys eggs is a whitening beginning at one end - this is due to expansion of the vitelline sac. From activation to hatching, a further 90 days elapses - although eggs have been known to hatch in as little as 65 days (Daddario, 1992). Eggs weigh up to 35 g, with a 28 g average for most species. The hatchlings measure approximately 50 mm x 38 mm (*R. punctularia*) but again are very variable from species to species. An egg from *R. p. manni* weighed 28.5 g and hatched on day 67 following incubation at 31°C. The hatchling weighed 20 g and initially fed on small earthworms.

SIEBENROCKIELLA CRASSICOLLIS (Gray, 1831)

Black marsh terrapin

General observations: A common turtle in Thailand, Java, Borneo, Malaya and Burma where its strong odour causes it to be known as "the bad-smelling turtle".

Taxonomy: *Siebenrockiella* is a monotypic genus. No subspecies of the Black marsh terrapin have been described.

Description: Carapace to 20 cm, although most specimens are much smaller. The carapace is entirely black, the plastron black and cream. The posterior marginals are strongly serrated. A medial keel is present, flanked by two indistinct lateral keels. The limbs are black, the head is black or grey with a pale, sometimes indistinct, post orbital spot. The head is large and broad. The feet are webbed.

Captive environment: As its colloquial name implies, this turtle is predominantly an inhabitant of marshes and swamps although it also occurs in other slow moving waterways such as canals. It spends much of its time immersed in mud where in hunts for molluscs, slugs, shrimp, carrion and similar prey. Wirot (1979) reports that it also feeds upon decaying aquatic vegetation and that it forages on land at night. The habits of this turtle are little studied and many details of its lifestyle remain unclear. In captivity, it is relatively undemanding, and is tolerant of a variety of water conditions. Water temperatures should be maintained in the range 25 - 29°C. A soft bottomed habitat with aquatic plants for cover is recommended. A shallow water environment is preferred. Because it spends so much time in the bottom of the tank, under-gravel filtration beds are subject to considerable disturbance (unless protected by a mesh cover) and a medium-sized external canister filter is therefore suggested. Some facility for basking should be provided, and the ambient air temperature above the water should be maintained in excess of 30°C.

Diet: It is relatively easy to provide this species with a diet very similar to that taken in the wild. It greatly appreciates earthworms and will also accept most prepared foods. It will also accept fruit and green vegetables.

Common health problems: None immediately evident.

Breeding: Infrequently bred in captivity. A clutch of eggs typically numbers one or two, and several clutches may be laid in a year. The eggs measure approximately 45 x 19 mm and can be incubated at 29 - 30°C in a high humidity environment on damp vermiculite and sphagnum. Studies have indicated that *Siebenrockiella* may possess an XY/XX chromosome model.

TERRAPENE Merrem, 1820

American box turtles

General observations: Box turtles are so named because they have unusually kinetic plastral hinges which in most cases enable to tortoise to withdraw completely behind a protective 'draw-bridge'. The location of these hinges are important, as they must not be confused with the African Hinge-back (*Kinixys* spp.) tortoises that achieve a similar result but by means of a hinge in the rear of the carapace. This is an effective defence mechanism and examples of the same evolutionary solution to a common problem are found not only in the New World genera *Terrapene* and *Rhinoclemys*, but also in the Asiatic genera *Cuora* and *Pyxidea*.

Taxonomy: American box turtles belong to the Emydid genus *Terrapene*. In North America two species occur each of which is further divided into subspecies as follows; *Terrapene carolina* which is currently considered to have four geographical subspecies; *Terrapene carolina carolina* (the common or Eastern box turtle), *T. c. triunguis* (the Three-toed box turtle), *T. c. major* (the Gulf Coast box turtle) and *T. c. bauri* (the Florida box turtle). The second north American species is *Terrapene ornata* which has two subspecies; *Terrapene ornata ornata* (the Eastern ornate box turtle) and *T. o. luteola* (the Salt Basin or Texas ornate box turtle). Two rare and endangered Mexican forms of *Terrapene carolina*, *T. c. yucatana* and *T. c. mexicana*, also occur but are seldom encountered in captivity (Buskirk, 1993). Mexico also has two other rare species of box turtle, *Terrapene coahuila*, which is highly endangered and *Terrapene nelsoni*, which is also rarely encountered in captive collections.

Description: Box turtles have characteristically high domed carapaces which in some forms is somewhat ridged or keeled in the vertebral region. *Terrapene carolina carolina* occurs from Maine to the deep south; it is quite variable in colouration, but often features yellow or orange streaks and blotches on a brown coloured ground. *T. c. triunguis* occurs in Georgia, eastern Texas and Missouri; again it is variable in colour, some specimens are merely olive or reddish brown, whilst others display a fine pattern of radial flecks on a brown-red ground. Its main diagnostic feature is that it has three toes on its hind legs rather than the usual four - although this is by no means an infallible indicator and it is not always easy for the inexperienced observer to tell *T. c. carolina* and *T. c. triunguis* apart. They are both of similar proportions, most adults attaining approximately 120 - 130 mm SCL and weighing around 470 g. Indeed, any description of north American box turtles can only be regarded in a general sense as a great deal of hybridisation appears to occur between certain races and evident intergrades are frequently encountered. The Gulf Coast box turtle, *T. c. major* is very much more distinctive in both appearance and size. This, the largest of the North American box turtles, occurs from south-west Georgia to eastern Texas. A female specimen in our own collection measures 160 mm SCL and weighs 635 g. *T. c. major* is uniformly dark in colour, almost black, with radiating light marks and blotches on the carapace - although these can be absent on some individuals. The feet of *T. c. major* are more evidently webbed than in other members of the *T. carolina* group. The last of the *T. carolina* assemblage is *T. c. bauri*, the Florida box turtle. The carapace of this race is similar in appearance to that of *T. ornata*, but typically the plastron is unpigmented and featureless and it boasts two yellow head stripes in contrast to the characteristic orange-white irregular spotting of *T. c. triunguis* and *T. c. carolina*. The Ornate box turtle, *Terrapene ornata* is a smaller, very attractively marked species normally featuring distinctive bright green-yellow eyes. This box turtle's feet show little evidence of webbing, a testimony to its more terrestrial habits than *T. carolina*. The two subspecies are very similar, but are considered separate on the basis of a lack of plastral pattern, typically less distinct carapace radiations and yellowish head scales in *T. o. luteola*. This yellow colouration is more evident in females than males that are typically a more greenish yellow colour.

Captive environment: The various species and subspecies of American box turtles occupy a variety of alternative habitats. These range from open woodlands in the case of *T. carolina carolina* to wet marshes in the case of *T. c. major*; given such a range of habitat preferences it is difficult to generalise even for a single species. However, despite their inclusion in the Emydid family, they are all basically terrestrial in habit. From the captive point of view, the main essential variable is the degree of preferred humidity and the time spent in or very near water. Some box turtles, notably *T. c. bauri* and *T. c triunguis* are more aquatic than others; these turtles will swim in a pond and even dive to the bottom to forage among the weeds. They are most active in warm, wet weather. Thunderstorms are especially welcomed (this is also when eggs are most likely to be deposited). Others, including *T. ornata*, seem to prefer somewhat drier conditions. *T. ornata* in particular is essentially a prairie and river edge savannah species with a preference for pastures and open woodlands. All *Terrapene* species can be safely maintained out of doors in the United States and most of Europe at least during the spring, summer and early autumn months. The advice often seen in pet care manuals that a vivarium environment is ideal for these species is simply not true and undoubtedly leads to a high level of mortality and numerous health problems. Provided outdoor temperatures are approximately similar to those experienced in their native habitat, then an outdoor environment is infinitely preferable. The Tortoise Trust has maintained all of the North American species of box turtle in an outdoor terrarium area, very successfully, for several years. A vivarium environment is only employed with sick animals or those we wish to place under observation or to isolate for any reason. A good outdoor terrarium should provide several square meters of land area, a reasonable sized pond for drinking and swimming, and should be thoroughly escape and predator proof; ours is constructed of plywood with a removable wire-mesh top cover. One part can be glazed, thus creating a mini-greenhouse for extra warmth. A good range of weeds and plants should be allowed to grow within the terrarium, and some hollowed-out logs make ideal hides and retreats. Box turtles are generally shy creatures, and need to feel secure in order to feed well and to breed. Box turtles hibernate, typically from November to March, although some southerly populations are an exception. We normally allow the Tortoise Trust colony to hibernate out of doors naturally, the turtles burying themselves deeply under some large half rotted logs in mud, loam and leaf litter. We have also found that hibernating them artificially in a container of mulched coconut fibre and forest floor litter is satisfactory. There are reliable accounts

Three-toed box turtle, *Terrapene carolina triunguis.* Although frequently maintained as a pet, this species is actually fairly difficult and demands a carefully designed environment if illness is to be avoided.

Terrapene carolina major, the Gulf coast box turtle. This species requires a warm, humid environment and does not normally hibernate.

Mauremys caspica, the Caspian terrapin. A very robust aquatic species able to tolerate a wide range of water conditions.

Captive-bred *Testudo horsfieldi*, Horsfield's tortoise. This species is subject to very rapid initial growth, and good dietary management is essential if bone deformities are to be avoided.

of some box turtles choosing to hibernate over winter buried in the bottom mud of iced-over ponds; this is not a procedure which should be encouraged under normal captive conditions as natural ponds are biologically active to a much greater extent than artificial ones and problems could very easily occur if conditions are anything less than absolutely ideal. If they are to be overwintered, then a humid vivarium at a minimum of 21°C is necessary with additional basking facilities and preferably equipped with full spectrum fluorescent lighting. Do not allow it to become too dry, or ear and eye problems are almost certain to develop. In the wild, under prolonged drought or heat-wave conditions, box turtles aestivate, disappearing underground for weeks on end. Our experience is that Gulf Coast box turtles prefer higher temperatures to the other subspecies of *Terrapene carolina* with the exception of *T. c. bauri*. These we keep in a section of our tropical house at a daytime temperature of 27 - 32°C, with access to an outdoor terrarium if required. Because of the design of our tropical house, the section containing the box turtles is allowed to cool to about 20°C overnight. This temperature cycle seems well suited to these particular animals. Humidity within the tropical house is high, often above 95%. We also have found that Gulf Coast box turtles do best (at least in Britain) if overwintered. Overwintering temperatures are as given above for our tropical house. Florida box turtles (*T. c. bauri*) do not hibernate in the wild and should also be overwintered in a warm, humid environment. *Terrapene ornata* is another species which hibernates in the northern parts of its range, but remains at least semi-active in the south.

Diet: *Terrapene* species are omnivorous. In the wild they consume not only berries and other fallen fruit but also snails, insect larvae, caterpillars, earthworms, crickets, tadpoles, slugs and beetles in addition to toadstools and green plant material. Some have also been observed to attack small ground-nesting birds. Juveniles are noticeably more carnivorous in nature than fully grown adults. *Terrapene ornata* in particular retains these essentially carnivorous and insectivorous preferences throughout adulthood. Crickets and grasshoppers are a favourite of this species and will often tempt a reluctant animal to begin feeding. In captivity, if a natural outdoor type environment is adopted then a certain amount of the turtles' dietary needs will also be met from natural resources. Our own colony can often be observed hunting for small prey in the early morning and late evening, especially during or just after a heavy rainfall. Some supplementary feeding is, however, essential. This should comprise a wide range of berries and fruits such as cherries, apple, banana or melon plus additional vegetables and salad materials including cauliflower, green and red sweet peppers, lettuce, tomato, mushrooms and even surplus cooked potato. The animal protein requirement can be met from low fat dog food and whole dead mice, locusts and snails. Canned cat food is not recommended as a staple item as it is dangerously high in fat content. Rehydrated cat pellets are, however, much more suitable and are accepted readily. The food should be liberally dusted with a high ratio calcium supplement to counter the high levels of phosphorous present in the animal matter.

Common health problems: Ear abscesses. These require surgical excision but can often be prevented by good water and vivarium hygiene and by providing adequate levels of ambient humidity. Eye infections are also common and can be traced to the same causes. These usually respond well to antibiotic injections. The vast majority of health problems with captive *Terrapene* are directly attributable to environmental mismanagement. When faced with a sick box turtle requiring nursing, we have found that good hospital accommodation can be provided by means of a base-heated plastic covered seed propagator. A damp towel substrate is included to raise ambient humidity. This has proved consistently successful and is particularly well suited to cases of environmentally induced eye inflammation.

Breeding: Sexing box turtles can be somewhat difficult. However, in *T. carolina* males tend to have a red eye whilst females have a yellowish brown eye; sometimes this also applies to *T. ornata* (especially *T. o. luteola*) but by no means always as a bright yellow-green eye is more usually seen in this species. Males also have longer and thicker tails than do females. There is some difference in plastral concavity, typically very evident in the *T. carolina* group but entirely absent in *T. ornata.* American box turtles can all be captive bred under virtually identical conditions. *T. c. carolina* and *T. c. triunguis* for example typically lay 3 - 5 elongate eggs (occasionally as many as 8) which are somewhat leathery in texture and on average measure approximately 32 mm by 20 mm. These should be incubated in a Type II incubator at high humidity (90%+) in a sphagnum moss or mixed peat and vermiculite substrate. Humidity is critical, as during incubation *Terrapene* eggs expand by absorption of environmental water. A lack of humidity will cause the eggs to dehydrate and collapse. If incubated at 26 - 28 °C hatching usually occurs in 70 - 85 days. This genus relies upon ESD, but the threshold may vary from subspecies to subspecies and with geographical origin. *T. c. carolina* and *T. c. triunguis* eggs incubated at 22.5°C to 27°C appear to produce predominantly male neonates, those incubated at 28.5°C and above result in exclusively females. Absolute safe limits for incubation appear to be 22°C minimum and 34°C maximum. The hatchlings, on average, measure 28 - 30 mm SCL and weigh approximately 7 g. The mating process of *Terrapene* species is most curious; at one stage the males' legs frequently become trapped in the posterior plastral hinge of the female - the process can also take several hours in contrast to the very rapid mating procedure of most terrestrial tortoises. This is preceded by a more typical biting, circling and shoving phase - during which the males frequently use their front legs to spin the females around. Hatchlings should be maintained in a high humidity environment at similar temperatures to adults.

TESTUDO GRAECA Linnaeus 1758

The North-American or Moorish tortoise

General observations: *Testudo graeca* was for years in Europe considered the archetypal pet tortoise. So much so that it became generally known as the "common tortoise". However, in reality this creature is little known and is very far from common throughout much of its natural range. It is found only in North Africa and small populations also occur in southern Spain and the Balearic islands.

Taxonomy: The taxonomy of the *Testudo graeca* complex is extremely confused and is also highly controversial. At present, 4 subspecies are generally recognised: *Testudo graeca graeca* from North Africa and Spain, *Testudo graeca ibera* from Greece, Turkey and the surrounding regions, the almost unknown *Testudo graeca zarudnyi* from the eastern sector of the central plateau of Iran (and possibly, from Afghanistan) and the enigmatic *Testudo graeca terrestris* which allegedly is found in Libya, Israel, Syria and south western Turkey. This scheme is based primarily upon the work of Robert Mertens who revised the taxonomy of *Testudo graeca* in 1946 with later modifications by H. Wermuth in 1958. Unfortunately, there are serious flaws in Mertens' comparative morphometric data and he manifestly fails to notice a range of morphological features which indicate that not only are there many more than four clearly defined races but that their relationship to each other as subspecies is highly questionable. Furthermore, the status of one "generally accepted" subspecies, *Testudo graeca terrestris,* is even more doubtful. This later has never been described in a meaningful way, lacks an extant holotype and both its description and distribution are extremely confused. It often seems that almost any small, yellowish coloured *Testudo*, no matter what its goegraphical origins, can claim title to this name. In 1990 the present author proposed a revised taxonomy of *Testudo graeca*. This scheme proposed that *Testudo ibera* and *Testudo zarudnyi* should revert to their original status as full species, that *Testudo graeca terrestris* should be discounted entirely for the reasons given above, and that within North Africa it is evident that massive diversity is present between populations, some of which deserve separate taxonomic recognition. Indeed, one population that occurs in Algeria had already been designated separately in 1836, as *Testudo whitei*. Another population that demonstrates major morphological divergence from normal (e.g. Moroccan) *T. graeca* is that of Tunisia and this population was also named separately as *Furculachelys nabeulensis* by the present author in 1990. The new genus name *Furculachelys* was proposed because certain osteological features of the Algerian and Tunisian populations do not conform to the accepted diagnostic criteria for *Testudo*. In fact, they appear to be half-way between *Testudo* and *Geochelone*. Their status at genus level is one issue, but another, more important issue is their status as the species level. This is far more important and relevant for practical conservation purposes. At present, the debate continues and it is hoped that recently initiated DNA studies may throw more light on the matter. This newly proposed taxonomy is presently not widely accepted in the USA, but in Europe, where these animals are much more frequently seen, acceptance is growing. Even if one rejects the proposal at genus level, it is difficult to see how it is possible to sustain the argument that the "giant" tortoises of Algeria, *F. whitei* and the "miniature" populations of Tunisia (*F. nabeulensis*) can possibly belong not only to the same species but must also belong to the same subspecies, *Testudo graeca graeca*, as present orthodoxy insists.

Description: True *Testudo graeca graeca* (as found in southern Algeria and Morocco) is a relatively small tortoise but is by no means as small as the Tunisian *F. nabeulensis*, from which they differ not only osteologically but also in terms of their external morphology and marking. Males typically attain no more than 145 mm SCL (the average is 130 mm) and weigh approximately 535 g. Females are considerably larger and demonstrate a high degree of dimorphism; 180 mm SCL and a weight in the region of 1,300 g would not be atypical. The maximum size for a female recorded in Morocco is 220 mm. In central coastal Algeria, females of 280 mm are common and "giants" which measure in excess of 300 mm are not unknown. These were separately described in 1836 as *Testudo whitei*. These Algerian tortoises can attain a mass of 4.8 kg. The carapace of Algerian specimens is much more elongate and often, especially in males, featuresstrongly flared rear marginal scutes very similar to those seen in *Testudo marginata*. The ground colour of the scutes in *Testudo graeca graeca* is bright yellow and features an irregular series of small black-brown flecks or spots. The areola of each large scute has a central black dot that is bordered laterally and anteriorly. The scales of the head and legs are yellow. The frontal vertebral scute is roundish in form, somewhat pinched in or depressed on the lower half. The rear marginals are not markedly flared or serrate, even on males. The supracaudal is not projected and is not ventrally introflexed. On occasions, animals with divided supracaudals may be encountered.

There are small tubercles or spurs on the upper thighs, next to the tail. Moroccan *T. g. graeca* demonstrate regional variations; in the south, tortoises are generally lighter in colour and males in particular possess a more elongate body form. In the north, especially in the mountains, melanistic and larger animals are commonplace. Many tortoises from southern Morocco possess reddish skin on the head, tail and hind limbs. This appears to correlate with the soil type upon which they live. The carapaces of such specimens are usually a light, dull brown and bear few distinct markings.

Captive environment: *T. graeca* (and all North African species generally) are extremely environmentally sensitive and cannot tolerate any mishandling. They usually tend to do badly in captivity and very few survive in the long-term. If mixed with other more robust, competitive and aggressive species such as *T. hermanni* or *T. ibera* they rapidly succumb to alien diseases and stress. They should be maintained separately. Activity in *Testudo graeca* ceases almost entirely when ambient temperatures exceed 28°C. In the wild, when conditions become too hot and dry, they aestivate underground. It is worth noting that these tortoises evolved to live in the once-vast forests of the region - sadly, these forests are now almost entirely destroyed due to the effects of overgrazing, agricultural intensification and burning. Only 5,000 years ago the climate and habitat of the region were very different from that of today. Some authors have mistaken *T. graeca* aestivating in August (when temperatures regularly soar as high as 48°C) as the beginning of their hibernation period. In fact, some coastal populations do not naturally hibernate at all - it never gets cold enough. The coldest months are January and February where it only rarely falls below 20°C. In December, in southern Morocco, temperatures in tortoise habitats are frequently above 26°C in the shade. In North Africa I have found tortoises grazing and otherwise behaving perfectly normally on Christmas Day. Inland populations at the higher altitudes are more inclined to hibernate - but only for a very short while. In the north of Morocco, temperatures are very different from those experienced in the south, and northern *T. g. graeca* (especially those living at higher altitudes) hibernate over winter for as long as 5 months.

Diet: Similar to *T. ibera*, *T. marginata* and *T. hermanni* but flowers appear to be a more important dietary constituent. These tortoises are all coprophagous to a greater or lesser extent, feasting whenever the opportunity arises on mammalian dung - in North Africa sheep, goat and camel droppings are all taken with relish. It is quite likely that this may play an important biochemical and digestive role but to date this aspect has been little studied. Faecal pellet analysis of *T. g. graeca* conducted by the author in southern Morocco revealed a high intake of snail shell particles. It is believed that these are consumed in order to meet the tortoises' demand for calcium.

Common health problems: "Runny Nose Syndrome"; pneumonia; stomatitis; flagellate problems. *T. graeca* complex tortoises should not be mixed with other species, subspecies or animals from a different geographical origin than themselves. Disease incidence rises sharply when mixed and reduces when maintained separately, according to geographic origin.

Breeding: Unlike *T. hermanni*, *T. marginata* or *T. ibera*, North African *T. graeca* are rarely bred at all in captivity. In addition, very little data is available on their natural reproductive biology or behaviour. Over the past few years however the Tortoise Trust has succeeded in captive breeding North African tortoises from several different localities including true *T. graeca graeca*. The eggs are much smaller and rounder than those of *T. ibera* typically measuring 30 mm long by 27 mm wide. The hatchlings weigh a diminutive 7 - 8 g and measure approximately 28 mm SCL. A typical clutch consists of 4 - 5 such eggs (the typical clutch size of Algerian *F. whitei,* is by comparison, 12 - 14 eggs of similar dimensions). Incubation is best accomplished at between 30.5 °C and 31.5 °C in a Type I unit at medium humidity (75 - 80%). At this temperature range incubation takes approximately 68 - 80 days. Hatchlings first pierce the egg and once their requirement for oxygen is satisfied may then choose to stay there for up to 72 hours whilst any remaining egg-sac is absorbed. The hatchlings are light brownish-yellow in colour without distinct markings which develop as they grow. They usually begin feeding within 48 hours of hatching. By 1 year of age they are approximately half the size of *T. ibera* hatched at the same time. Hatchlings are accommodated initially in covered seed tray propagators warmed by an external basking lamp. When weather permits they are removed to a secure, mesh-covered outdoor unit. This is both escape and predator proof.

TESTUDO HERMANNI Gmelin, 1789

Hermann's tortoise (Rookie)

General observations: *Testudo hermanni* enjoys a relatively wide distribution (as two currently recognised subspecies) which includes eastern Spain, southern France, Italy and the Balearic islands, the Balkan peninsula, Yugoslavia, Albania, Bulgaria, Romania, Greece and Turkey. It is also found on Corfu, Sicily and Sardinia.

Taxonomy: There are, as indicated above, two currently recognised subspecies of *Testudo hermanni*. However, these are not as frequently cited in most field guides and other works of reference *"Testudo hermanni hermanni"* in respect of the eastern (Balkan) race and *"T. h. robertmertensi"* in respect of the western (French, Spanish and Italian) race. By virtue of taxonomic priority the western race is actually the nominate form and should be cited as *Testudo hermanni hermanni* GMELIN 1789 with a designated Type Locality of Collobrieres, France. At the same time, the eastern race should be cited as *Testudo hermanni boettgeri* MOJSISOVICS 1889 with a designated Type Locality or *terra typica* of Orsova, Romania. The western population, *Testudo hermanni hermanni* is relatively homogenous and is certainly very distinctive. Specialist field workers who are familiar with the species can detect a number of regional variations involving colouration and size even within the currently accepted subspecies.

Even so, it is clear that the western populations of *T. h. hermanni* are very convergent in all external characters. The same cannot be said of the eastern subspecies *T. h. boettgeri* which is by no means contiguous and which displays an alarming range of shapes, sizes, colours and patterns within what is supposed to be a single (subspecific) form . It is almost certain that further research will eventually lead to the identification of certain populations that may require separate taxonomic consideration. It may also be necessary to view the entire *T. hermanni* conglomerate as a complex of many very divergent individual populations than as two simple and clearly defined geographical subspecies.

Description: *Testudo hermanni* was first differentiated from *T. graeca* because of the horny tip it bears upon its tail and its lack of thigh tubercles. Unlike *T. graeca*, *T. ibera* and all other Mediterranean or Asiatic terrestrial species except for *T. horsfieldi* it has a fixed and rigid xiphiplastron. It is typically a flattish animal with a broad, low carapace that bears black markings upon an olive-yellow base. The western population of *T. h. hermanni* are typically smallish tortoises approximately 120 - 130 mm SCL, whilst certain eastern populations *of T. h. boettgeri* can easily reach double this length. In both cases there is marked dimorphism, with western males attaining a typical absolute maximum of 165 mm and females 190 mm. I have measured several (female) tortoises from Bulgaria however which exceed 260 mm SCL and which weigh in excess of 3,400 g. An eastern Bulgarian *Testudo h. boettgeri* collected in 1918 and now in a museum is believed to be the largest example of this species ever recorded, at 303 mm SCL (Buskirk, pers. comm.). Most of the tortoises of Yugoslavia, although considerably larger than *T. h. hermanni* at an average of 180 - 200 mm SCL does not attain such dramatic dimensions as these. Curiously, the "giant" Hermann's tortoises from Eastern Europe I have observed have all possessed 4 claws on all feet. This character is usually associated with *T. horsfieldi*, although it is not known how widespread this trait is generally among populations of *T. h. boettgeri.* It is frequently alleged that it is possible to distinguish between the western and eastern populations of *T. hermanni* by determining if the supracaudal shield is divided or undivided. It is also sometimes claimed that *T. hermanni* can be distinguished from *T. graeca* using the same criteria. In fact, neither claim is true and this character is of little value in specific determination. One finds that *T. h. hermanni* does indeed almost always posses a divided supracaudal shield, but one also finds that approximately 20% of *T. h. boettgeri* also share the character. The plastral markings of *Testudo hermanni hermanni* are characteristically formed of two almost solid dark bands running longitudinally down the plastron. Every specimen of this subspecies examined by the author (several hundred in France, Spain and Italy) have possessed this feature. The plastral markings of the eastern *form T. hermanni boettgeri* appears to be somewhat more variable. Some specimens examined have possessed plastrons with dense markings which almost approach that of *T. h. hermanni* so this character should not employed in isolation to diagnose speciation. Most bear a diffuse series of blotches, however. The ground colour of *T. h. hermanni* is typically a bright golden yellow. This contrasts sharply with most specimens of the eastern *T. h. boettgeri* where the ground colour could best be described as a greenish-yellow. Similarly, the carapace markings of the western population seem to be unusually clear and well defined compared to most eastern specimens.

Captive environment: The natural habitat of *T. hermanni* is evergreen Mediterranean oak forest; this habitat has however been substantially degraded and reduced as a result of human activity. Present-day populations are therefore found in (secondary) maquis type environments which typically comprise coarse, arid and scrubby hillsides. In only very few places does *T. hermanni* continue to inhabit surviving primary forest. In captivity *T. hermanni* is a comparatively resilient and adaptable tortoise. It seems equally at home in arid or even moderately damp environments but plenty of sun and warmth is essential. An ideal captive situation would provide a large outdoor enclosure, planted with low growing herbs and shrubs on well-drained soil. There should be a slope or gentle hill to encourage basking and to provide a nesting site. Mediterranean tortoises maintained by the Tortoise Trust are provided with a securely fenced paddock which is south-facing to encourage basking and nesting. This enclosed habitat includes a number of introduced native Mediterranean shrubs and several areas where natural fodder plants are encouraged to grow. This greatly reduces the need for artificial feeding and generally provides for a healthier, higher quality diet.

For overnight accommodation, a wooden hut can be provided, although most tortoises will make a scrape under a suitable bush. In the wild, *T. hermanni* hibernates from November to April throughout most of their range.

Diet: The natural diet of *T. hermanni* consists of herbaceous and succulent plants native to the Mediterranean zone. In captivity as wide a range of weeds and green vegetation as possible should be provided. Lettuce alone is far from an adequate substitute. A natural grazing area is much better than artificial feeding. Although most *T. hermanni* enjoy fruits, an excess should not be given as their sugar content can increase the probability of digestive problems and diarrhoea. *T. hermanni* requires a diet which is very high in fibre and will often take dried leaves in preference to fresh. Just occasionally in wet weather *T. hermanni* will take advantage of a passing slug or snail but this does not comprise a significant dietary component. They should not be provided with any meat-based food items in captivity; if they are, then serious consequences may be encountered in the long-term. During heavy rain *T. hermanni* raise themselves on their back legs and place their noses to the ground in order to drink from shallow puddles; typically they also void urine at the same time. As with many arid-adapted reptiles they normally choose not to lose fluid unnecessarily until it can be easily replenished. It is important to note that, as with all Mediterranean tortoises, seasonal variations in the quantity, quality and constituency of the food intake is an important factor. In spring, abundant moist food is available as fresh shoots and flowers but in summer the land becomes dry and is unable to support much green vegetation. During this period the tortoises consume food with a higher dry-weight ratio than they do earlier in the year. In extreme conditions the tortoises may actually aestivate during this barren period. The early autumn rains result in a renewal of green vegetation allowing for a final feeding period before hibernation. In captivity, it is important to avoid reliance upon a supermarket salad type diet; provision of a natural grazing area as described above will assist greatly in achieving this objective.

Common health problems: None, although viral stomatitis and viral hepatitis have been recorded. A common site for deep-seated subcutaneous abscesses in *T. hermanni* is just above the tail, where the skin joins the carapace. This site should be inspected regularly.

Breeding: The breeding behaviour of *T. hermanni* is very different from that of all other Mediterranean species. Unlike *T. graeca* or *T. ibera* male *hermanni* do not engage in the same degree of violent ramming activity during courtship, instead resorting much more to head and leg biting which can become quite vicious in nature to the extent of occasionally drawing blood. The horny tip of the tail is also used to stimulate the females cloacal region. Males are also frequently observed apparently resting on females backs almost mechanically stroking the carapace of the female with the front legs. This behaviour, which is conducted in a seemingly trance-like state can persist for hours. It is not known what purpose it serves, if any. The behaviour has not been observed in any other Mediterranean species. Mating is a vigorous affair, accompanied by high pitched squeaks from the male during copulation. Egg laying in the wild takes place from April to June and hatching usually occurs immediately following the first rains of September. There is a very marked difference both in clutch density and egg size between the western *T. h. hermanni* and eastern *T. h. boettgeri*; the average clutch size of *T. h. hermanni* in France is 3, whilst in eastern *T. h. boettgeri* it is typically 5 - 8 and can be as high as 12. The eggs of *T. h. hermanni* are fairly small at 30 mm long by 24 mm wide on average, whilst those of *T. h. boettgeri* are, by comparison, enormous at 40 mm long by 29 mm wide. Hatchling *T. h. hermanni* typically weigh 9 - 10 g or so, whilst eastern *T. h. boettgeri* hatchlings weigh in at an average of 12 - 14 g. Statistically and in taxonomic terms, these are very significant differences. Both subspecies frequently lay more than one clutch per year. In captivity artificial incubation at 30.5 - 33 °C normally results in hatching at about the 8th or 9th week. Recent research on ESD in *Testudo hermanni boettgeri* suggests that the threshold temperature for this race is 31.5°C (Eendebak, 1995).

TESTUDO HORSFIELDI Gray, 1844

The Afghan or Steppe tortoise

General observations: The Afghan tortoise has to date been little studied and much remains unclear concerning its biology, taxonomy and ecology. In Pakistan *T. horsfieldi* occurs in Baluchistan and at very low densities in the North West Frontier Province. It also occurs in the former U.S.S.R where it is subject to heavy exploitation, and since the disintegration of the Soviet Union, greatly expanded illegal collecting and export trade from territories such as Kazakhstan.

Taxonomy: At the species level there is little dispute, although recently two subspecies have been proposed; *Testudo horsfieldi kazachtanica* from Kazakhstan to Turkmeniya (Chkhikvadze 1988) and *Testudo horsfieldi rustmovi* from south-western Turkmenistan (Chkhikvadze, Amiranashvili and Ataev 1990). The nominate race, *T. h. horsfieldi* occurs in Pakistan, Afghanistan, Iran and China. At genus level, its taxonomic status is very confused. The morphological evidence is conflicting. The cranial characters suggest a close affinity with *Testudo*, but the carapace osteology is sufficiently different for it to be allocated to the genus *Agrionemys* by several authorities. Externally, it expresses a marked phenetic relationship to *T. hermanni* with which it shares the morphological features of fixed xiphiplastron and horny tip to the tail - although this later is reduced compared to *T. hermanni*.

Description: The carapace is typically flattish, roundish and yellow-green or olive in colouration. There are some ill defined dark brown markings on the larger scutes. The plastron is typically blotched with black, or may be black all over on some examples.
There is typically a group of enlarged scales or tubercles to each side of the tail; these appear to be larger on males than females. The tail has a hard, horny tip. The feet all have four claws. The skin is yellowish. A breeding pair of male and female *T. horsfieldi* now maintained by the Tortoise Trust measure 140 mm/590 g and 187 mm/1,390 g respectively.

Captive environment: In the former USSR this species occurs principally on sandy steppes, although loamy habitats have also been recorded. In Pakistan, Minton (1966) found *T. horsfieldi* exhibited a preference for grassy areas close to springs in generally rocky and hilly terrain. This species is well known for its digging abilities; tunnels up to 2m long with widened chambers at the end are frequently excavated in steep hillsides or under overhanging stones (Mylnarski and Wermuth, 1971). The disused burrows of rodents are also colonised and adapted. The burrows of the marmot and hedgehog appear to be particularly favoured. Similar behaviour has recently been observed by this author in relation to arid south Moroccan habitats of *T. graeca graeca* where abandoned mammal burrows are used by aestivating tortoises (Highfield, unpublished observations). This tortoise is reported not to occur in coastal areas, preferring instead the mountains inland. In the former USSR the species is active for only 3 months of the year, usually March, April and May. From late May onwards activity sharply decreases and the tortoises spend most of their time hidden in their burrows. In the northern parts of its range, *T. horsfieldi* hibernates in winter deep within its burrow; in the southern parts of its range aestivation occurs in summer (Ernst and Barbour, 1989). In Pakistan, captive tortoises were observed to bury themselves from October to March and aestivation occurred from June to August (Roberts, 1975). This tortoise is also found at unusually extreme altitudes: Minton (1966) found them at altitudes between 1,600 and 2,300 m. A more typical altitude in the former soviet sector of their range would appear to be between 800m. and 1,600 m. In captivity, *T. horsfieldi* cannot tolerate damp but otherwise can be successfully maintained under similar conditions to *T. hermanni.* Burrowing and climbing facilities should, however, always be provided.

Diet: As for *T. hermanni.* Some reports state that *T. horsfieldi* rarely feed upon grass, but I have found that they very much enjoy young green shoots and consume them enthusiastically.

Common health problems: Trade animals are often infected with *Hexamita parva.* Viral stomatitis and hepatitis have also been recorded in this species. Serious skin infections can occur if *T. horsfieldi* is allowed to hibernate in damp earth.

Breeding: In the wild, most mating occurs early on in the season. In the former Soviet part of their range, Terentjef and Chernov (1949) report that mating commences in March and lasts until June, with deposition in May and the first weeks of June. Hempel (1988) notes that mating commences almost immediately upon emerging from hibernation. Males are frequently very aggressive. They chase females, biting at their head and legs with sufficient ferocity to regularly draw blood. Two males will often fight viciously if confined together in the breeding season, but at other times seem to co-exist peacefully.

Males court females by means of a strange head nodding ritual, staring directly into the females face whilst simultaneously jerking their head up and down in a rapid motion. They emit a series of high pitched squeaks during copulation. The eggs are usually laid within 8 weeks of successful mating, and typically measure some 47 mm long by 34 mm wide but considerable variability is seen between individual females. Eggs usually weigh between 23 - 25 g. Clutch density is usually between 3 - 5, but again, this is very variable.

Terentjev and Chernov (1949) note that two to three clutches of eggs may be laid per season, and this observation is confirmed by the behaviour of *T. horsfieldi* in the Tortoise Trust collection. In the former Soviet Union, Sergeev (1941) reported 4 clutches per year. Hempel

Testudo (g.) ibera, the Turkish spur-thighed tortoise. This species also occurs in Greece.

Plastron of *Testudo hermanni hermanni*, the rare Western race of *T. hermanni*. Typical size of adult male. This race is much smaller than the more common Eastern race.

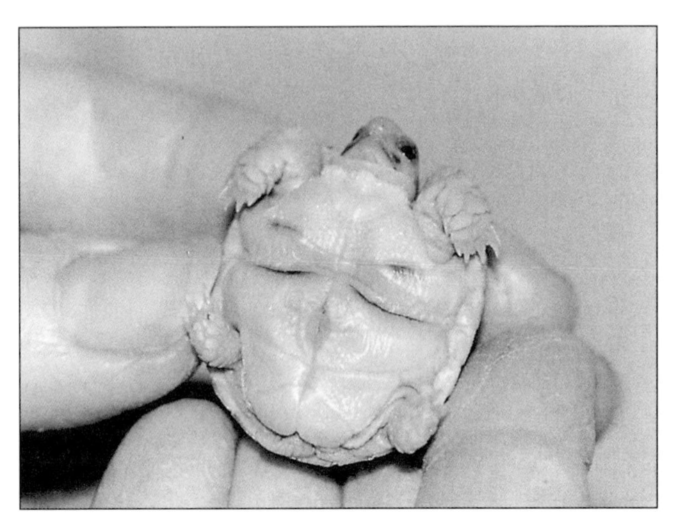

Newly hatched *Testudo kleinmanni*, the Egyptian tortoise. At 4.5 grams on leaving the egg this is the smallest of the Mediterranean tortoises, and attains adult dimensions no greater than 130 mm. Males are typically less than 115 mm.

Testudo marginata, the Marginated tortoise. Note elongate carapace, and highly flared rear marginals. This is a male specimen. Females are broader at the waste.

(1988) records that a captive female laid several clutches of 2 - 4 eggs per clutch and in the United States, Slavens (1989) observed a large captive female lay 2 clutches of 7 and 9 eggs at the end of August and another clutch of 3 eggs in September. According to Mylnarski and Mertens (1971) an individual female may lay as many as 20 eggs per season in 3 or more clutches. In the wild, incubation usually takes 80 - 110 days, but if incubated at moderate humidity in a Type I incubator at a more or less constant temperature of 30.5°C 60 - 75 days is more usual. The new hatchlings typically measure between 32 - 34 mm long and weigh from 9 - 12 g. In their first year, they tend to grow more quickly than *T. hermanni* and maturity is believed to be attained in 7 - 10 years (Roberts, 1975, Terentjev and Chernov, 1949).

TESTUDO IBERA Pallas 1814

The Greek or Turkish Spur-thighed tortoise

General observations:: This tortoise occurs throughout Turkey, north-eastern Greece, Bulgaria, Romania, western Iran, Syria, Jordan, Iraq and the Republic of Georgia in the former U.S.S.R. from where the type specimen was taken in 1814. There is a considerable degree of morphological variation throughout this very considerable range, principally in respect of colour but also in size; specimens from Asiatic Turkey and Syria tend to be very much lighter and often feature a bright yellow head and limbs. Certain of these have been enthusiastically labelled "*Testudo graeca terrestris*" or "*terrestris-ibera*" intergrades by some observers. In north-western Turkey *T. ibera* tend to be much more melanistic, and are, on occasions, almost entirely black. An introduced colony of *T. ibera* also exists on Sardinia where it is sympatric with not only similarly introduced *T. hermanni* but also *T. marginata*.

Taxonomy: In 1946 the German herpetologist Robert Mertens designated *Testudo ibera* PALLAS 1814 as a subspecies of *Testudo graeca* LINNAEUS 1758 but this suggestion appears seriously flawed in the light of recent investigations. The point needs to be made that *Testudo ibera* was described and named as a full species by Pallas in 1814. This was generally accepted as such until 1946 when Mertens downgraded it on the basis on an analysis of a dozen specimens of questionable origin. There are major structural, biotypic and behavioural differences between *T. graeca* and *T. ibera* which Mertens (and most subsequent authors) have completely overlooked. Therefore, in the opinion of the present author, this tortoise should be considered separately from *T. graeca* which it only very superficially resembles. Within the very large and widely distributed population of *T. ibera* however, there are a considerable number of very distinct geographical forms or races some of which occur in relative isolation, some of which appear to represent extremes of clines; only a few of these have so far received separate systematic recognition. To date only *Testudo (graeca) nikolskii* from north-west Transcaucasia and *T. (graeca) anamurensis* from south-western Turkey have been proposed. It should be noted that although assigned by their respective authors as subspecies of "*Testudo graeca*", if *T. ibera* is considered a true and separate biological species these would instead be amended to *T. ibera nikolskii* and *T. ibera anamurensis*. The author has recently made a series of further field-trips to Turkey in order to examine the localities occupied by the proposed subspecies *T. (graeca) anamurensis* and the questionable "*T. graeca terrestris*" populations. Of *T. (g.) anamurensis*, I must provisionally concur with the late H. Weissinger who described them; these tortoises demonstrate sufficient divergence from "normal" *Testudo (graeca) ibera* to warrant further detailed study. More work is undoubtedly required in order to finally determine their taxonomic status and distribution, however. They are markedly elongate, possess a profound rear marginal flare almost of marginata proportions, and have an unusually blotched plastron. Their entire carapace profile is quite different from what one normally finds in *T. ibera*. Of the "*terrestris*" forms said to inhabit the region of Turkey neighbouring Syria and centred upon the ancient city of Antakya (Antioch), these tortoises have for long posed a considerable mystery. For what I believe to be the first time, colour plates of these enigmatic tortoises are presented here. Immediately evident are the light yellow masks on face and head; also the yellow colour of the carapaces. These tortoises are also considerably smaller than "normal" *ibera*. However, analysis of the scute structure and other morphological characters proves beyond doubt that these tortoises are a variant form of *Testudo ibera* (as would be expected, given their geographical situation) and are far removed from North African *T. graeca*. In this region, summers are long and hot and aestivation of tortoises occurs. As has been observed in other localities, e.g. Murcia in Spain, where these climatic conditions prevail there are evolutionary pressures that favour smaller, lighter coloured tortoises. It is also worth pointing out that by no means every tortoise in this locality is bright yellow - in the same field as several yellow specimens we found a melanistic male. If the colouring is due to locally dominant genetic factors, then it would not be surprising if an occasional animal demonstrating a recessive trait should appear. It may be that one could justifiably propose these as another subspecies of *Testudo ibera*, but however one views them they should not be tainted with the name "*terrestris*", which is essentially worthless, so confused has it become.

Description: The nominate race of *T. ibera* is readily distinguished from *T. graeca*; it is considerably larger with males typically reaching 180 mm SCL and females 201 mm SCL, although even larger examples are very frequently seen (the very largest examples appear to be found in Bulgaria, which is, curiously, also home to the largest examples of *T. hermanni*). It is also much broader and flatter than *T. graeca* which is characteristically high domed in lateral profile (the length-height-width ratios of *T. graeca* and *T. ibera* are totally dissimilar). The ground colour of *T. ibera* is quite variable but ranges from a greenish horn colour to light orange-brown. The carapace markings are brownish-black and the vertebral and costal scutes typically feature a dark central areola with anterior and lateral borders. Very aged specimens sometimes lose the outer layer of keratin revealing large irregular bright orange areas underneath. Another carapace character that distinguishes *T. ibera* from *T. graeca* is found at the 1st vertebral scute which is very angular compared to the rounded form of *T. graeca*. The head (and underlying cranium) of *T. ibera* is quite different from that of *T. graeca graeca*, the nose in particular is broader and blunter and the eyes are characteristically much larger by comparison. The limbs are, by comparison to North African *T. graeca graeca*, much thicker and shorter (there are acute osteological differences involving certain limb bones). The supracaudal shield is only occasionally divided and the thighs feature either a single or double spur. Some geographic populations have significantly flared or serrate posterior marginals, occasionally upturned or reverted, a character that is more prevalent in males than it is in females. Finally, it should be noted that all of the above forms, or races, are capable of presenting with a divided supracaudal scute. This character is not common, but most certainly does occur in a minority of animals. This author once bred 5 *T. ibera* hatchlings from parents with undivided supracaudals, only to discover that 3 hatchlings had inherited the trait and two lacked it. Tortoises with divided supracaudal shields have also been observed in the wild. As such, this character should not be relied on to differentiate *T. ibera* (or *T. graeca*) from *T. hermanni* as is suggested in many works of reference.

Captive environment: Generally as for *T. hermanni. Testudo ibera* are a relatively tenacious and robust species capable of withstanding considerable extremes of climate. Along with *T. hermanni* they tend to do well under captive conditions and breed very readily.

Diet: As for *T. hermanni.*

Common health problems: None immediately evident.

Breeding: For best breeding success, pairs should be closely matched on the basis of general colouration and markings. Although dissimilar pairs can and do produce viable offspring, this is noticeably less consistent than is the case if pairs are more closely matched. Clutch density ranges from 4 - 12 but more typically numbers 6 - 8. Large females tend to produce higher clutch densities than smaller specimens. The eggs of *T. ibera* throughout its range appear remarkably consistent in both size and weight; on average they measure 36 mm long by 30 mm wide and weigh about 18 - 20 g. They can be incubated in a Type I incubator in a medium humidity environment and at a more or less constant temperature of 31°C can be expected to hatch in 60 - 80 days. The hatchlings typically weigh in the region of 14 - 16 g and measure 32 - 34 mm SCL. Contrary to popular belief the hatchlings can usually be hibernated without difficulty - indeed, it is preferable that they should hibernate if at all possible. However, under artificial conditions the greatest care must be taken to ensure temperatures remain at between 4 - 6°C and that excessive weight loss does not occur. Due to the reduced body mass of hatchlings, their core temperature fluctuates much more rapidly than that of adults in response to sudden environmental temperature changes. A temperature deviation that might cause no problem for a large adult can easily kill a tiny hatchling. Nor should hibernation periods be excessively long - between 65 - 80% of the normal typical hibernation period in the wild is usually the advisable maximum. We believe, however, that even a short hibernation is beneficial - provided it is correctly managed. There is simply no room for error. If overwintering is preferred for the first year, then a heated and illuminated vivarium will be required.

TESTUDO KLEINMANNI Lortet, 1883

The Egyptian tortoise

General observations: The miniature Egyptian tortoise is seriously threatened by habitat loss and illegal collecting. Only a handful of captive breeding successes have been achieved at the time of writing. The following data is derived from the author's experience of captive breeding of this species for the first time in mainland Britain in November 1994 at the Tortoise Trust. Because a number of enthusiasts and institutions now have this species in their collections, and the lack of published data on maintenance and breeding, both topics are covered here in some detail.

Taxonomy: Regional variations do occur, but no subspecies have been proposed. The genus *Pseudotestudo* was once proposed to contain *kleinmanni*, but this is no longer generally accepted.

Description: The unfamiliarity of this species to many authorities has resulted in a number of errors in previous publications relating to basic diagnostic characters and descriptions. Stubbs (1989) states, for example, that *Testudo kleinmanni* features "scutes possessing a small black patch in the centre". This is misleading, as such a feature, if found in *kleinmanni*, would be quite exceptional and is not at all typical of he species. In terms of coloration, there are three principal features that may be considered reliably diagnostic.

Plastron: The plastron of the vast majority of specimens features two "V" shaped brown or black markings upon the abdominal scutes. The only other Mediterranean tortoise with similar markings is the much large *Testudo marginata*. This feature is present on all but very few individuals and is quite different from the abdominal marks seen on the plastron of "*graeca*" complex tortoises. This author has seen and photographed a small number of *kleinmanni* from Libya with entirely unmarked plastrons, but these are extremely unusual and are atypical of *kleinmanni* as a whole. The ground of the plastron is pale straw-coloured. *Carapace:* The ground of the carapace ranges from extremely pale dull yellow to bright straw coloured with a hint of yellowish-green. The anterior and lateral margins of the vertebral scutes are delineated in dark brown to black. The anterior and external lateral margins of the costals are similarly distinguished. In some specimens these markings are much diminished. The centres of the scutes are unmarked and lack the typical dark aureole of "*graeca*" complex animals. *Skin coloration:* The skin of the head and limbs are very pale yellow to ivory colour. Again, the only other Mediterranean tortoise to feature similar skin coloration is *Testudo marginata*. In *marginata*, however, the head is dark brown to black and is much more elongate in form than that of *kleinmanni*. Unlike *Testudo graeca*, *Testudo kleinmanni* has no thigh tubercles. The tail also lacks a terminal claw (as seen in *T. hermanni*, for example) although several published diagnostic keys have erroneously asserted that it does possess this feature (for example, see Iverson, 1992). The most obvious distinguishing characteristic of *Testudo kleinmanni* (compared to *T. graeca*) is its remarkably diminutive size. Males are smaller than females, and have an average Straight Carapace Length of only 95 mm. The largest female recorded until recently had an SCL of 127 mm (Flower, 1933). A specimen with an SCL of 128 mm has now come to light, however (Highfield, unplublished data).

The marginal scutes are often strongly reverted, or upturned. This feature is not restricted to males, but is encountered in both sexes. The supracaudal scute is typically entire, but sometimes divided (two of the seven adult animals in the Tortoise Trust colony have divided supracaudals). The nuchal shield in *kleinmanni* is normally very broad. Rarely, a specimen with a narrow nuchal may be seen. A very major diagnostic feature of *Testudo kleinmanni* is evident if the scales on the front legs are compared to those of *T. graeca*. In *kleinmanni* the scales number three in longitude, and are broad in form. In graeca, there are typically 5 or more much narrower scales.

Captive environment: Each of our *T. kleinmanni* units measures 500 mm x 2 m and are further sub-divided into two to allow separation of males and females. It consists of a plywood base surrounded by a 150 mm high coated chipboard wall. Lighting is simple in the extreme, consisting of a single 40W mini-spot light situated in each section. During winter, when the tortoises are not allowed outside, this is supplemented by Vita-lite full spectrum tubes. Each section features a potted plant (for decoration and shade) plus a number of rocks to encourage climbing activity and a 60% dry loam 40% sand substrate. Overnight heating is provided by low-wattage heat pads. Ambient daytime temperatures are maintained in the region of 17 - 24°C, with most activity occurring in the middle of this range. It is a common error of *kleinmanni* husbandry to employ ambient temperatures that are far too high. Geffen (1985) and Geffen and Mendelssohn (1989) found that in the wild peak activity almost always occurred in the same temperature range. At higher temperatures (30°C and above) activity decreases and under natural conditions the tortoises will aestivate. It is difficult to replicate conditions for safe aestivation in captivity, and for this reason our specimens are maintained at moderate temperatures that permit all-year round activity.

Diet: *T. kleinmanni* in the Tortoise Trust collection are maintained on a 100% vegetable diet with as high a proportion of wild-picked foods as practicable. The overall balance of the diet is geared towards a high fibre, low protein and high calcium intake. No fruit is provided (other than the occasional piece of tomato) and water is available at all times if required. Calcium and vitamin D3 are provided by means of Nutrobal® or Rep-Cal® sprinkled liberally on each daily feed.

Common health problems: Respiratory disease; pneumonia; *Hexamita* infection. Strict isolation from all other tortoises is essential.

Breeding: The most remarkable feature of breeding behaviour in *T. kleinmanni* concerns vocalisation. Both male and female *kleinmanni* are very vocal compared to most tortoises and the males in particular produce a sound not unlike a dove calling during mating. Considering the diminutive size of the tortoises, the volume produced is astonishing. This sound is quite unlike that of any other Mediterranean tortoise. Amorous males circle females, do not appear to engage in biting behaviour, but do ram the female's shell, possibly in an attempt to cause her to remain static. Mating often lasts 20 minutes or more. Typically, males do not show interest in mating when females are carrying eggs.

In the wild, *T. kleinmanni* nests are excavated to a depth of 3 - 5 cm in a sandy substrate. In captivity, our indoor unit allowed an excavation depth of no more than 2.5 cm but this did not seem to inhibit laying. One egg was laid in an outdoor sand-pit on a particularly hot summer's day. The eggs are elongate and range from 31.5 mm long x 22.5 mm wide to 41 mm long x 29 mm wide with an average of 32.5 mm long x 23.5 mm wide. The eggs weigh between 7 - 9 grams. Females typically lay one egg at a time, but on occasions two are laid simultaneously. Large females may lay up to 4 eggs simultaneously, but this is not common. One 122 mm female in the Tortoise Trust collection laid 3 eggs in one clutch with the largest egg measuring 41.5 x 29 mm. Laying normally occurs at monthly intervals, and continues until a clutch of 4 to 5 eggs has been deposited. This is then followed by two to four months without laying during which males show increased interest in mating.

The normally suggested incubation temperature for most *Testudo* species is approximately 30 - 31°C, and at this temperature *T. hermanni*, *T. marginata* and *T. graeca* will usually hatch in 8 - 9 weeks. Climatic and research data, however, suggests that in the case of *T. kleinmanni* a higher average temperature is more appropriate. Geffen and Mendelssohn (1991) recorded sand temperatures at a depth of 5 cm to a peak of 38.5°C in July in Israel in the natural habitat of this species. Our incubator was adjusted to provide a constant 33°C, a temperature which in *Testudo graeca* would typically produce all-female neonates, although for a period of 28 days during the middle-third period in the estimated incubation cycle, we raised this temperature to 35°C to approach peak temperatures experienced under natural conditions. This peak temperature is above the normal safe maximum for incubation of other *Testudo* species, which is generally recognised as 34°C. Above this temperature developmental malformations are common in *T. graeca* and *T. hermanni*. Clearly, this is not the case with *T. kleinmanni*. We have also recorded success by incubating at a range of temperatures from 29.5 to 31°C.

Jersey Zoo's 1990 hatchlings were incubated at a constant 30°C, and hatched in 85 to 95 days. All five hatchlings proved to be males. Mendelssohn (1982) also incubated kleinmanni eggs at a constant 30°C and noted hatching between 97 - 117 days. Hobbs and May (1993) recorded hatching between 96 - 123 days at an incubation temperature of 30.5°C. Our own first two in 78 days and 111 days respectively. Subsequent hatchlings have emerged at intermediate periods. In the wild, hatching can occur in as little as 70 days.

One interesting observation on *Testudo kleinmanni* incubation is that both embryonic development and the incubation period are very unpredictable. Periods of arrested development seem commonplace. Geffen and Mendelssohn (1991) report one case of an egg that contained a living embryo after 10 months of incubation. We have certainly noted that development is usually extremely slow for the first month to 6 weeks, then accelerates rapidly. In one instance, 3 months passed before any noticeable development occurred. Following initial pipping of the egg, the neonates may remain within the egg for several days whilst any remaining yolk-sac is fully absorbed. On emergence, the hatchlings measured between 28 - 30 mm in length and weighed 4 grams. They drank water from a shallow dish almost immediately, and began feeding upon desiccated dandelion leaves within 12 hours.

Diet and environmental temperature for hatchlings are as for adults. Due to their extremely small size and fragility we place neonate *kleinmanni* in a covered, but well ventilated, seed-tray propagator. Some gentle base heating is provided, in addition to radiant heat from a basking lamp suspended above the propagator. For the first few weeks of life a paper towel substrate is employed. As the juveniles grow, they can be removed to a smaller version of the adult accommodation. The growth of these juveniles is rapid.

Female *Testudo graeca graeca*, photographed under a cactus hedge in southern Morocco.

Libyan origin *T. g. graeca*. Libyan specimens feature an unusual 'spotted' carapace pattern and different body shape from Moroccan examples. They have been exploited in great numbers in recent years.

Female (left) and male (right) *Testudo horsfieldi*, the Horsfield's or Central Asian tortoise.

Most soft-shell turtles are relatively undemanding in terms of temperature stability, but substrate type is critical. They are easily injured on sharp surfaces. A high dissolved oxygen content is also important.

TESTUDO MARGINATA Schoepff, 1792

The Marginated tortoise

General observations: *Testudo marginata* is one of the largest circum-Mediterranean tortoises (comparable only to Algerian *F. whitei* which surpasses it in body mass) and is distinguished not only by its extremely flared, serrate and projecting rear marginals (from which it takes its name) but also by its unusually marked plastron which is unique among the tortoises of the region. The main population concentration of *T. marginata* occurs in the Peloponnese and along the associated Greek coast to Mount Olympus. Smaller populations occur on several Aegean islands and an introduced population occurs on Sardinia. A small population also survives to this day in Tuscany, Italy, where it is assumed to have been introduced by the Etruscans.

Taxonomy: This tortoise was described by Schoepff in 1792 and has since acquired a number of synonyms including "*T. nemoralis*" and the rather descriptive "*T. campanulata*". The Marginated tortoise is distinctive both visually and zoogeographically and its status has rarely been the subject of any dispute. Early records of alleged "*T. marginata*" from North Africa (of which there are many) are the result of confusion either with the similarly sized *F. whitei* of Algeria or, just as surprisingly, with the diminutive *Testudo kleinmanni*; despite all the other differences, this little tortoise does feature an approximately similar set of markings on its plastron.

Description: In addition to the obviously flared posterior marginals noted above, *T. marginata* feature several other key distinguishing features. The soft skin of the upper limbs and tail is typically very creamy pale; much more so than on either *T. ibera* or *T. hermanni* and very noticeably so in young animals. The plastron of *T. marginata* characteristically features a large brown-black triangular marking on each of the larger scutes. The head is relatively small and the eyes are also smaller and more almond-shaped than those of *T. ibera*. It has been claimed that *T. marginata* have 5 claws on all feet and that the rear plastral lobe is not mobile; neither statement is true. Adult females typically measure approximately 240 - 280 mm SCL and weigh on average between 2 - 3 kg, whilst males are normally somewhat longer than females of equivalent age measuring 250 - 295 mm SCL but weigh in the same range. Length for length females typically weigh more than a male of identical SCL but are considerably broader in girth. The assumed homogenous genetic continuity of T. *marginata* is thrown into some doubt, however, by recent morphometric results which indicate that in at least some populations adult males do not exceed 230 mm SCL and females do not exceed 215 mm. Other dimorphic indicators typical of males in this species include tail length, a considerably narrower mid-line and more prominent marginal flares.

Captive environment: As for *T. ibera* and *T. hermanni*.
Diet: As for *T. ibera* and *T. hermanni*.

Common health problems: None immediately evident.

Breeding: *T. marginata* breed readily in captivity. Possibly the fact that there appears to be relatively little genetic diversity from one part of their range to another (except for the miniature populations noted above) plays a part in this. Certainly, almost any male will mate successfully with almost any female and viable eggs will usually result. Clutch density is typically 8 - 10 (occasionally more) and the eggs measure on average 30.5 mm long by 28 mm in width. They normally weigh between 16 - 18 g. If incubated at approximately 31°C hatching usually occurs in 60 - 70 days. Incubation humidity does not appear to be especially critical, good results having been noted in low (- 65%), medium (80%) and high (90% +) environments. One of the most successful breeders of *T. marginata* I know has used a simple water-jacket based incubator powered by a submersible aquarium heater for several years and invariably succeeds in hatching large numbers of this species every year. The hatchlings usually measure some 30 mm SCL and weigh between 10 - 14 g. Juveniles are roundish in overall shape, lacking both the elongate body form and flared marginals of the adults.

TRACHEMYS SCRIPTA (Schoepff, 1792)

Slider

General observations: A beautiful and under-rated turtle, the subspecies *T. s. elegans* are exploited in vast numbers for the low-value pet trade and all too frequently killed through ignorance. Ex-captive animals have now been released (both accidentally and deliberately) on every continent and in some instances threaten to displace autochthonous species. *T. s. elegans* is captive-bred commercially in vast numbers, and some breeders specialise in producing unusual colour morphs and albino specimens.

Taxonomy: Formerly referred to *Chrysemys* or *Pseudemys* and still a matter of some controversy. Three subspecies are currently recognised from North America; *T. s. scripta* (Yellow-bellied slider), *T. s. elegans* (Red-eared slider) and *T. s. troostii* (Cumberland slider). Up to another 16 subspecies occur if South American populations are taken into account. The taxonomy of these is highly confused and controversial. The situation is further complicated by the fact that some subspecies or races hybridise, and intergrades are known to occur.

Description: *T. s. elegans* must surely be one of the world's most familiar turtles. The other subspecies are much less familiar to most, and those familiar only with captive-bred trade animals may be also surprised to discover the range of variation present between natural populations of *T. s. elegans*. SCL to 280 mm. Females are much larger than males, who typically do not exceed 200 mm and often not more than 170 mm SCL. Males are also distinguished from females by having longer tails and fore-claws.

Captive environment: As for *C. picta*. *T. scripta* occupies a wide range of habitat types and is an enthusiastic basker. In southern parts of its range *T. scripta* remains active throughout the year, but in northern parts it hibernates beneath the ice. In captivity in Britain, I have observed *T. s. elegans* remain remarkably active even at very low temperatures. I once retrieved several from beneath 100 mm of ice only to find that within 10 minutes of removal to a warmer tank they were demanding food. The turtle bowls often sold in pet stores for accommodating this species are totally inadequate. Sliders also need high quality filtration; a combination of under-gravel and internal canister filters will suffice for small to medium sized specimens. Large specimens will require an external filter. Where possible, *T. scripta* should be housed in ponds rather than in tanks.

Diet: Omnivorous, feeding upon aquatic plants, small fish, crustacea, insect larvae and carrion. Juveniles are considerably more carnivorous than adults. In captivity, it is sadly all too common to see this species suffering from a wide range of dietary deficiencies, especially calcium, D3 and vitamin-A. Provision of a varied diet, with adequate levels of supplementation, will result in healthy and colourful turtles with excellent bone formation. Some commercial turtle foods advertised as ideal for sliders are nutritious and well balanced in terms of mineral content but others are worse than useless. Purchase with caution and read content analyses carefully. Commercial foods should not be relied upon exclusively. Sliders will do best on a mixed diet of trout-chow, rehydrated dog, cat and koi pellets and vegetation supplemented on a regular basis with additional minerals and vitamins.
Common health problems: Skin and shell infections; ear abscesses

Breeding: Very similar to *C. picta* (above). Pre-nuptial behaviour involves the males waving their long fore-claws in the female's face. The eggs of *T. scripta* are subject to ESD with temperatures below 27°C producing exclusively males and those of 30°C producing exclusively females. Interesting new research also suggests that the sex of neonates may be influenced by carbon dioxide levels, with high levels predisposing development towards females (Etchberger, et. al. 1992).

TRIONYX (APALONE) SPP. Geoffroy, 1809

Soft-shelled turtles

General observations: A widely distributed group of turtles, large specimens of which are noted for their highly aggressive temperament and lightening fast reactions. Even small examples can inflict dangerous bites and should be handled with great care.

Taxonomy: There is dispute at the generic rank as to whether numerous *Trionyx* species should be included instead in the genus *Apalone* (or, indeed, into 8 other proposed genera including *Palea, Pelodiscus, Rafetus, Nilssonia* and *Aspideretes*). It is clear from recent research (Meylan, 1987) that the *Trionyx* group is a complex one and that future research is likely to result in further extensive revisions to status and nomenclature. The most frequently encountered New World species are *T. (Pelodiscus) sinensis* (Chinese soft-shell, 25 cm, introduced), *T. (Apalone) spinifera* (Spiny soft-shell, 54 cm), *T. (Apalone) mutica* (Smooth soft-shell, 35 cm) and *T.(Apalone) ferox* (Florida soft-shell). Asiatic species sometimes encountered in specialist collections include *T. (Aspideretes) gangeticus* (Indian soft-shell, 94 cm), *T. (Pelochelys) bibroni* (Asian Giant soft-shell, 168 cm), *T. (Dogania) subplana* (Malayan soft-shell, 35 cm), *T. (Aspideretes) hurum* (Peacock soft-shell, 60 cm) and *T. (Amyda) cartila-*

geneus (Asiatic soft-shell, 70 cm). Rarely, African soft-shells such as the giant *T. triunguis* (Nile soft-shell, 95 cm) may also be seen in institutional collections.

Description: Soft-shelled turtles, which form the family *Trionychidae*, are distinguished by their lack of horny laminae upon the carapace, which is instead covered by leathery skin. Internally, the bony elements of the shell are greatly reduced. The snout is long, thin and snorkel-like. The neck is long and extensible. The fore and hind limbs each bear 3 claws.

Captive environment: The most important point to stress with regard to maintaining soft-shelled turtles in captivity, especially large ones, is that their ability to inflict serious injuries should never be underestimated. Novices are advised not to attempt to handle any large soft-shell. Large specimens have been known to bite straight through a boat's paddles, and I have seen a 70 cm specimen bite through thick rubber boots. Their long and agile necks permit rapid strikes at any handler unwise enough to approach from the front or side. Some can strike back as far as half the length of their carapace. The safest method of holding a soft-shell is to grasp it firmly from behind in the last quarter of its length. To provide additional grip, I find partially wrapping the turtle in a large towel often helps. All soft-shell turtles are highly aquatic, most species preferring natural habitats with soft bottoms, such as swamps, creeks and sandbars. If injuries to the plastron are to be avoided, soft-bottomed captive environments (e.g. silt substrates) are also advised, although some keepers obtain good results with plain glass tanks. Cutaneus injuries and infections in soft-shell turtles have been linked to sand and gravel substrates (Korolev, et. al. 1983). These ceased upon changing to a natural soft pond-silt substrate. Basking facilities are not normally provided for soft-shell turtles, but when they are, they seem to be enjoyed so a land area suitable for basking is recommended. Captive environments for soft-shell turtles should be devoid of any sharp or abrasive object, and heaters should be well protected, as these all of these turtles injure easily. It is especially important that haul out areas or basking positions are entirely smooth. For juveniles, floating polystyrene blocks have proved both safe and effective. Minor injuries have a tendency to become infected very quickly. The use of Stress-coat and acriflavine often helps minimise the incidence of secondary infections occurring. Good water quality is also important in minimising the risk of skin diseases. Adequate filtration and regular water changes are essential. Water temperature preferences vary somewhat from species to species, but most will feed well and reproduce if temperatures are maintained at 24 - 26°C. Species that normally hibernate (for example, *T. sinensis, T. muticus and T. spinifera*) can also be over wintered at these temperatures. If a winter hibernation or rest period is required, water temperatures can be reduced to between 7 - 8°C. It should be noted that whilst some Asiatic species hibernate, others do not. It is important to study the specific range and natural history of the species in question to determine appropriate captive management techniques. Some species are tolerant of brackish water conditions (I once observed a large soft-shell in a very brackish lagoon in Turkey). Most soft-shell species seem reasonably tolerant of water pH but it is best to avoid alkaline conditions and to aim instead for a pH in the 6.5 to 6.8 range as this has proved consistently satisfactory with all species.

Diet: Most *Trionyx/Apalone* species are highly carnivorous; their natural diet includes insects and their larvae, snails, fish, worms, crayfish and amphibians. Some species are omnivorous to a certain degree. Larger species, such as *T. ferox* are also known to consume other species of turtle if the opportunity arises. For this reason, and also because of their general aggressiveness, soft-shelled turtles are best maintained in isolation. In captivity, *Trionyx* species will almost always accept hydrated trout-chow, koi pellets, tinned pet foods, frozen foods (including rodents) and feeder fish. Juveniles can often be tempted to feed initially upon chopped earthworm.

Common health problems: Secondary infections at injury sites (see above).

Breeding: Males grasp females by the neck, and this can result in injuries. Exposure may need to be limited. Egg dimensions and clutch density vary considerably from species to species, but most soft-shells are prolific layers. Even smaller species are possess high reproductive potential, e.g. *T. (Pelodiscus) sinensis* can lay up to 5 clutches per year of 20 - 30 eggs that measure about 22 mm in diameter and have a mass of approximately 3.8 grams. Incubated at 27°C at a relative humidity of 90% hatchling occurs in 55 - 60 days. The pH of the incubation media may play an important role in influencing viability, as hatching rates often improve if sphagnum and peat are combined with vermiculite. Hatchlings of *T. (P.) sinensis* typically measure 23 mm SCL and weigh between 3 - 4 grams. The eggs of *T. (Dogania) subplanus* are typically slightly larger, at 24 - 30 mm and if incubated at 28°C and 90% humidity hatching occurs in 65 - 80 days. Some of the giant soft-shells (e.g. *T. (A.) gangeticus*) lay round eggs measuring up to 35 mm in diameter. Typical clutch densities for this species are in the region of 25 - 35 and are laid at regular monthly intervals for most of the year. In the natural bioclimatic zone, incubation takes between 217 - 287 days (Das, 1991). Research on *T. muticus, T. spinifera* and *T. sinensis* demonstrates that the sex of offspring is not determined by temperature as in most other turtles. Incubation at a range of temperatures typically results in a 1:1 male-female hatchling ratio. This characteristic may be shared by other members of this fascinating family. In captivity, juveniles attain sexual maturity as early as 4 years old. Juveniles of some species are mutually aggressive and they should not be maintained at high densities. Water quality is especially critical in the case of hatchlings and UV sterilisation in conjunction with a high quality external filter is recommended in order to reduce the risk of slight injuries becoming infected via water-borne pathogens. Hatchlings of most species will feed initially upon earthworms.

GLOSSARY

ACID - Water or substrate with a pH of less than 7.
ACTIVATED CARBON - A chemical filtration medium.
ADAPTION - Morphological or behavioural modifications evolved over a period in response to environment or mode of life.
AESTIVATE - Summer or dry season dormancy. Not to be confused with hibernation.
ALKALINE - Water with a pH higher than 7.
ALLANTOIS - Sac-like growth surrounding an embryo. Assists with respiration and waste management.
AMNION - A fluid filed sac enclosing an embryo.
ANOXIA - Lack of oxygen. Suffocation.
ANTERIOR - Towards the front or head.
ANTIBRACHIAL - Pertaining to the fore-limb.
AQUATIC - Living in water.
AREOLA - The central region of the scute. May be marked or raised.
AUTOCHTHONOUS - Indigenous.
BARBELS - Sensory organs located on the chin.
BASKING - Behaviour designed to gain maximum absorption of heat from the sun. Often involves positioning on slopes.
BEAK - The horny outer covering of the jaws.
BIMODALITY - The term used to describe non simultaneous hatching.
BIOCLIMATIC RANGE - The distribution of a species as affected by climatic controls.
BODY TEMPERATURE - The interior rather than exterior surface temperature of the body. Usually measured per cloaca.
BRACKISH - Slightly salty, often estuarine, water.
BRUMATION - An alternative term for hibernation in reptiles.
CALCAREOUS - Containing calcium carbonate.
CARAPACE - The hard bony upper shell of the tortoise or turtle.
CARNIVORE - An animal which eats the flesh of other animals. Not common in tortoises but frequent in freshwater turtles. e.g. Snapping turtles.
CAUDAL - Pertaining to the tail region.
CHARACTER - Any key feature used to diagnose species or sex.
CHELONIAN - A shield reptile. Tortoises, turtles and terrapins.

CIRCUM -MEDITERRANEAN - From around the Mediterranean sea.
CLINE - A gradual morphological variation within a species from one part of its range to another.
CLOACA - The chamber and vent in the tail.
CLUTCH - The collective term for all the eggs laid by a female at one time.
CLUTCH DENSITY - The number of eggs in a single clutch.
CONTIGUOUS - A sequential or unbroken series or distribution.
COPROPHAGOUS - Dung or faeces eating.
COSTAL - The series of plates located at the side and middle of a testudines shell between the vertebrals and marginals.
CRANIAL - Pertaining to the skull.
CUTANEOUS - Of or pertaining to the skin.
DICHROMATIC - In the context of sex, refers to difference in coloration between males and females of a species.
DIMORPHISM - Two distinct forms within a species. Sexual dimorphism is the existence of morphological divergence between male and female.
DIURNAL - Variation between day and night. Animals which are active during the day.
DORSAL - Pertaining to the upper part.
DYSTOCIA - See egg-binding.
ESD - Acronym for Environmental Sex Determination.
ECOSYSTEM - The natural symmetry between organisms and their environment.
ECTOPARASITE - A parasite that lives outside the body or on its surface.
ECTOTHERM - An organism which mainly relies upon environmental sources to sustain its body temperature.
EGG BINDING - A condition which occurs in female tortoises involving difficulty in laying eggs (dystocia).
EGG CARUNCLE - A small projection on the beak of hatchlings used for the purposes of piercing the egg.
EGG TOOTH - See egg caruncle.
ENDEMIC - Zoogeographically restricted species, race or form.
ENDOPARASITE - An internal parasite, e.g a 'worm'.
ENDOTHERM - An animal which self-generates heat by metabolic action, e. g. a mammal.
EXOTHERM - See ectotherm.
FSL - Acronym for Full Spectrum Lighting, 'artificial sunlight'.
FAMILY - The taxonomic category below Order and above Genus.
FAUNA - The animal life of a locality.
FENESTRATED - Pierced. With gaps or holes.
FORM - A population or 'variety'; not necessarily deserving of separate systematic recognition but also sometimes denoting a true species or subspecies.
GENETIC - Pertaining to genes and inheritance.
GENUS - The taxonomic category below Family and above Species. Contains one or more species.
GESTATION - In tortoises, the period between fertilisation of an egg and laying.
GREGARIOUS - Tending to congregate in groups.
GULAR - Pertaining to the throat region; in tortoises usually refers to the plastral scutes below the head.
GUT - The alimentary canal, especially the intestine.

HABITAT - The environment in which an animal lives.

HATCHLING - The young animal just after it leaves the egg; any juvenile phase tortoise to about 6 months.

HEPATIC - Pertaining to the liver.

HERBIVORE - An animal which eats plants rather than other animals. A vegetarian.

HERPETOLOGY - The science and study of reptiles and amphibians.

HIBERNATION - Winter dormancy characterised by specific biological and biochemical changes including lowered blood pressure and respiration rate.

HINGE - A mobile suture; as seen in Box turtles or Hinge-back tortoises which allows part of the shell to be closed.

HOMOGENOUS - A relatively intact distribution of genetic material within a population. Little diversity from one locality to another within the range.

HYBRID - An individual resulting from a mating of parents which are not genetically identical, e.g which belong to different species.

HYPERTROPHIED - Abnormally enlarged.

INCUBATION - The developmental phase of an egg prior to hatching which requires warmth.

INFRARED - Invisible heat rays beyond the visible light spectrum.

INTERGRADE - A hybrid form.

INTRODUCED - A species not native to a region but which now occur there as a result of artificial transport or escapes from captivity.

INTROFLEXED - Turned inwards.

JUVENILE - Not sexually mature.

KEEL - A ridge sometimes seen in the vertebral region of the carapace.

KERATIN - A tough fibrous protein present in epidermal structures such as carapace shields, beaks and claws.

KINESIS - Mobile. As in a Box turtle or Hinge-back shell.

LATERAL - Pertaining to the side.

MARGINAL - The series of smaller scutes at the very edge of the carapace. Usually 11 on each side in most species.

MELANISTIC - Darker or blacker than normal.

MESIC - An intermediate humidity habitat.

METABOLIC RATE - The rate of energy expenditure by an organism.

METABOLISM - The chemical or energy changes which occur within an animal necessary to sustain life.

MICROCLIMATE - The climate immediately surrounding an animal. May differ profoundly from the general climate, especially in the case of burrowing tortoises.

MORPHOLOGY - Pertaining to shape and form.

MORPHOMETRY - The technique of measuring and comparing shapes, e.g. the shape of a turtle shell.

MYELITIS - Tissue destruction due to infection. Usually pertains to bone tissue.

NARES - Paired openings of the nasal cavity.

NASAL - Pertaining to the nose or nares.

NECROSIS - Tissue death. Usually due to infection.

NEUTRAL - Water with a pH of 7.

NITRATE - Final stage of biological filtration, after production of ammonia and nitrite.

NITRITE - Toxic compound produced during breakdown of metabolic wastes.

NOCTURNAL - Active at night.
NUCHAL - A small scute at the front of the carapace, above the head.
OCCLUSION - Refers to alignment between the upper and lower jaws.
OEDEMA - Fluid retention. Can signify renal disease or bruising. Any swelling.
OMNIVORE - An animal which feeds on both plant and animal tissue.
ONTOGENETIC - Pertaining to the process of ageing.
OPTIC - Pertaining to the eyes.
OSTEOLOGICAL - Pertaining to the bones and their structure.
OVIPOSITION - The act of egg laying.
P.O. - Preferred Optimum.
PALUDARIUM - A 'shore aquarium'; in practice, most aquatic turtle aquaria will conform to this definition. Paludaria feature a water section and a raised land area.
PARENTERAL - Via injection.
pH SCALE - Relative measure of acidity or alkalinity
PHENETIC - Apparent similarity on the basis of external characters.
PHYLOGENY - Pertaining to evolutionary relationships.
PLASTRON - The lower surface of the testudine shell.
POIKILOTHERM - See ectotherm.
POPULATION - A group of the same species living in a discreet geographical area.
POSTERIOR - The rear or back part.
PPM - Parts per million.
RACE - A population of a species distinguishable from the rest of that species. A sub-species.
RADIAL - Like the spokes of a wheel.
RENAL - Pertaining to the kidneys.
RH - Relative humidity. Expressed as a percentage.
SAVANNAH - A habitat of open plains and low grassy vegetation.
SCL - Acronym for Straight Carapace Length (not measured over the curve).
SCUTE - The horny plates of a testudine shell.
SERRATED - Jagged or saw-like.
SUBSPECIES - A subdivision of a single species given a unique name which is expressed after the generic and species name. See race.
SUBSTRATE - In herpetology, usually refers to vivarium flooring material.
SUPRA - Pertaining to above.
SUPRACAUDAL - The scute above the tail.
SUTURES - The 'seams' between two boney or horny plates.
SYMPATRIC - Living in the same geographical area.
SYNONYM - One of several different names applied to an identical taxonomic category only one of which is valid. The invalid names only are called synonyms. The valid name is selected by priority.
SYSTEMIC - Whole body treatment. Not topical. Usually by injection.
TAXON - A taxonomic category, e.g a Family, Genus or Species.
TAXONOMY - The science of classification.
TEMPERATE - Latitudes where summer and winter seasons are experienced.
TERRAPIN - In this work, applied to fresh water aquatic testudines.
TERRESTRIAL - Living on the ground. Not aquatic.
TOPICALLY - Pertaining to surface application.

TORTOISE - In this work, applied to exclusively terrestrial testudines.
TRICARINATE - Featuring three keels or ridges.
TUBERCLE - The 'spur' on a tortoises thighs.
TURTLE - In this work, applied to semi-terrestrial testudines and marine testudines. Sometimes applied interchangeably with 'tortoise'.
TYMPANITIC - Pertaining to the ear.
TYPE - The original specimen upon which a species is erected.
TYPE LOCALITY - The place where the Type was collected or originated.
VENTRAL - Pertaining to the underside.
VERTEBRAL - Pertaining to the spinal region. The central row of scutes along the top of the carapace.
VIVARIUM - An indoor artificial environment containing animals.
XIPHIPLASTRA - The rearmost pair of plastral bones.
XEROPHYTIC - Dry or semi-arid environments.
ZOOGEOGRAPHY - The science of animal distribution.

APPENDIX ONE

Values of dietary constituents and additives

1. CALCIUM SUPPLEMENTS

Some forms of calcium are more easily absorbed or utilised than others, and some in themselves contain high levels of phosphorous. The best forms are those which have a high calcium percentage (Ca) and a low percentage of phosphorous (P). The approximate average Ca:P ratios of some commonly available additives are given below. From this it will be noted that calcium carbonate is a very good additive whilst calcium phosphate is a comparatively poor source.

	% Ca	**% P**
Calcium borogluconate	8.50	00.00
Calcium carbonate	40.00	00.00
Calcium gluconate	9.25	00.00
Calcium lactate	18.00	00.00
Calcium phosphate - monobasic	17.00	26.00
Calcium phosphate - dibasic	30.00	23.00
Calcium phosphate - tribasic	39.00	20.00
Standard bone meal	30.00	15.00

2. NUTRITIONAL ANALYSIS OF SOME WILD FOODS

All figures are approximate averages - content varies seasonally.
As food items consumed in the wild by tortoises are not 'commercial' crops, in many cases little or no data is available on their precise formulation.

Item	% protein	% fibre	% dry matter	% fat	% Ca	% P
Grass (winter)	4.00	37.00	40.00	1.00	0.75	0.06
Grass (summer)	6.00	n/a	n/a	2.00	0.35	0.20
Grass (lawn)	3.00	12.00	35.00	1.30	0.10	0.09
Forbs	9.00	n/a	n/a	2.75	1.80	0.40
Brome	8.50	31.00	35.00	1.00	0.28	0.23
Threeawn	6.30	35.00	n/a	1.50	0.60	0.09
Clover hay	11.00	30.00	n/a	1.90	1.00	0.20

3. NUTRITIONAL ANALYSIS OF COMMON SUBSTITUTE (CAPTIVE) FOODS

All figures are approximate averages in grams per 100g.

Item	Protein	Fibre	Fat	Ca (mg)	P (mg)	Vit A (IU)
Apple	0.20	1.00	0.60	7.00	10.00	90.00
Aubergine	1.20	0.90	0.20	12.00	26.00	10.00
Avocado	2.20	1.50	17.00	10.00	42.00	290.00
Beet greens	2.20	1.30	3.00	119.00	40.00	6100.00
Broccoli	3.60	1.50	0.30	103.00	78.00	2500.00
Brussels Sprouts	0.00	1.60	0.40	36.00	80.00	550.00
Cabbage	1.30	0.80	0.20	49.00	29.00	130.00
Carrot	1.10	1.00	0.20	37.00	36.00	1100.00
Cauliflower	2.70	1.00	0.20	25.00	56.00	60.00
Celeriac	1.80	1.30	0.30	43.00	115.00	00.00
Chicory greens	1.70	0.80	0.30	86.00	40.00	4000.00
Cucumber	0.90	0.60	0.10	25.00	27.00	250.00
Endive	1.70	0.90	0.10	81.00	54.00	3300.00
Fennel	2.80	0.50	0.40	100.00	51.00	3500.00
Lettuce	1.20	0.50	0.20	35.00	26.00	900.00
Lettuce, romaine	1.30	0.70	0.30	68.00	25.00	300.00
Lettuce, iceberg	0.90	0.50	0.10	20.00	22.00	1700.00
Peas, green	6.30	2.00	0.50	26.00	120.00	640.00
Peppers, sweet	1.20	1.40	0.22	9.00	22.00	420.00
Sprouting beans	3.80	0.70	0.20	19.00	64.00	20.00
Spinach	3.00	0.60	0.30	93.00	38.00	8100.00
Tomato	1.10	0.50	0.20	13.00	00.27	900.00
Turnip greens	3.00	0.80	0.90	246.00	58.00	7500.00
Watercress	2.20	0.70	0.30	151.00	55.00	4900.00

APPENDIX TWO

USEFUL ADDRESSES

The following specialist testudine organisations can usually provide additional information on the captive care requirements of most species. Many publish regular newsletters or journals of interest to the tortoise and turtle enthusiast. Some organisations are mainly concerned with the turtle hobbyist, others are directly involved in tortoise or turtle conservation work. All offer useful information and access to expert advice. In addition to these specialist organisations, the national or regional general herpetological societies of most countries can usually provide technical advice on testudines.

California Turtle and Tortoise Club,
P.O. Box 7300
Nan Nuys
California ,CA 91409-7300
U.S.A.

CARAPAX Project,
Centro Tartarughe,
C. P. 34,
58024 Massa Marittima,
Grosseto,
Italy.

National Turtle and Tortoise Society Inc.,
P.O. Box 9806,
Phoenix,
Arizona,
AZ 85068-9806,
U.S.A.

New York Turtle and Tortoise Society,
163 Amsterdam Avenue,
Suite 365,
New York,
NY10023,
U.S.A.

Sacramento Turtle and Tortoise Club,
25 Starlit Circle,
Sacramento,
California,
CA 95831,
U.S.A.

San Diego Turtle and Tortoise Society,
P.O. Box 519
Imperial Beach
California
CA 91933-0519
U.S.A.

S.O.P.T.O.M.,
Village des Tortues,
B.P. 24 ,
3590 Gonfaron,
France.

Tortoise & Turtle Club of Florida
P.O. Box 239
Sanford
Florida 32772-0239
U.S.A.

The Tortoise Trust,
BM Tortoise,
London,
WC1N 3XX,
England. Tel/Fax: (01267)-211578
E-Mail 100105.555@compuserve.com

TORT-Group,
5157 Poncho Circle,
Las Vegas,
Nevada 89119,
U.S.A.

APPENDIX THREE

Useful formulae and conversions

Temperature

To convert °C to °F multiply by 1.8 and add 32
To convert °F to °C subtract 32 and multiply by 5 and divide by 9

Water boils at 212°F and 100°C
Water freezes at 32°F and 0°C

Length

Inches to centimetres	multiply by 2.54
Centimeteres to inches	multiply by 0.394
Feet to metres	multiply by 0.30
Yards to metres	multiply by 0.91
1 foot	= 30.50 cm
1 inc	= 25.4 mm
1 centimetre (cm)	= 0.394 inches
1 metre	= 3.28 feet
1 metre	= 1.09 yards

Weight

1 ounce = 28.3 grams
1 pound = 454 grams
1 gram = 0.035 ounces
1 kilogram (kg) = 2.2 pounds

To convert grams to ounces multiply by 0.035
To convert pounds to kilos multiply by 0.454

Volume

1 cubic inch = 16.4 cubic cm
1 cu foot = 0.028 cubic metres
1 cu yard = 0.765 cubic metres

Fluid volume

Imperial gallons to litres	multiply by 4.55
Litres to imperial gallons	multiply by 0.22
US gallons to litres	multiply by 3.79
Litres to US gallons	multiply by 0.26
US fl oz to ml	multiply by 29.5625
US pints to litres	multiply by 0.473
US fl oz to imperial fl oz	multiply by 0.960

5 imperial gallons	= 6 US gallons
1 fl. ounce	= 28.4 mililitres (ml)
1 pint	= 0.568 litres

Area

1 sq inch	= 6.45 sq cm
1 sq foot	= 929 sq cm
1 sq foot	= 0.093 sq metres
1 sq yard	= 0.836 sq metres

BIBLIOGRAPHY AND RECOMMENDED FURTHER READING

Arranged by genus and subject matter for ease of use

ACANTHOCHELYS

Horne, B. D. 1993. Courtship behaviour and oviposition of captive *Acanthochelys pallidipectoris* Freiberg. Herpetological Review 24(1): 25

Richard, E. 1991. Oviposition of *Acanthochelys pallidipectoris* (Freiberg) in captivity. (Chelonii: Chelidae). Bull. Maryland. Herpet. Soc. 27(2):107-109.

ALDABRACHELYS

See under *Geochelone*.

ASTEROCHELYS

See under *Geochelone*.

BATAGUR

Blanco, S., Behler, J. H. and Kostel, F. 1990. Propagation of the Batagurine turtles *Batagur baska* and *Callagur borneoensis* at the Bronx zoo. In: Proc. 1st Int. Symp. on Turtles and Tortoises: Conservation and Captive Husbandry. Eds. Beaman, Caporaso, McKeown and Graff. 63-65.

Das, I. 1991. Colour Guide to the Turtles and Tortoises of the Indian subcontinent. R&A Publishing, Avon, England.

Davenport, J., Wong, T. M. and East, J. 1992. Feeding and digestion in the omnivorous estuarine turtle *Batagur baska* (Gray). Herpetological Journal (2):133-139.

Tikader, B.K. and Sharma, R. C. 1985. Handbook Indian Testudines. Zoological Survey of India, Calcutta. 156 pp.

CARETTOCHELYS

Dorrian, C. 1994. Captive management of the Pig-nosed turtle, *Carettochelys insculpta*. Herpetofauna (Sydney) 24(1):15-18.

Georges, A. 1987. The Pig-nosed turtle Warradjan. Australian Natural History. 22(5):230-234.

Georges, A. and Rose, M. 1993. Conservation biology of the Pig-nosed turtle, *Carettochelys insculpta*. Chelonian conservation and Biology 1(1):3-12.

CHELODINA

Cann, H. 1978. Tortoises of Australia. Angus and Robertson, Sydney.

Cogger, H. G. 1975. Reptiles and Amphibians of Australia. A.H. & A.W. Reed, Sydney.

Feldman, F. 1979. Mating observed in captive New Guinea snake-neck turtles. Notes from Noah 7(3):9

Georges, A. 1988. Sex determination is independant of incubation temperature in another chelid turtle, *Chelodina longicollis*. Copeia 1988:248-254.

Nichol, E. B. 1985. Breeding of *Chelodina novaeguinae* and *Chelodina longicollis*. Bull. Chi. Herp. Soc. 20(2):29-34.

CHELUS

Ferguson, M. W. J. 1981. Extrinsic microbial degradation of the Alligator eggshell. Science (214):1135-1137.

Hartline, P. H. 1967. The unbelievable fringed turtle. Int. Turtle and Tortoise Soc. J. 1(6):24

Hausman, P. 1968. Matamata. Int. Turtle and Tortoise Soc. J. 2(4):18

Lehmann, H. 1987. Hypothetische uberlegungen zur schlupfproblematik von kunstlich inkubierten gelegen sudamarikanischer Schildkrotenarten de familie *Chelidae*. Salamandra 23(2/3):73-77.

CHELYDRA

Feldman, M. 1983 Effects of rotation on the viability of turtle eggs. Herp. Review. 14 (3):76-77

Miller, K. 1987. Hydric conditions during incubation influence locomotor performance of hatchling snapping turtles. J. Exp. Biology. 127:401-412.

Wilhoft, D. C., Hotaling, E. and Franks, P. 1983. Effects of temperature on sex determination in embryos of the snapping turtle, *Chelydra serpentina*. J. Herpetology. 17:38-42

CHERSINA

Boycott, R. C. and Bourquin, O. 1988. The South African Tortoise Book. Southern Book Publishers, Johannesburg.

Krzystyniak, S. 1984. Notes on the Angulate tortoise:*Testudo angulata*. The Herptile. 9(2):36-39.

CHINEMYS

Burke, C. H. 1988. Caring for Reeves' turtles. The Carapace, Oct/Nov 1988:2-4.

Lovich, J. E., Ernst, C. H. and Gotte, S. W. 1985. Geographic variation in the Asiatic turtle *Chinemys reevsii* (Gray) and the status of *Geoclemys grangeri* Schmidt. J. Herpet. 19:238-245.

Mao, S. H. 1971. Turtles of Taiwan. Commercial Press, Taipei. 128 pp.

Pope, C. H. 1935. Natural history of Central Asia. Vol. 10. The reptiles of China. Am. Nat. Hist. Mus.

Smith, M. 1991. Reeves' turtle, *Chinemys reevesii*.Tortuga Gazette 27(8):1-2.

CHRYSEMYS

Cox, W. R., Rapley, W. A. and Barker, I.K. 1980. Herpesvirus-like infection in a painted turtle. J. Wildl. Diseases (16):445-449

Ernst, C. H., Lovich, J. E. and Barbour, R. W. 1994. Turtles of the United States and Canada. Smithsonian Institution, Washington. 578 pp.

CLEMMYS

DeLisle, D. 1992. The Bog turtle. Tortuga Gazette. 28(2): 1-3.

Harding, J. H. 1991. Spotted Turtle *Clemmys guttata*. Tortuga Gazette 27(5):3-4.

Hermann, D. W. 1990. Captive Husbandry of the Eastern *Clemmys* group at Zoo Atlanta. In Proc. 1st Int. Symp. on Turtles and Tortoises: Conservation and Captive Husbandry. Eds. Beaman, Caporaso, McKeown and Graff. 54-62.

Norris, P. 1984. Notes on the spotted turtle (*Clemmys guttata*). The Herptile 9(3):114-115.

Tryon, B. W. and Hulsey, T. G. 1977. Breeding and rearing the Bog turtle. Int. Zoo Yearbook (17).

Zovickian, W. H. 1971. Humidity as a growth factor in hatchlings of *Clemmys muhlenbergii*. Bull. Md. Herp. Soc. 7(4): 93-95

CUORA

Bartlett, R. D. 1981. Observations on the Asian box turtle *Cuora flavomarginata* in captivity. Notes from NOAH 8(5):4-6.

Ernst, C. H. and McCord, W. P. 1987. Two new turtles from Southeast Asia. Proc. Biol. Soc. Washington. 100: 624-628.

Harding, J. 1989. Courtship behaviour in the Chinese box turtle *Cuora trifasciata*. Herpet. Review. 20(4):85.

Inskeep, R. 1984. A note on the captive breeding of the box turtle *Cuora amboinensis* (Daudin 1802). Brit. Journ. Herpetology. (6):385-386.

Inskeep, R. 1984. Second breeding of *Cuora amboinensis* (Daudin) 1802. Brit. Herp. Soc. Bull. (9):28.

Mao, S. H. 1971. The Turtles of Taiwan. Commercial Press Ltd., Taipei. 128 pp.

Rummler, H. K. & Fritz, U. 1991. Geographische variabilitat der Amboina-scharnierschildkrote *Cuora amboinensis* (Daudin, 1802) mit beschreibung einer neuen unterart, *C. a. kamaroma* subsp. nov. Salamandra 27:17-45

CYCLEMYS

Das, I. 1991. Colour Guide to the Turtles and Tortoises of the Indian subcontinent. R&A Publishing, Avon, England.

Tikader, B.K. and Sharma, R. C. 1985. Handbook Indian Testudines. Zoological Survey of India, Calcutta. 156 pp.

Ewart, M. A. 1989. In: Turtles, Perspectives and Research. Ed. Morlock, H. and Harless, M. Krieger Publishing Ltd. Florida.

EMYDOIDEA

Ernst, C. H., Lovich, J. E. and Barbour, R. W. 1994. Turtles of the United States and Canada. Smithsonian Institution, Washington. 578 pp.

Hunter, M. L., Albright, J and Arbuckle J. (eds.) 1992. The Amphibians and Reptiles of Maine. Univ. of Maine. Bulletin 838.

EMYDURA

Corwin,W. 1985. The Reproductive behaviours of two Australian chelid turtles *Emydura macquarii* &. *E. latisternum* at the Dallas Zoo. 9th Int. Herpet. Symp. on Cap. Prop & Hus. Ed. S. McKeowan, F. Caporaso and K. H. Peterson. San Diego.

Green, D. 1991. News from Down Under. Tortuga Gazette. 27(4):6.

Nichol, E. 1993. Red-bellied short-necked turtle *Emydura subglobosa*. Tortuga Gazette 29(2):1-3.

EMYS

Fritz, U. 1993. Weitere Mitteilung zur inartlichen Variabilitat, chronologie und zoogeographie von *Emys orbicularis* (Linnaeus, 1758). Herpetozoa 6(1/2):37-55.

Fritz, U. 1995. Zur innerartlichen Variabilitat von *Emys orbicularis* (Linnaeus, 1758). Zool. Abhandlungen. Dresden. 48 (13):185-242.

Pieau, C. 1971. Sur la proportion sexuelle chez les embryons de deux chelonians issus d'oeufs incubes artificiellement. C. R. Hebd. Seanc. Acad. Sci. Paris. (D) 272:3071-3074.

Pieau, C. 1975. Donnees recentes sur la differentiation en fonction de la temperature chez les embryons *d'Emys orbicularis*. Bull. Soc. Zool. France. 101(4):46-53.

Pieau, C. 1982. Modalities of the action of sexual differentiation in field developing embryos of the European pond turtle *Emys orbicularis*. J. Exper. Zool. (220):353-360.

GEOCHELONE

Anonymous. 1988. Yellowfoot and Redfoot tortoises: *Geochelone denticulata* and *Geochelone carbonaria*. T.E.A.M. 1(5):2-4.

Archer, W. H. 1948. The mountain tortoise (*G. pardalis*). Afr. Wildlife. 2(3):74-79.

Bacon, J. P. 1980. Some observations on the captive management of Galapagos tortoises. In Reproductive Biology and Diseases of Captive Reptiles (eds. Murphy, J. B. and Collins, J. T. SSAR.

Auffenberg, W. 1966. Land of the Chaco Tortoise. Int. Tort. & Turtle Soc. Journ. 3 (3):16-19, 36-37.

Bartlett, R. D. 1982. An incidence of twinning in the Malagassy tortoise, *Geochelone radiata*. Tortuga Gazette, April 1982:4.

Belmonte, F. T. 1991. Comportamiento reproductivo de *Chelonoidis chilensis* (Reptilia, Testudines) en cautiverio. Acta. Zoo. Lilloana XL(1):13-20.

Beltz, R. E. 1968. A world tour of the *Geochelone*. Int. Turtle Tortoise Soc. J. 2(1):12-17, 27-29.

Bennefield, B. L. 1982. Captive breeding of the tropical Leopard tortoise *Geochelone pardalis babcocki in* Zimbabwe. Testudo 2(1):1-5.

Boycott, R. C. and Bourquin, O. 1988. The South African Tortoise Book. Southern Book Publishers, Johannesburg.

Bowker, F. 1926. Tortoise eggs and nests. S. Af. J. Nat. Hist. 6:37.

Branch, W. R., Baard, E. and De Villiers, A. 1990. Some exceptionally large southern African chelonians. J. Herpet. Assoc. Africa. 37:53-54.

Broadley, D. 1989 in The Conservation Biology of Tortoises (eds. Swingland, I. and Klemens, M.) IUCN, Gland.

Buskirk, J. R. 1993. Distribution, Status and Biology of the Tortoise *Geochelone chilensis*, in Rio Negro Province, Argentina. Studies in Neotropical Fauna and Environment. (28): No. 4 233-249.

Censky, E. J. 1988. *Geochelone carbonaria* (Reptilia: Testudines) in the West Indies. Fla. Sci. 51(2):108-114.

Coakley, J. and Klemens, M. 1983. Two generations of captive-hatched Leopard tortoises *Geochelone pardalis babcocki*. Herp Review 14(2): 43-44.

Coles, R. W. 1985. Reproductive data: the Leopard tortoise (*Geochelone pardalis*). Herptile, 10(1): 28-29.

Daniel, J.C. 1983. The Book of Indian Reptiles. Bombay.

Davis, S. 1979. Husbandry and breeding of the Red-footed tortoise *Geochelone carbonaria* at the National Zoological Park, Washington. Int. Zoo Yearbook, pp.50-53. London, England.

Ernst, C. H. and Barbour, R. W. (1989) Turtles of the World. Smithsonian Institution Press, Washington.

Flint, M. 1977. Captive husbandry and reproduction of the Leopard tortoise *Geochelone pardalis babcocki.* Proc. 2nd. An. Reptile Symp. on Captive Propagation and Husbandry. pp.113-119.

Gonzalez, J. G. 1993. Reunion Island - Still a land of tortoises. Chel. Cons. and Biology. 1(1): 51-52.

Hine, M. L. 1980. Reproduction of the Leopard Tortoise in captivity. Testudo. 1(3):40-43.

Jakob, R. 1970. Notes on keeping and rearing the Jaboty tortoise *Testudo denticulata.* Rep. Jersey. Wild. Pres. Trust. 7:49050.

Juvick, J. Meier, D. and McKeown, S. 1990 Captive husbandry and conservation of the Madagascar Ploughshare tortoise *Geochelone yniphora.* In: Proc. 1st Int. Symp. on Turtles and Tortoises: Conservation and Captive Husbandry. Eds. Beaman, Cporaso, McKeown and Graff. California, USA.

Klemens, M. 1974. Captive breeding of the Leopard tortoise (*Geochelone pardalis*). Conn. Herp. Soc. Bull. 5:5-7.

Lambert, M. R. K. 1995. On geographical size variation, growth, and sexual dimorphism of the Leopard Tortoise, *Geochelone pardalis*, in Somaliland. Chel. Cons. and Biol. (1):4:270-278.

Legler, J. M. 1963 Tortoises (*Geochelone carbonaria*) in Panama: distribution and variation. American Midland Naturalist, 70(2): 490-503.

May, C. D. 1983. Some tips for choosing breeder tortoises (*G. carbonaria*). Notes from NOAH, 10(12).

Mowbray, L. S. 1966. A note on breeding South American tortoises *Testudo denticulata* at Bermuda Zoo. Int. Zoo. Yearbook. 6:216.

Moll, D. and Tucker, J. K. 1976. Growth and maturity of the red-footed tortoise *Geochelone carbonaria.* Bull. Md. Herpet. Soc. 12(3):96-98.

Pritchard, P. C. H. and Trebbau, P. 1984. The Turtles of Venezuela. SSAR, Ohio.

Rottman, J. 1969. Zucht der Argentinischen Landschildkrote (*Testudo chilensis*). DATZ (22):282-284.

Rowe, J. and Janulaw, J. 1980. A noteworthy conservation achievement. Chelonologica, 1(3):125-131.

Shaw, C. E. 1967. Breeding the Galapagos tortoise - success story. Oryx 9(2): 119-130.

Stearns, B. C. 1988. Captive husbandry and propagation of the Aldabra giant tortoise *Geochelone gigantea.* Int. Zoo. Yearbook. (27):98-103.

Stearns, B. C. 1989. The captive status of the African spurred tortoise *Geochelone sulcata*: recent developments. Int. Zoo Yearbook. (28):87-98.

Vokins, A. M. A. 1977. Breeding the red foot tortoise *Geochelone carbonaria* (Spix 1824). Dodom 14:73-80.

Wermuth, H. 1967. Die Argentinische landschildkrote, *Testudo chilensis.* DATZ (20):58-61.

Wilson, V. J. 1968. The Leopard tortoise *Testudo pardalis babcocki* in eastern Zambia. Arnoldia Rhodesia, 3:1-11.

GEOEMYDA

Yasukawa, H. Ota, H. and Kikida, T. 1992. Taxonomic re-evaluation of the two subspecies of *Geoemyda spengleri* (Gmelin, 1789) (Reptilia: Emydidae). Jap. J. Herpetology 14:143-159.

GOPHERUS (XEROBATES)

Anonymous. 1981. Care of adult tortoises. Tortuga Gazette, July 1981:3-6.

Anonymous. 1983. Care of California and Texas Desert tortoise hatchlings. Tortuga Gazette, July 1983. pp. 7-9.

Anonymous. 1985. How to adopt and care for Desert tortoises. Tort-Group, Nevada.

Appleton, A. 1985. Breeding the Bolson tortoise. Tortuga Gazette, Feb. 1985:6-7.

Arata, A. A. 1958. Notes on the eggs and young of *Gopherus polyphemus* (Daudin). Quart. Journ. Florida. Acad. Sci. 21: 274-280.

Auffenberg, W. 1976. The Genus *Gopherus* (Testudinidae):1. Osteology and Relationships of extant Species. Bull. Florida State Museum. 20(2):47-110.

Berry, Kristin. 1990. Commonly asked questions about the Desert tortoise and answers. Tortoise Tracks, 11(1).

Bour, R. and Dubois, A. 1984. *Xerobates*: a synonym older than *Scraptochelys*. Bull. Mens. Soc. Linn. Lyon. 53(1):30-32.

Bramble, D. M. 1982. *Scraptochelys*: Generic division and evolution of gopher tortoises. Copeia 1984(4):862-867.

Brame, A. H. and Peerson, D. J. 1969. Tortoise ID. Int. Tortoise and Turtle. Soc. J. Sept-Oct. 1969. pp.8-12.

Brown, D. A. 1965. Nesting of captive *Gopherus berlandieri* (Agassiz). Herpetologica, 15:101-102.

Connor, M. J. 1989. Molecular biology and the Turtle; the Desert tortoise and its relatives. Tortuga Gazette, 25(8): 10-11.

Fowler, M. E. 1980. Comparison of respiratory infection and hypovitaminosis-A in Desert tortoises. Comparative Pathology in Zoo Animals, Washington.

Hansen, R. M. , Johnson, M. K. and Van Devender, T. R. 1976. Foods of the Desert tortoise *Gopherus agassizi* in Arizona and Utah. Herpetologica 32:247-251.

Jackson, G. and Trotter, J.A, T.H. and M. W. 1976. Accelerated growth rate and early maturity in *Gopherus agassizi.* Herpetologica 32:139-145.

Iverson, J. B. 1980. The reproductive biology of *Gopherus polyphemus. Chelonia, Testudinidae.* Am. Midland Nat. 103(2):353-359.

Kirchman, V. 1976. Gopherus Tortoise Care Sheets. San Diego Turtle and Tortoise Soc. pp.6.

Lamb, T., Avise, J. C. and Gibbons, J. W. 1989.Phylogeographic patterns in mitochondrial DNA of the desert tortoise (*Xerobates agassizi*) and evolutionary relationships among the North American gopher tortoises. Evolution, 43: 76-87.

Lee, H. H. 1964. Egg laying in captivity by *Gopherus agassisi.* Herpetologica 19: 62-65.

Legler, J. M. 1959. A new tortoise, genus G*opherus*, from Northcentral Mexico. Univ. Kansas. Pub. Mus. Nat. Hist. II: 335-343.

McGinnis, S. M. and Voight, W. G. 1971. Thermoregulation in the Desert tortoise, *Gopherus agassizi.* Comp. Biochem. Physiol. 40A:119-126.

Nichols, U. G. 1957. The desert tortoise in captivity. Herpetologica 13: 141-144.
Poorman, F. & R. 1971. *agassizi* Vs. *berlandieri*. Int. Tortoise and Turtle Soc. J. Jan-Feb. 1971:14-16.
Rosskopf, W. J. 1981. Initial three year mortality study on Desert tortoises. Tortuga Gazette, May 1981. pp. 4-5.
Rosskopf, W. J. 1990. The upper respiratory syndrome in captive desert tortoises: Diagnosis, treatment and management. Proc. First Intnl. Symp. Turtles & Tortoises. Chapman University, CA. 108-112.
Spotila, J. R. and Standora, E. A. 1986. Sex determination in the desert tortoise: A conservative management strategy is needed. Herpetologica 42:694-702.
Trotter, J. 1973. Incubation made easy. Int. Turtle and Tortoise Soc. J. Jan-Feb 1973. pp.26-31.
Woodbury, A. M. 1952. Hybrids of Gopherus *berllandieri* and *G. agassizii*. Herpetologica 8:33-36.

GRAPTEMYS

Caldwell, J. P. and Collins, J. T. 1981. Turtles in Kansas. AMS Publishing, Lawrence, Kansas.
Connor, P. 1993. Cagle's map turtle. Tortuga Gazette (29) 10: 1-4.
Ernst, C. H., Lovich, J. E. and Barbour, R. W. 1994. Turtles of the United States and Canada. Smithsonian Institution, Washington. 578 pp.
Ewart, M. A and Nelson, C. E. 1991. Sex determination in turtles: diverse patterns and some possible adaptive values. Copeia 1991:50-69.
Jacobson, E. R., Gaskin, E. R. and Wahlquist, H. 1982. Herpesvirus-like infection in map turtles. JAVMA (181):1322-1324.
Killebrew, F. C. 1991. Habitat characteristics and feeding ecology of Cagle's map turtle (*Graptemys caglei*) within the proposed Cuero and Lindenau Reservoir sites. Texas Parks and Wildlife Dept.

HEOSEMYS

Das, I. 1991. Colour Guide to the Turtles and Tortoises of the Indian subcontinent. R&A Publishing, Avon, England.
Tikada, B. K. and Sharma, R. C. 1985. Handbook of Indian Testudines. Zool. Surv. India, Calcutta.

HOMOPUS

Barzyk, J. E. 1994. Husbandry and captive breeding of the parrot-beaked tortoise, *Homopus areolatus*. Chelonian conservation and Biology. 1 (2). 138-141.
Boycott, R. C. and Bourquin, O. 1988. The South African Tortoise Book. Southern Books, Johannesburg. 148 pp.
Branch, W. R. 1992. *Homopus 'bergeri'* - A wrong name for a new tortoise from Southern Namibia. Proceedings of the 2nd H. A. A. Symposium. J. Herpt. Assoc. Africa. (40):11,
Branch, W. R. 1989. *Homopus areolatus*. In: The Conservation biology of tortoises. Swingland, I. R. and Klemens, M. W. (eds.) IUCN, Gland. 72-74.
Eglis, A. 1963. Nesting of a Parrot-beaked tortoise. Herpetologica (19):66-68.
Silverman, L. 1993. Cited in: NYTTS Breeder's Notebook. Newsnotes IV(1):19-20.
Palmer, M. 1993. Husbandry of the Parrot-beaked tortoise (*Homopus areolatus*). The Carapace IX(3):11-14.

HYDROMEDUSA

Dillon, C. D. 1992. The Argentine Snake-necked turtle. Tortuga Gazette 28(5):1-2.

Souza, F. L. and Abe, A. S. 1995. Observations on feeding habits of *Hydromedusa maximiliari* (Testudines : Chelidae) in Southeastern Brazil. Chel. Cons and Biol. 1(4):320-323.

INDOTESTUDO

Biswas, S., Acharjyo, L. N. and Mohapatra, S. 1978. Notes on distribution, sexual dimorphism and growth in captivity of *Geochelone elongata*. J. Bombay Nat. Hist. Soc. (75):928-930.

Das, I. 1991. Colour Guide to the Turtles and Tortoises of the Indian subcontinent. R&A Publishing, Avon, England.

Dunn, R. W. 1976. Breeding the Elongate tortoise at Melbourne Zoo. Int. Zoo Yearbook, London: 73-74.

Hoveling, M. and van Putten, P. 1994. *Indotestudo elongata*. De Schildpad 20(4):10:18

Lackey, B. 1980. Turtle of the Month: Elongated tortoise. Tortuga Gazette, April 1980:3-4.

McCormick, B. 1992. The Elongated tortoise. Tortuga Gazette (28) 3:1-3.

Sane, L. S. and Sane, S. R. 1989. Some observations on growth of the Travancore tortoise (*Geochelone travencorica*). J. Bombay Nat. Hist. Soc. 85(1):109.

Spencer, B. 1988. The Elongated tortoise and its management at the Minnesota Zoo. Bull. Chicago. Herpetological Soc.. 23(3):37-40.

Tikader, B.K. and Sharma, R. C. 1985. Handbook Indian Testudines. Zoological Survey of India, Calcutta. 156 pp.

KACHUGA

Agarwal, A. K., Wadhwan, B. S. and Lavania, R. K. 1986. Sexual dimorphism in the Indian freshwater turtle *Kachuga tecta* (Gray).Bionature 6(2):94-97,

Das, I. 1991. Colour Guide to the Turtles and Tortoises of the Indian subcontinent. R&A Publishing, Avon, England.

Moll, E. O. 1987. Survey of the freshwater turtles of India. Part II. The genus *Kachuga*. J. Bombay Nat. Hist. Soc. 84(1):7-25.

Tikader, B.K. and Sharma, R. C. 1985. Handbook Indian Testudines. Zoological Survey of India, Calcutta. 156 pp.

Vijaya, J. 1982. *Kachuga tecta* hatching at the Snake Park. Hamadryad 7(3):14-15.

Vyas, R. and Patel, B. H. 1993. Captive breeding of the Indian Roofed terrapin *Kachuga tecta* (Gray). J. Bombay Nat. Hist. Soc. 90: 8-113

KINIXYS

Archer, W. H. 1968. The Tortoise with a difference. Int. Turtle Tortoise Soc. J. 2(4):11-13, 35-36.

Broadley, D. G. 1981. A review of the populations of *Kinixys* (Testudinidae) occurring in south-eastern Africa. Ann. Cape. Prov. Mus. 13:195-216.

Chin, D. 1993. Captive maintenance and breeding of *Kinixys belliana*, the Bell's hinge-back tortoise. NYTTS Newsnotes IIV (2): 14-16.

Highfield, A. C. 1989. *Kinixys belliana*. The Carapace. 5(5):9-10.

Kuchling, G. 1986. Biology of *Kinixys belliana* at Nosy Faly, Madagascar. in: Studies in Herpetology (ed. Rocek, Z.). Charles U. P., Prague. pp.435-440.

Kuchling, G. 1989. Okologie, Lebensweise und Uberlebenchancen der Landschildkroten Madagaskars. Salamandra, 25(3/4):169-190.

Laurent, R. F. 1962. On the races of *Kinixys belliana* Gray. Breviora, Mus. Comp. Zool. 176:1-6.

Morris, L. 1994. Western hinge-back tortoise *Kinixys belliana nogueyi*. Tortuga Gazette 30(1):1-3.

Pond, S and L. 1989. Experiences with captive breeding of the African Hinge-back tortoise, *Kinixys belliana*. Plastron Papers, XIX (2): 12-14.

Sachsse, W. 1980. Zur biologie und Fortpflanzung von *Kinixys belliana nogueyi*. Salamandra 16.

Villiers, A. 1958. Tortues et crocodiles de L'Afrique Noire Francaise. I.F.A.N., Dakar. pp. 1-354.

Woods, A. 1993. *Kinixys erosa* (Schwiegger, 1812). Tortoise Trust Newsletter, Winter 1993 edition.

KINOSTERNON

Cox, W.A., Nowak, M. C. and Marion K. R. 1980 Observations on Courtship and Mating Behavior in the Musk Turtle, *Sternotherus minor* J. Herpetol. 14, 200 - 204

Ernst, C. H., Lovich, J. E. and Barbour, R. W. 1994. Turtles of the United States and Canada. Smithsonian Institution, Washington. 578 pp.

Mahmoud, I. 1968. Feeding behaviour in Kinosternid turtles. Herpetologica 24(4):300-305.

Mahmoud, I. 1969. Comparative ecology of the Kinosternid turtles of Oklahoma. Southwest. Natur. 14:31-66.

Pewtress, R. K. 1990. The Stinkpot Musk turtle; its natural history and captive maintenance.In: Reptiles (ed. J. Coote). Proc. of the 1988 U.K. Herp Soc. symposium on captive breeding.

MALACLEMYS

Davenport, J. and Macedo, E. A. 1990. Behavioural osmotic control in the euryhaline diamondback terrapin *Malaclemys terrapin*: responses to low salinity and rainfall. J. Zool. Soc. Lond. 220:487-496.

Dimond, M. T. 1987. The effects of incubation temperature on hatching time, sex and growth of hatchlings of the diamondback terrapin, *Malaclemys terrapin* (Schoepff). Pranikee 8:1-5.

MALACOCHERSUS

Darlington, A. F. and Davis, R. B. 1990. Reproduction in the Pancake tortoise *Malacochersus tornieri* in captive collections. Herp. Review. 21 (1):16-18.

Dickson, J. 1992. Maintenance & Breeding of the Pancake tortoise at Bristol Zoo. International Zoo News 39 (3): 29-34.

Eglis, A. 1960. Notes on the Soft-shell tortoise *Malacochersus tornieri* (Siebenrock). Herpetologica 16:12-14.

Eglis, A. 1964. Flat and fast - the Pancake tortoise. Animal. Kingd. 68:107-110.

Juvik, J. O. 1971. Chimney climber. Int. Turtle Tortoise Soc. J. 1(2): 29, 44-45.

Ireland, L.C. and Gans, C. 1972. The adaptive significance of the flexible shell of the tortoise *Malacochersus tornieri* Anim. Behav. 20, 778 - 781

Shaw, C. E. 1970. The hardy (and prolific) Soft-shelled tortoise. Int.Tortoise and Turtle Soc. J. Jan-Feb 1970:6-31.

MANOURIA

Espenshade, W. and Buskirk, J. (1994) *Manouria impressa* (Gunther 1882): A summary of known and anecdotal information. Tortuga Gazette 30(5):1-5

Huang, Q. 1991. Experimental captive breeding of *Manouria impressa*. Sichuan J. Zoology 10(1):37 (in Chinese).

McKeown, S., Juvik, J. O. and Meir, D.E. 1982. Observations on the reproductive biology of the land tortoises *Geochelone emys* and *Geochelone yniphora* in the Honolulu zoo. Zoo Biol. 1:223-235.

McMorris, J. R. and Burns, D. M. (1975) Notes on *Geochelone impressa*. Chelonia 2(2):5-7.

Moll, E. (1989) *Manouria impressa* Impressed tortoise. *In* Conservation Biology of Tortoises, IUCN SSC #5, Gland, Switzerland.

Nabhitabhata, J. (1991) Impressed tortoise *Manouria impressa*. Endangered Species and Habitats of Thailand. Ecolog. Res. Dept. Thai. Inst. Sci. Tech. Res. Bangkok. pp. 200-201.

Weissinger, H. (1987) Haltung von *Manouria impressa* Gunther 1882 (Testudinidae). Elaphe 9(1):9-10.

Wirot, N. (1979) The Turtles of Thailand. Bangkok.

MAUREMYS

Busack, S. D. and Ernst, C. H. 1980. Variation in Mediterranean populations of *Mauremys* Gray, 1869. Ann. Car. Mus. (49):251-264.

Fritz, U. and Freytag, O. 1993. The distribution of *Mauremys* in Asia Minor, and first record of *M. caspica caspica* (Gmelin, 1774) for the internally drained basin of Anatolia. Herpetozoa 6(3/4):97-103.

Highfield, A. C. (1996, in press) An introduction to the *Mauremys* turtles of the Mediterranean. Reptile and Amphibian Magazine.

Sidis, I. and Gasith, A. 1985. Food habits of the Caspian terrapin (*Mauremys caspica rivulata*) in unpolluted and polluted habitats in Israel. J. Herpetology. 19(1):108-115.

MELANOCHELYS

Das, I. 1991. Colour Guide to the Turtles and Tortoises of the Indian subcontinent. R&A Publishing, Avon, England.

Das, I. 1990. Distributional records for chelonians from Northeastern India. J. Bomb. Nat. Hist. Soc. 87(1):91-97.

Tikader, B.K. and Sharma, R. C. 1985. Handbook Indian Testudines. Zoological Survey of India, Calcutta. 156 pp.

PELOMEDUSA

Boycott, R. C. and Bourquin, O. 1988. The South African tortoise book. Southern Book Publishers, Johannesburg.

Harding, J. H. 1981. Observations on the African helmeted turtle, *Pelomedusa subrufa*, in captivity, with comments on breeding behaviour. Bull. Chi. Herp. Soc. 16(4):86-94.

Wood, R. C. 1973. A possible correlation between the ecology of living African pelomedusid turtles and their relative abundance in the fossil record. Copeia (3):627-629.

PELUSIOS

Branch, Bill. 1988. Field guide to the snakes and other reptiles of Southern Africa. New Holland Publishers, London.

Levine, D. 1994. African side-neck turtles *Pelusios niger* and *P. subniger*. Tortuga Gazette: 30(8):1-3.

PHRYNOPS

Goode, M. 1988. Reproduction and growth of the chelid turtle *Phrynops (Mesoclemmys) gibbus* at the Columbus zoo. Herp. Review 19(1):11-13.

Harding, J. P. and Ewart, M. 1989. Notes on reproductive behaviour in captive *Phrynops gibbus*. Bull. Chic. Herp. Soc. 24(3).

Pritchard, P. C. H. and Trebbau, P. 1984 The Turtles of Venezuela. SSAR.

PLATEMYS

Buskirk, J. 1991. The Spiny-neck turtle (*Platemys spixii*) in and out of captivity. The Vivarium 3(2):16,30-31.

Dillon, C. D. 1994. Twistneck turtle *Platemys platycephala*. Tortuga Gazette 30(2):1-3.

Harding, J. H. 1983. *Platemys platycephala* (twistneck turtle). Reproduction. Herp Rev. (14):22.

PLATYSTERNON

De Koningh, H. L. 1968. An oriental big-head. Int. Tort. Turtle. Soc. J. (2):17-14

Nutaphand, W. 1979. The Turtles of Thailand. Bangkok. 222 pp.

PODOCNEMIS

Alho, C. J. R., Danni, T. M. S. and Padua, L. F. M. 1984. Influencia da temperatura de incubacao na determinacao do sexo da tartaruga da amazonia *Podocnemis expansa* (Testudinata: Pelomedusidae). Revista. Brasil. Biol. 44(3):305-311.

Belkin, D. A. and Gans, C. 1968. An unusual turtle feeding niche. Ecology (49):768-769.

Medem, M. F. 1964 Morphologie, Oekologie und Verbreitung der Schildkrote *Podocnemis unifilis* in Kolumbien. Senkenb. Biol. (45):353-368.

Pritchard, P. C. H. and Trebbau, P. 1984 The Turtles of Venezuela. SSAR.

PSAMMOBATES

Boycott, R. C. and Bourquin, O. 1988. The South African Tortoise Book. Southern Books, Johannesburg. 148 pp.

Branch, W. R. 1989. *Psammobates* . In: The Conservation biology of tortoises. Swingland, I. R. and Klemens, M. W. (eds.) IUCN, Gland.

Turner, E. H. 1971. *Psammobates*: The delicate one. Int. Tortoise and Turtle Soc. J. 5(2):4-5.

PYXIDEA

Buskirk, J. 1993. *Pyxidea mouhotti*. NYTTS Breeder's Notebook. NYTTS Newsnotes IV (1):19.

Das, I. 1991. Colour Guide to the Turtles and Tortoises of the Indian subcontinent. R&A Publishing, Avon, England.

Nutaphand, W. 1979. The Turtles of Thailand. Bangkok. 222 pp.

Sachsse, W. 1973. *Pyxidea mouhotti*, eine lanbewohnende Emydide Sudostasiens. Salamandra 9(2):49-53.

Tikada, B. K. and Sharma, R. C. 1985. Handbook of Indian Testudines. Zool. Surv. India, Calcutta.

RHINOCLEMMYS

Daddario, B. & B. 1992. *Rhinoclemmys pulcherrima manni*. NTYYTS Breeder's Notebook. NYTTS Newsnotes III (2):5.

Hidalgo, H. 1982. Courtship and mating behaviour in *Rhinoclemmys pulcherrima incisa*. Trans. Kansas. Acad. Sci. (85):82-95

Monge-Najera, J., Morera, B. and Chavez, M. 1988. Nesting behaviour of *Rhinoclemmys pulcherrima* in Costa Rica. Herpet. Journal 1(7):308.

Pritchard, P. C. H. and Trebbau, P. 1984. The Turtles of Venezuela. SSAR, Ohio.

SIEBENROCKIELLA

Nutaphand, W. 1979. The Turtles of Thailand. Bangkok. 222 pp.

TERRAPENE

Allard, H. A. 1935. The natural history of the Box turtle. Sci. Monthly, 41:325-338.

Allard, H. A. 1948. The Eastern box turtle and its behaviour. J. Tennessee Acad. Sci. 23:307-321.

Anonymous. 1989. Caring for your Box turtle. Voice of the Turtle, 18(10):5-6.

Beaman, K. R. 1989. Turtle of the Month: Common Box turtle *Terrapene carolina*. Tortuga Gazette, 25(11):3-4.

Beezley, C. 1969. Gentle Hermit. Texas Parks and Wildlife. XXVII(4).

Behler, J. L. and King, F. W. 1979. The Audubon Society Field Guide to North American reptiles and amphibians. A. Knopf, New York.

Buskirk, J. 1993. Yucatan box turtle: *Terrapene carolina yucatana*. Tortuga Gazette 29(5):1-4.

Carpenter, C. C. 1957. Hibernation, Hibernacula and associated behaviour of the Three-toed box turtle (*Terrapene carolina triunguis*). Copcia, 4: 278-282.

Cohen, H. J. 1977. Breeding Report: *Terrapene carolina carolina*. Chelonia, 3(3):5.

Conant, R. 1975. A Field Guide to the reptiles and amphibians of eastern and central North America. Houghton Mifflin, Boston.

Ditmars, R. L. 1934. A review of the box turtles. Zoologica (N.Y.) 17: 1-44

Englehardt, G. P. 1916. Burrowing habits of the box turtle. Copeia, 1916:42-43.

Ernst, C. H., Lovich, J. E. and Barbour, R. W. 1994. Turtles of the United States and Canada. Smithsonian Institution, Washington. 578 pp.

Highfield, A. C. 1993. The fate of American *Terrapene* Box Turtles imported into Britain. A Disturbing Report on the Box Turtle trade. New York Tortoise & Turtle Society Newsnotes Vol. IV:(1) 16-18.

Labrecque, J. 1982. Turtle of the Month: The American Box turtle. Tortuga Gazette, August 1982. 5-8.

Legler, J. M. 1960. Natural history of the ornate Box turtles *Terrapene ornata ornata* Agassiz. Univ. Kansas. Publ. Mus. Nat. Hist. 11: 527-669.

Marquard, K. H. 1988. Bericht aus dem Alltag zweir Dreizehen Dosenschildkroten (*Terrapene carolina triunguis*). De Schildkrote 2(2):32-36.

Metcalf, E. and Metcalf, A. L. 1970. Observations on ornate box turtles (*Terrapene ornata ornata* Agassiz). Kansas Acad. Sci. Trans. 73(1): 96-117.

Penn, G. H. and Pottharst, K. E. 1940. The reproduction and dormancy of *Terrapene c. carolina* in New Orleans. Herpetologica, 2:25-29.

Pope, C. H. 1949. Turtles of the United States and Canada. Knopf, N. Y.

Stettler, P. H. 1990. Experiences with Box turtles. Reptile Keeper International 1(5):17-18.

Whetmore, A. 1920. Observations on the hibernation of Box turtles. Copeia, 77:3-5.

TESTUDO

Anderson, S. C. 1979. Synopsis of the turtles, crocodiles and amphisbaeans of Iran. Proc. Calif. Acad. Sci. 41(22):501-528.

Andreu, A. C. and Villamor, M. D. C. 1986. Reproduction of *Testudo graeca graeca* in Donana, SW Spain. *In* Studies in Herpetology, Prague. ed. Rocek. pp. 589-592.

Bour, R. 1987. L'identite' des Tortues terrestres europenes: specimens-types et localites-types. Revue fr. Aquariol., 13 (1986) pp. 111-122.

Bour, R. 1989. Caracteres diagnostiques offerts par le crane des tortues terrestres du genre *Testudo*. Mesogee 48:13-19.

Bruekers, J. M. B. M. 1986. Schildpadden in Zuid-Frankrijk. Lacerta (44):4 63-65.

Bruekers, J. 1994. *Testudo graeca anamurensis*. De Schildpad 20(4):46-51.

Brushko, Z. K. and Kubykin, R. A. 1977. Data of reproduction of the Steppe tortoise in the Southern Balkhash Lake region. Proc. Zoo. Inst. Acad. Sci. UUSR. 74:32-34.

Buskirk, J. 1985. The Endangered Egyptian tortoise *Testudo kleinmanni*: Status in Egypt and Israel. 9th Int. Symp. Captive Proparagtion and Husbandry. Eds. McKeowan, Caporaso and Peterson. San Diego, CA.:35-51.

Connor, M. J. 1993. *Testudo kleinmanni*, notes on captive husbandry. Tortuga Gazette 29(1):5.

Buskirk, J. 1967. Turtles of the Holy Land. Int.Turtle Tortoise Soc. J. 1:20-23.

Buskirk, J. 1993. An annotated bibliography of the Egyptian tortoise, *Testudo kleinmanni* Lortet 1883. Tortuga Gazette 29 (1):1-4.

Cheylan, M. 1981. Biologie et Ecologie de la tortue d'Hermann *Testudo hermanni* GMELIN 1789. Mem. Trav. E.P.H.E Inst. Montpellier (13):1-404

Chkhikvadze, V. M. 1988. Systematic classification of contemporary land turtles of middle Asia and Khazachstan. Acad. Sci. Georgian S. S. R. Biol. Ser. 14:110-113

Chkhikvadze, V. M., Amiranashvili, H. G. and Ataev, C. 1990. A new subspecies of tortoise from southwestern Turkestan. Izvest. Akad. Nauk. Turkmenskoi S. S. R. Ser. Biol. 1:72-75

Collins, P. W. P. 1980. The Captive Breeding of Mediterranean tortoises in Britain. in. British. Herp. Soc.: Care and Breeding of Captive Reptiles. pp.21-36.

Devaux, B. 1988. La Tortue Sauvage. Sang de la terre, Paris.

Dickinson, P. 1985. Maintenance, behaviour and breeding of African Spur-thighed Tortoise. Int. Zoo News No. 194. 32(6):3-19.

Eendebak, B. T. 1995. Incubation period and sex ratio of Hermann's tortoise, *Testudo hermanni boettgeri*. Chel. Cons. & Biol. 1(3):227-231.

Geffen, E. and Mengelssohm H. 1991. Preliminary study on the breeding pattern of the Egyptian tortoise, *Testudo kleinmanni*, in Israel. Herpetological Journal (1):571-577.

Hempel, Wolfgang. 1988. Haltung und Nachzucht bei *Agrionemys horsfieldi*. De Schildkrote 2(2):12-19.

Highfield, A. C. 1989. Embryonic anoxia and the incubation of turtle eggs. Plastron Papers. Vol. XIX No.2. p. 31.

Highfield, A. C. 1990. Preliminary report on the Taxonomic, Biotypic and Conservation status of the Land Tortoises of Tunisia. Tortoise Survival Project, London.

Highfield, A. C. 1989. Diagnostic characters of Tortoises (1): Division of the Supracaudal scute in *Testudo* and its relevance as a taxonomic Diagnostic Character. British Herpetological Society Bulletin. 30:14-18.

Highfield, A. C. 1988. A new size record for *T. hermanni* GMELIN 1789?. The Rephiberary 132;5-6.

Highfield, A. C. & Martin, J. 1989 *Testudo whitei* BENNETT 1836; New light on an old carapace - Gilbert White's Selborne tortoise re-discovered. Journal of Chelonian Herpetology (1):1 13-22.

Highfield, A. C. & Martin, J. 1989 A Revision of the Testudines of North Africa, Asia and Europe, Genus: *Testudo*. J. Chel. Herp. (1):1 1-12.

Highfield, A. C. & Martin, J. 1989. An introduction to a conservation project for the North African tortoise, including a description of *Testudo flavominimaralis*, n.species. Tortoise Trust, London.

Highfield, A. C. 1989. Revision of Taxonomic Status and Nomenclature; Genus *Testudo*; A brief chronology. The Rephiberary nr. 141.

Highfield, A. C. 1989 Tortoise Survival Project. Voice of the Turtle, San Diego Tortoise & Turtle Society. 18:(11).

Highfield, A. C. 1990. New record size for North African *Testudo*. British Herpetological Soc. Bulletin. 31:29-30.

Highfield, A. C. 1990. Keeping and Breeding Tortoises in Captivity. R&A Publishing Ltd.

Highfield, A. C. 1989. 200 years of Tortoise Taxonomy. The Rephibiary. ASRA Newsletter No. 145.

Highfield, A. C. 1987. Causal Factors of Mortality in Captive Collections. Lecture at University of Bristol Symposium. Published in Testudo, 2(5).

Highfield, A. C. 1993. Mysterious Tortoise Deaths in Wild Populations and Captive Collections in Europe and America. Reptilia & Amphibia: Proceedings of the 16th annual ABWAK symposium. 15-20.

Highfield, A. C. 1993. The Horsfields Tortoise: *Testudo horsfieldi* (Gray) 1844 A Brief Review of its Biology, Ecology & Captive Breeding. ASRA Monographs: Captive Breeding. Oxford.

Highfield, A. C. 1992. Report from Turkey. Tortoise Trust Newsletter 1992. No. 3:8-11.

Highfield, A. C. 1991. Report from Morocco. T.T. Newsletter 1991 No.1:7-8.

Highfield, A. C. 1991. Introducing *Testudo kleinmanni*. T.T. Newsletter 1991 No. 5 & 6:15-17.

Highfield, A. C. 1993. Conservation of Mediterranean tortoises. Proc. Int. Symposium on Reptiles and Amphibians. BOA and ALBA Norkopping, Sweden.

Highfield, A. C. 1994 In Search of little-known tortoises in Southern Turkey with notes on *Testudo (graeca) anamurensis* and *Testudo graeca terrestris*. Tortoise Trust Newsletter.(9):1

Highfield, A. C. 1994 Ecology and Conservation of tortoises in North Africa and the Mediterranean. Proc. Int. Herpetological Symp. New Orleans, U.S.A.

Highfield, A. C. 1992. Observations of *Testudo (graeca) ibera* in Lycia, Turkey. The Tortuga Gazette, CTTS, California Vol. 28:9. 1-3.

Highfield, A. C. 1992 Spotlight - On Tortoises. Biological Sciences Review Vol. 4:(4) 28-30.

Highfield, A. C. 1989. Terrestrial Chelonia; Incubation of Eggs & Care of Hatchlings. The Tortoise Trust, London. 29pp.

Highfield, A. C. 1986. Safer Hibernation & Your Tortoise. Tortoise Trust, London, 28pp, reprinted as serial in The Carapace, NL of Nat. Turtle & Tortoise Society, Inc. Phoenix, Arizona. 1989.

Highfield, A. C. 1989. Artificial incubation techniques in relation to *Testudo graeca* and *T. hermanni* with notes on Embryonic Anoxia as a possible factor in hatchling mortality in captive breeding programs. Voice of the Turtle 18(12), San Diego, CA.

Highfield, A. C. 1989. Feeding your tortoise. Tortoise Trust, London.

Highfield, A. C. 1989. General care of tortoises. Tortoise Trust, London.

Highfield, A. C. 1994. The Feeding Manual. Tortoise Trust, London.

Hine, M. L. 1982. Notes on the Marginated tortoise (*Testudo marginata*) in Greece and in Captivity. Bull. Brit. Herpet. Soc. No.5.

Hobbs, L. L. and May, P. A. 1993. A *kleinmanni* breeding. 13th Ann. Texas Herpet. Symposium.

Khozatsky, L.I and Mlynarski, M. 1966. *Agrionemys* - nouveau genre de tortues terrestres (Testudinidae). Bull. Ac. Polon. Sci. (2):123-125.

Kirsche, W. 1979. The housing and regular breeding of Mediterranean tortoises *Testudo* spp. in captivity. Int. Zoo Yearbook, 19:42-49.

Lambert, M. R. K. 1981. Temperature, activity & field sighting in the Mediterranean spur-thighed or common garden tortoise tortoise *Testudo graeca* L. Biological Conservation. (21):39-54.

Lambert, M. R. K. 1982. Studies on the growth, structure and abundance of the Mediterranean spur-thighed tortoise, *Testudo graeca* in field populations. J. Zool. Soc. London, 196:165-189.

Lambert, M. R. K. 1988. Natural bioclimatic range and the growth of captive-bred Mediterranean *Testudo* L. in northern Europe: Implications for conservation farming. B.H.S. Bulletin, 24:6-7.

Loveridge, A. and Williams, E.E. 1957. Revision of the African tortoises and turtles of the suborder Cryptodira. Bull. Mus. Comp. Zool. Harv. Coll. 115:163-557.

Madge, D. 1985. Temperature and sex determination in reptiles with reference to Chelonia. Testudo 2(3):8-13.

Mertens, R. 1946. Uber einige mediterrane Schildkrotenrassen. Senckenbergiana Biol. 27:111-118.

Obst, F. J. and Meusel, W. 1969. Die Landschildkroten Europas. Die Neue Brehm-Bucherei. Wittenberg-Lutherstadt.

Pelaz, M. P. 1988. Aspectos historicos para la actual corologia de *Testudo hermanni* en la Mediterraneo Occidental. Vida Silvestre nr. 64 (ICONA - Madrid) 28-35.

Terent'ev, P. V. and Chernov, S. A. 1965. Key to the Amphibians and Reptiles. 3rd ed. Prog. Sci. Trans. Jerusalem, Israel.

Wermuth, H. 1952. *Testudo hermanni robertmertensi* n. subsp. und ihr Vorkommen in Spanien. Senckenbergiana, 33:157-164.

Wermuth, H. 1958. Status und nomenklatur der maurischen land-schildkrote, *Testudo graeca*, in S. W. Asien und N. O. Africa. Senck. Biol. 39:149-153.

TRACHEMYS

Connor, M.J. 1992. The Red-eared slider. Tortuga Gazette 28(4):1-3.

Etchberger, C. R., Phillips, J. B., Ewart, M. A., Nelson, C. E. and Prange, H. D. 1992. Physiological responses to carbon dioxide in embryonic Red-eared slider turtles, *Trachemys scripta*. J. Exp. Zool. 264:1-10.

Gibbons, J. W. 1990. Life history and ecology of the Slider turtle. Smithsonian Institution Press.

Harding, J. and Holman, J. A. 1990. Michigan Turtles and Lizards. Michigan State University.

Vosjoli, P. de. 1992. The General care and maintenance of Red-eared sliders and other popular freshwater turtles. Advanced Vivarium Systems, California.

TRIONYX

Korolev, A. V., Kudrayavtsev, S.V and Frolov, V. E. 1983. Some special aspects of the husbandry of soft-shell turtles (Reptilia, Testudines, Trionchidae) at the Moscow Zoo. 7th Annual Reptile Symposium on Captive Propagation & Husbandry. Dallas, Texas. 54-58.

MISCELLANEOUS AND VETERINARY REFERENCES

Anonymous. 1961. Tortoise growth. Zoonooz 34(1):12.

Acuna-Mesen, R. A. and Hanson, Paul E. 1990. Phorid fly larvae as predators of turtle eggs. Herp. Review. 21(1):13-14.

Adams, J. W. 1989. A plague upon a turtle's house: "Shell Rot" or ulcerative shell disease. Plastron Papers, XVIII. No. 7: 17-18.

Avery, R. A. 1986. The physiology of reproduction. Testudo 2(4): 8-13.

Bellairs, A. 1969. The Life of Reptiles (2 Vols.). Weidenfeld and Nicholson, London.

Bellairs, A. and Cox, C. B. (eds) 1976. Morphology and Biology of Reptiles. Academic Press, London.

Bowers, W. S., Ohta, T., Cleere, J. S., and Marsella, P.A. 1976. Discovery of insect anti-juvenile hormones in plants. Science 193:542-547.

Boyer, D. R. 1965. Ecology of the basking habit in turtles. Ecology, 46:99-113.

Branch, Bill. 1988. Field guide to the snakes and other reptiles of Southern Africa. New Holland Publishers, London.

Brattstrom, B. H. and Collins, R. 1972. Thermoregulation. Int. Tortoise and Turtle Soc. J. 6(5):15-19.

Bull, J. J. 1980. Sex determination in reptiles. Quart. Rev. Biol. 55:3-21.

Carr, A. 1952. Handbook of Turtles. Cornell U. P. New York.

Congdon, J. D. and Gibbons, J. W. 1985. Egg components and reproductive characteristics of turtles: relationships to body size. Herpetologica 41(2): 194-205.

Congdon, J. D and Gibbons, J. W. 1987. Cracks in the egg theory. Science News, July 11, p. 24.

Cooper, J. E. and Jackson, O.F. 1981. Diseases of the Reptilia. Academic Press, London.

Cox, W.A., Wyatt, S. T., Wilhelm, W.E and Marion, K. R. 1988. Infection of the turtle *Sternotherus minor*, by the Lung Fluke, *Heronimus mollis*:incidence of infection and correlations to host life history and ecology in a Florida Spring. Journ. of Herpetology 22(4):488-490.

Ernst, C. H. and Barbour, R. W. 1972. Turtles of the United States. U.P. Kentucky.

Ernst, C. H. and Barbour, R. W. 1989. Turtles of the World. Smithsonian Institution Press. Washington, D.C.

Ewart, M. A. and Nelson, C. E. 1991. Sex determination in turtles: diverse patterns and some possible adaptive values. Copeia (1):50-69.

Foust, Allen. 1992. Incubating turtle eggs. NYTTS Newsnotes III (2):4-5.

Frye, F. 1973. Husbandry, Medicine and Surgery in Captive Reptiles. V.M. Publications, Kansas.

Frye, F. 1974. The role of nutrition in the successful maintenance of captive reptiles. Cal. Vet. Med. Assn. 86th Ann. Seminar. Sylabus. pp. 5-15.

Frye, F. 1981. Biomedical and Surgical aspects of captive reptile husbandry. V. M. Publications, Kansas.

Frye, F. 1991 Reptile Care: An Atlas of Diseases and Treatments. Vol.II. TFH Inc. New Jersey.

Frye, F. L. and Williams, David L. 1995. Self-assessment colour review of reptiles and amphibians. Manson Publishing, London.

Galbraith, D. A. 1993. Multiple paternity and sperm storage in turtles. Herpet. Journ. 3:117-123.

Gans, C. (ed.) 1969 onwards in 13 Vols. Biology of the Reptilia. Academic Press, London.

Groombridge, B. 1982 The IUCN Amphibia-Reptilia Red Data Book part 1. IUCN, Switzerland.

Harless, M. and Morlock, H. (eds) 1979 Turtles: Perspectives and Research. John Wiley and Sons, New York.

Highfield, A. C. 1987. Electronic temperature Measurement and Control for Incubators and Vivaria. The Herptile. Journ. International. Herpet. Soc. Vol.12 (4):130-133.

Highfield, A. C. 1988. Husbandry Notes; Force-feeding chelonians supportive therapy techniques. The Rephiberary, nr. 131.

Highfield, A. C. 1988. Husbandry Notes; Observations on Dehydration in Reptiles. The Rephiberary, nr. 130.

Highfield, A. C. 1989. Flagellate & Ciliate Protozoan infections in Tortoises. The Herptile, 14(1):4-8.

Highfield, A. C. 1989. Notes on dietary constituents for Herbivorous terrestrial chelonia and their effects on Growth and Development. ASRA (U.K) Journal, Vol.3 (3):7-20.

Highfield, A. C. 1992. When Tortoises Won't Feed. The Reptilian. Vol.1 (1):26-28.

Holt, P. 1978. Radiological studies of the alimentary tract in two Greek tortoises. Vet. Record 103:198-200.

Inskeep, R. 1983. Incubator construction. Testudo, 2(2): 40-42.

Iverson, J. B. 1986. A checklist with distribution maps of the Turtles of the World. Richmond, Indiana.

Jackson, O. F. and Fasal, M. D. 1981. Radiology in Tortoises, Terrapins and Turtles as an aid to diagnosis. J. Small Animal Practice. (22):705-716.

Kaplan, H. M. 1957. The care and diseases of laboratory turtles. Proc. Anim. Care Panel. 7:259-272.

Keymer, J. F. 1978. Diseases of chelonians: (1) Necropsy survey of tortoises. Vet. Record. 103: 548-552.

Klingenberg, R. J. 1993 Understanding reptile parasites. The Herpetocultural Library, Lakeside, CA.

Kuchling, G. 1989 Assessment of ovarian follicles and oviductal eggs by ultrasound scanning in live freshwater turtles, *Chelodina oblonga*. Herpetologica (45):89-94

Kuchling, G. 1989 New hope for recovery from the brink of extinction: *Pseudemydura umbrina*, the rarest turtle on earth breeds again. IUCN Tortoise & Freshwater Turtle Specialist Group Newsletter. No.4:16-18.

Lang, T. and Clutterbuck, C. 1991 P is for Pesticides. Ebury Press, London.

Lawrence, K. 1983. The treatment of disease in reptiles. ASRA (U.K.) J. 2(2):18-25.

Lawrence, K. and Needham, J. R. 1985. Rhinitis in long term captive Mediterranean tortoises (*Testudo graeca* and *Testudo hermanni*). Vet. Record. 117:662-664.

Marcus, L. 1981. Veterinary biology and medicine of captive amphibians and reptiles. Lea and Febiger, Philadelphia.

Millichamp, N. J. 1980. *In:* The Care and Breeding of Captive Reptiles. BHS, London.

Murphy, J. B. n.d. A Brief outline of suggested treatments for diseases of captive reptiles. SSAR and Kansas Herpet. Soc.

Murphy, J. B. 1973. A review of diseases and treatment of captive chelonians. HISS News-Journal. 1(1):5-8.

Movchan, N. A. 1964 Antibiotic properties of the egg albumin of the Steppe tortoise (*Testudo horsfieldi* GRAY). Vestn. Leningrad Univ. Biol. 15(3):18-25.

Movchan, N. A. 1966 Fungicidal properties of the albumin of the Steppe tortoise *Testudo horsfieldi*. Vestn. Leningrad Univ. Biol. 3(1):59-69

Obst, F. J. 1986. Turtles, Tortoises and Terrapins. Macmillan of Australia, Melbourne.

Pfeiffer, C. 1980. Foods for Tortoises. Chelonologica, 1:(1):5-13.

Pritchard, P. C. H. 1979. Encyclopedia of Turtles. TFH, New Jersey.

Ross, Richard A. 1984. The Bacterial diseases of Reptiles. Institute for Herpetological Research, California.

Smith, R. N. 1985. The tortoise egg. Testudo 2(3):7.

Tryon, B. 1975. How to incubate reptile eggs: a proven technique. Bull. N. Y. Herp. Assoc. 11(3-4): 33-37.

Wallach, J. 1969. Medical care of reptiles. J. Am. Vet. Assn. 155:1017-1034.

Wallach, J. 1971. Environmental and nutritional diseases of captive reptiles. J. Am. Vet. Assn. 159(11):1632-1643.

Welch, K. R. G. 1994. Turtles, Tortoises and Terrapins. A Checklist. R&A Research and Information Ltd. Somerset, U.K.

Young, J. D. 1950. The structure and some physical properties of the testudian eggshell. Proc. Zool. Soc. Lond. 120:455-469.

Yntema, C. L. 1976. Effects of incubation temperature on sexual differentiation in the turtle *Chelydra serpentina*. J. Morphol. 150(2): 453-462.

Zimmermann, E. 1986. Breeding terrarium animals. TFH, N.J.

Zwart, P. and Truyens, E. H. A. 1975. Hexamitiasis in tortoises. Vet. Parasitology. 1:175-183.

Zwart, P. 1987. Advances in the veterinary care of chelonians over the past 20 years (1967-1987). Testudo 2(5): 1-14.

INDEX